GCSE Design & Technology

Resistant Materials

Gerald Eyers • John Huxtable

with contributions by Ian Fawcett

Series Editor: Geoff Hancock

www.heinemann.co.uk

✓ Free online support
✓ Useful weblinks
✓ 24 hour online ordering

01865 888058

Heinemann [illegible]
Harcourt Education Limited

First published 2005

09 08 07 06 05
10 9 8 7 6 5 4 3 2 1

10-digit ISBN: 0 435413 47 3
13-digit ISBN: 978 0 435413 47 7

British Library Cataloguing in Puplication Data is available from the British Library on request

Designed by Wild Apple Design
Produced by Kamae Design

Printed and bound in the UK by CPIBath

Index compiled by Ian D Crane

Original illustrations © Harcourt Education Limited, 2005

Illustrated by John Storey and Kamae Design

Photographic acknowledgements
The authors and publisher would like to thank the following for permission to reproduce photographs:
Alamy pages 9 left, 34 left, 39 top, 53 top, 68, 89 left, 120 top, 122 left and 123; Alessi/Alessandro Mendini page 39 bottom; Alessi/Guido Venturini page 8 bottom; BSI pages 32 and 41 both; Bridgeman Art Library page 19; Construction Photography page 52 right; Corbis pages 34 right, 40, 64 left, 66 left and 89 right; Corbis/Harcourt Education pages 9 right, 101, 105 top left & bottom left; David Colwell page 10; Debbie Rowe page 47; Dyson pages 115 and 130 bottom three; Faber Maunsell page 53 bottom; Forest Stewardship Council page 37 right; Frank Gehry/Vitra/Hans Hansen page 29; Fujitsu page 37 left; Gerald Eyers 66 right; Getty pages 43, 121 and 130 top; Harcourt Education Ltd/Rob Judges – Blue School pages 11 left, 14, 15, 21, 27 right, 33, 44, 64 right, 72, 74 both, 76, 78, 79 both, 87 both, 88, 92 all, 99 both, 100, 103 both, 104, 125 top, 135, 136, 139, 142, 147, 148 and 150; Harcourt Education Ltd/Rob Judges – Clares page128 and 129; Harcourt Education Ltd/Rob Judges – Eurotech pages 124 all and 125 bottom three; Harcourt Education Ltd/Victoria Townsley page 67 left; Harcourt Education Ltd/Natalie Gray page 67 right; IKEA pages 8 top, 62 all, 85, 116 right, 117, 132 and 141; John Makepeice page 11 right; Nokia page 120 bottom; Oak Ridge National Laboratory page 90; Panos page 35 right; Petcore page 36 bottom; Polydron page 63; Prince page 52 left; Recycle Now/www.wrap.org.uk page36 (textile recycling & paper recycling); Rex pages 16, 103 top right & bottom right and 116 left; Roy Tam/www.eco-furniture.co.uk page 30; Russell Hobbs/Salton Europe page 54 right; Science and Society page 69; Science Photo Library pages 35 left, 83, 112, 118 and 122 right; Sony page 20; Superstock pages 46 and 127; Technology Enhancement Programme page 54 left; Techsoft page 107, 110 and 111; Victoria & Albert Museum pages 7 and 31; www.alupro.org.uk page 36 (aluminium recycling); www.britglass.org.uk page 36 (glass recycling); www.cansmart.org page 36 (steel recycling); www.3trpd.co.uk page 131 right; www.3trpd.co.uk/Zaha Hadid Ltd page 131 top left & bottom left.

Thanks also to Focus Educational Software Ltd for permission to use screenshots of Focus on Resistant Materials on pages 26 and 45; Google USA for permission to use a screenshot of their website on page 141; The Product Development Company for permission to use screenshots of Pro DESKTOP on pages 23, 27 left, 108 all and 109 both; The Technology Enhancement Programme at the University of Warwick for permission to use a screenshot of Materials Selection and Processing on page 45.

Thanks also to Clares Retail Services Ltd and Eurotech Moudlings Ltd for their help in producing the case studies.

Cover photograph by Science Photo Library
Cover design by Wooden Ark

Picture research by Bea Ray and Natalie Gray

The publisher would like to thank the following for permission to reproduce copyright material:

AQA material is reproduced by permission of the Assessment and Qualification Alliance. Where sample answers and examiners' comments have been provided, these are the responsibility of the author and have not been provided or approved by AQA.

A special thanks to the students who allowed their coursework to be reproduced in this publication.

Introduction

is book has been written to meet the requirements of the full d short course AQA specifications for GCSE Resistant Materials chnology. The AQA specification is designed to meet the ational Curriculum Orders and GCSE subject criteria for Design d Technology.

e programme of study for Design and Technology at Key age 4 requires you to develop your Design and Technology pability by applying knowledge and understanding of resistant aterials when developing ideas, planning, making products and aluating them. This book has given particular emphasis to the ewer elements of the subjects, such as industrial practices, ICT d CAD/CAM.

QA specification

e specification provides opportunities for you to develop Design d Technology capability throughout your course. It requires you combine skills with knowledge and understanding in order design and make quality products in quantity. It also provides pportunities for you to acquire and apply knowledge, skills and nderstanding through:

- analysing and evaluating existing products and industrial processes
- undertaking focused practical tasks to develop and demonstrate techniques
- working out how to develop ideas, and plan and produce products
- considering how past and present design and technology affects society
- recognising the moral, cultural and environmental issues in design and technology situations
- using ICT.

ow will you be assessed?

ou will be assessed in two ways. You will complete a coursework roject making up 60% of your GCSE mark. You will also omplete a two-hour ($1\frac{1}{2}$ hour for the short course) written exam t the end of the course that will make up 40% of your GCSE ark. In both the coursework and the written exam, you will be ssessed on how you demonstrate your knowledge, skills and nderstanding in three ways:

- of materials, components, processes, techniques and industrial practice (20%)
- when designing and making quality products in quantity (60%)
- when evaluating processes and products and examining the wider effects of design and technology on society (20%).

Most of your marks (60%) will be awarded for designing and making. Most of your designing and making will be completed in your coursework project.

How to use this book

This book will help you:

- develop your resistant materials skills
- develop your knowledge and understanding of resistant materials and all the related topics required within the AQA specification
- understand what is required for internal assessment (coursework) and how to get the best grades
- prepare for and revise for the written exam and understand how to get the best grades
- develop key skills of communication, application of number, information and communications technology, working with others, problem solving and improving your own learning through your resistant materials work.

This book is divided into the following parts:

- Part 1 What you need to know: this is the main part of the book and contains sections 1–7
- Part 2 Doing your coursework project: this contains section 8 and gives advice on how to plan and produce your coursework, helping you get the best marks possible
- Part 3 Preparing for the exam: this comprises section 9 and gives advice on what examiners are looking for, how to prepare for the exam and how to get the best marks you can.

This book is written in double-page chapters. Each chapter includes:

- specification links to show which modules of the AQA specification are covered by the chapter
- an introduction showing what you will learn from the chapter
- activities that reinforce and develop learning
- a summary of the chapter to help with revision.

AQA Resistant Materials 10.5 and 10.6

Numbering is used on each double-paged chapter to show which section of the AQA Resistant Materials Technology specification the chapter matches.

D1 Some chapters of Part 1 are also useful for the coursework project. This is identified by showing the relevant coursework assessment criteria at the top of the chapter. Here, 'D' refers to designing and 'M' refers to making. Along with the numbering, these are taken from the coursework project assessment criteria for grade A given in section 16.3 of the AQA specification.

Some chapters might also include:

- coursework boxes: these show how particular chapters in Part 1 are relevant to your coursework, so you should keep this information in mind when completing your project. You will also need to make sure you read Part 2 so that you understand exactly what you need to do for your project
- case studies: these give real examples of how the processes and knowledge you are learning are applied in real life.

At the end of each section there are relevant examples of exam questions and the marks available. These will help you practise and revise for the exam.

Finally, there is also a glossary at the end of the book to explain words identified in bold text. This will be useful as you are going through your course and also when you come to revise for the exam or do your coursework.

Websites

There are links to relevant web sites in this book. In order to ensure that the links are up-to-date, that the links work, and that the sites aren't inadvertently linked to sites that could be considered offensive, we have made the links available on the Heinemann website at www.heinemann.co.uk/hotlinks. When yo access the site, the express code is 3473P.

Short course

If you are following the short course you will need to use just some of the chapters in this book. You will also need guidance from your teacher on how to use this book and which chapters to use.

1 Designing

his section looks at the knowledge and nderstanding you need to design effectively nd links these with the designing skills you ill need use to develop and communicate ur ideas. The subjects covered in this ection will help you to be more creative in ur designing and provide you with a 'toolkit' f designing skills and approaches to help you explore and develop your design ideas.

art 2, Doing your coursework project, looks pecifically at what is required in your design lder.

What's in this section?

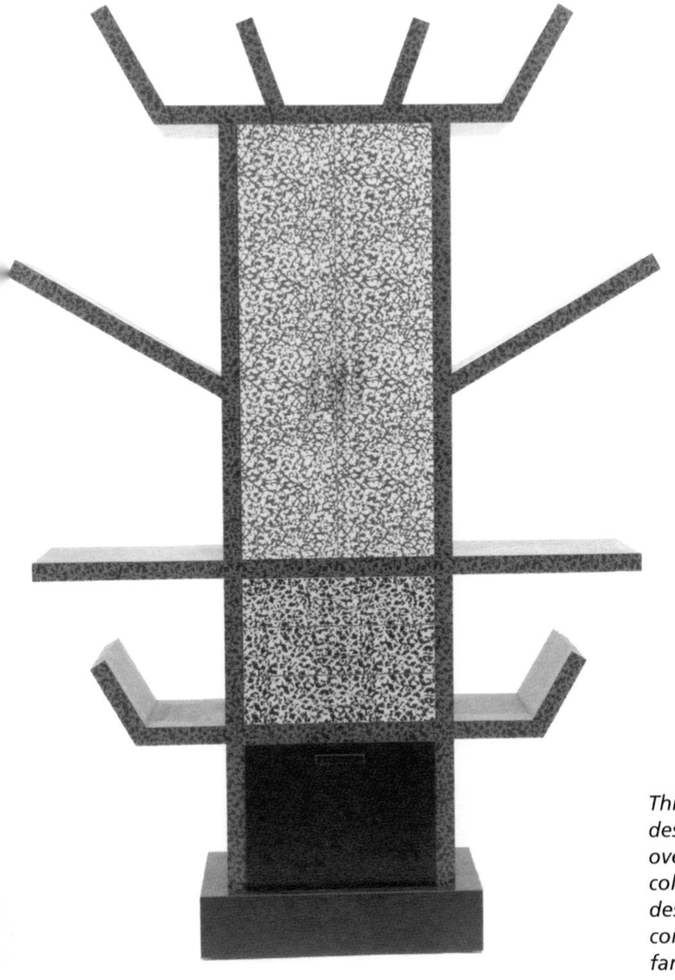

This Casablanca sideboard design by Ettore Sottsas is over 20 years old. Its bold colours and strange form were designed to be something completely new and it is still far from ordinary today

Basic design principles

In this chapter you will learn about:

★ the basic design principles and how to use using them in your work.

Focus on the detail

You are surrounded by well-designed objects of many kinds. You look at them every day, but how much do you *really* see and understand about the details in the designs? The designers of these products will have considered carefully such details as the **line**, **shape**, **form**, **colour** and **texture** of the products. These are the basic building blocks for all designing.

Line

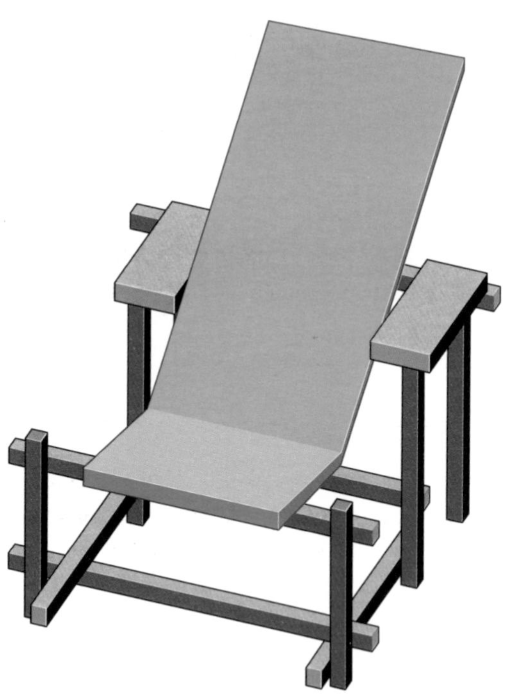

Line is used to create shape, pattern and movement

Line can be used to:

- emphasise shape and volume: vertical lines make things look taller, horizontal lines make things look wider
- suggest direction and movement, often referred to as the **dynamic aesthetic**
- separate colours, tones and textures in a product
- create texture and **pattern**.

Shape

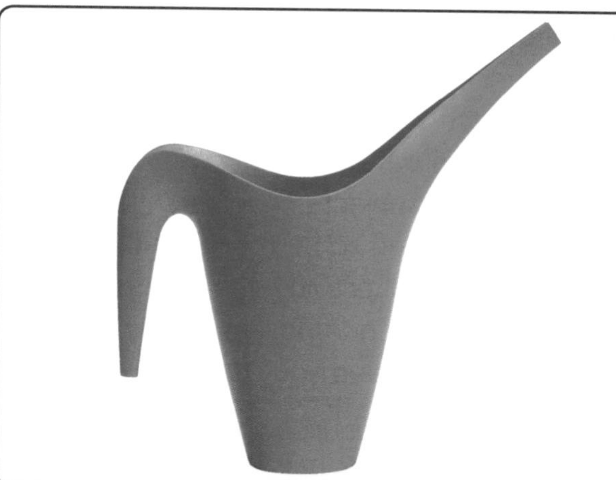

Striking designs are often very simp

Shapes are two-dimensional elements of design. The simplest shapes are geometric shapes such as circles, rectangles and triangles. Natural free-flowing shapes, such as those found in plants, are organic shapes. Shape can be used to:

- make objects suit and fit with the user (e.g. a comfort scissors handle) as part of ergonomics
- accentuate form as a part of the aesthetic styling of a product (e.g. stripes on cars)
- indicate the **function** (the way the product works) of an object (e.g. push/pull/open).

Form

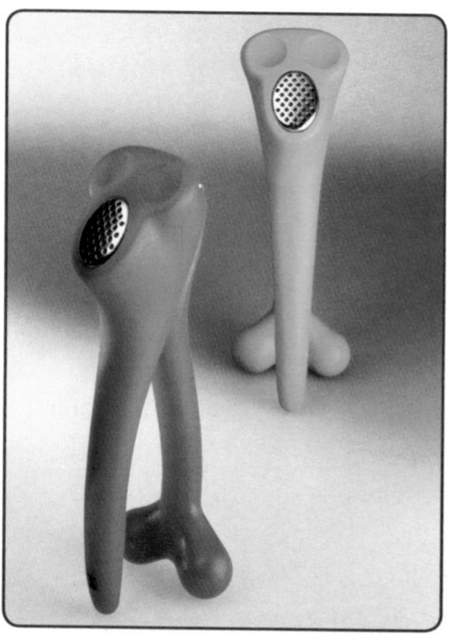

Bold forms an striking colours mak these garlic presse very appealin

ɔrms are three-dimensional (they have width and height). ıe simplest forms are spheres, cubes and pyramids. atural forms such as fruits and plants are called organic ›rms. Form can be used to:

- mould products to fit the three-dimensional form of the human body
- increase the tactile (touching) and visual qualities of an object
- emphasise the aesthetic style of an object.

;olour

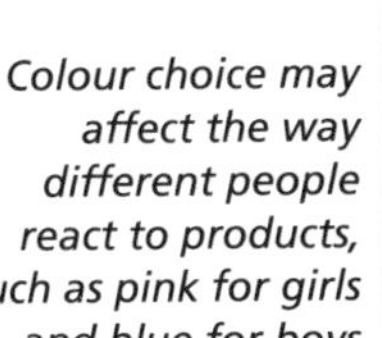

Colour choice may affect the way different people react to products, uch as pink for girls and blue for boys

›pplying colour to an object can have a big impact on the ⁄ay people react to it. Bright colours make people think ıe product is fun. A single colour may suggest a use; for xample, yellow is often associated with sport and red with anger. Colours are sometimes linked to the identity of ɔmpanies, teams and events. Colour can be used to:

- suggest a use
- convey an emotion
- show identity
- carry a warning or meaning
- reflect a gender preference
- make you smile.

Texture

'exture is linked to the qualities of **materials**. For example, ɴetals are sometimes glossy and shiny and sometimes matt ınd silky. Texture can be:

- as a result of materials and finishes, such as the satin sheen of well-finished wood
- brought about by a manufacturing **process**, such as blow moulding
- used to enhance the function of an object by aiding grip, such as a tennis racquet handle
- added to create patterned shapes and to improve the aesthetic qualities of an object, such as the textured panels on an MP3 player
- used to make powerful impact – one product will often display a wide range of textures and patterns.

The texture and patterns found in natural forms are a valuable source of inspiration

Coursework

Start at the beginning. Understanding basic design principles is an essential foundation for your coursework project.

Activities

1 Create a large collage of a collection of images that show each of the design principles used to enhance product design. Paste up the images and label the principles.

2 Keep a sketchbook of interesting designs. This is a good way to build up a resource that you can use while designing.

Summary

★ Think of the design principles as a set of resources you have to design with, just as an artist has a set of colours on a palette to paint with.

1.2 A designing 'toolkit'

In this chapter you will learn about:

- ★ the different ways to begin a design project
- ★ how designers use the work of others to inspire them
- ★ how to combine a range of approaches to design.

A range of approaches

Professional designers use different approaches to make sure their ideas are original, but they also need to save time, ensure quality and prevent mistakes if new designs are to be successful. The following approaches will help you to be more creative and to be successful when you are designing.

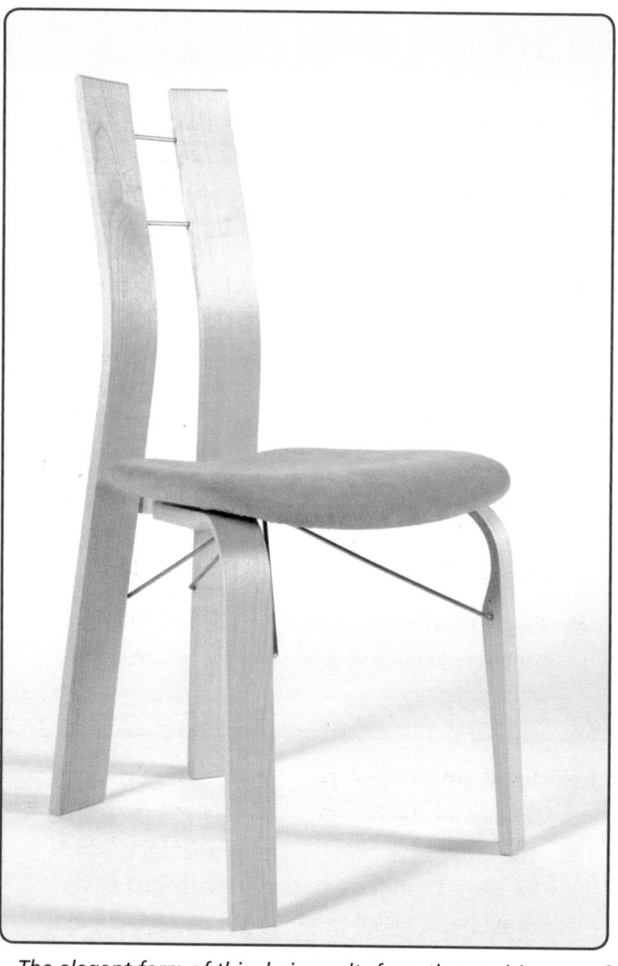

The elegant form of this chair results from the sensitive use of materials and processes

Basic design principles

Knowing about the basic design principles of line, shape, form, colour and texture, and understanding how they can be applied, is the first step to good design.

Exploring the work of others

Look in depth at existing designs to discover which materials have been used, how the parts are cut and joined, what components and finish have been used. Compare the cost and quality of the product with others on the market. This is an effective way of learning a great deal about a product in a short time.

Looking at and learning from other ideas is valuable, but beware that you are not so influenced by their ideas that you end up copying them. Designers legally protect their designs by either registering or **patenting** their ideas. This prevents their designs being used without permission and payment.

Product analysis

Detailed analysis of the design and manufacture of products is a powerful design tool as it allows you to learn from other people's experience. By looking at the **aesthetics** (the overall look and feel of the product), you can see how the designer has used the principles of design to create a successful product. Look at the function and consider how the designer has ensured that the design will be good to use (**ergonomics**) and how it will fit a range of users (**anthropometrics**). Finally, look at how all these aspects have been combined to create the style and fashion of the product and how this has been targeted at a specific group of **consumers** (people who may buy the product).

Exploring new materials and processes

Sometimes designers wish to use new materials and processes. Spending a short time exploring and experimenting to see what can be done can be a step. Understanding materials and processes is an important part of designing.

New components or technologies can create opportunities for new projects. Exploring a range of **knock-down (KD)**

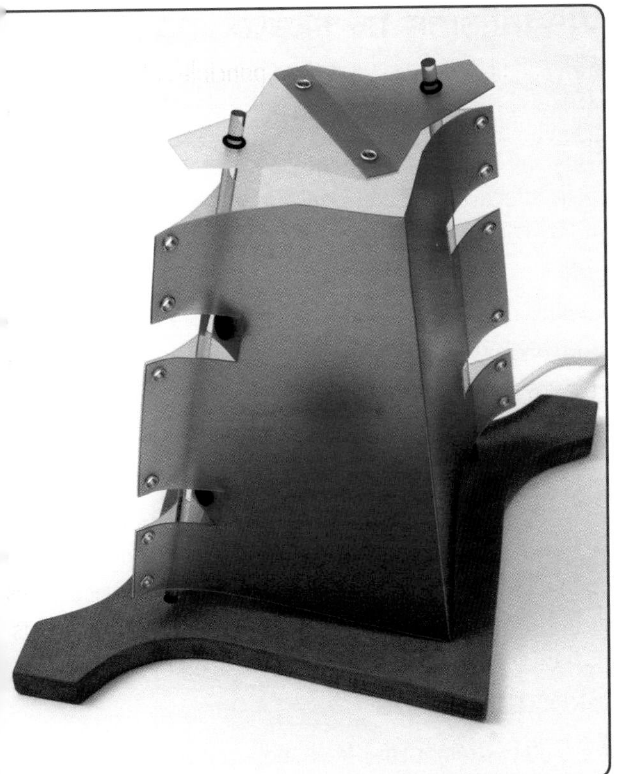

)eveloping designs that adapt and use architectural forms on a nuch smaller scale can be effective, as this student lamp shows. It is made from riveted polypropylene sheet with an MDF base

Designers use these abstracts to create new, imaginative ideas that draw on the beauty, elegance and purity of nature

ittings (quick assembly fittings) and the sorts of joints ney can be used to make could be an effective way to egin designing an original piece of furniture.

nspiration

ietting inspiration for new designs is not easy. How can ou be inspired? Looking into different areas such as nature nd architecture can be a great stimulus.

Architecture: look at modern buildings to find interesting shapes and forms.

Nature: the natural world is full of beautiful shapes, forms, structures, patterns and colours. Sometimes designers use these directly and at other times they abstract parts (select interesting sections and use them in different ways).

Coursework

Use this design 'toolkit' to help you be more creative and to come up with some original ideas to meet your design brief.

Activities

1 Find a photo of an interesting modern building, such as the 'Gherkin' or the Lloyds building in the City of London. Make a drawing of the most interesting features of the building.

2 Draw two ideas for an original desktop light that uses the form of the building as a starting point. Use only a biro for the drawing and work entirely freehand.

3 Try the same activity with a natural seedpod.

Summary

★ There are many ways to help you to produce original designs effectively. Working with stimulus material is a good way to help you to be creative.

★ Looking at other designers' work will help you to see what can be done.

1.3 Visualising by quick sketching

In this chapter you will learn about:
- ★ **visualising your ideas by quick modelling and sketching**
- ★ **how to use a range of sketching techniques to explore design ideas.**

Turning ideas into reality

We all have the ability to see and to imagine ideas in our 'mind's eye'. Transferring these ideas into sketches and models is a vital skill for designers as it enables them to:
- think more clearly about form and function
- develop and clarify their ideas further
- share their ideas with others
- evaluate ideas to decide which ones to develop.

In the early stages of designing, quick sketches or quick models can both be effective. Designers often move quickly from one to the other, making a quick model in minutes, looking at it, changing it, making a quick sketch of the model, drawing it again and possibly remodelling. One of the best ways to visualise your design ideas is to use both sketching and modelling together and to switch between them.

Visualising by sketching

A3 paper of medium weight (80 gsm), possibly with a simple underlay sheet with a 10 mm square grid, will mak sketching easier. A fine-point marker or even a biro can be really effective for initial ideas. Draw freehand and keep the size of drawings reasonably compact. You cannot rub out ideas, forcing you to draw in a particular way, which is effective for first ideas. As your ideas develop, you may wis to change to a sharp HB pencil.

Use the following steps for the early stages of your work:
1. Draw simple 2D views at a fairly small scale, then add a little spot colour for emphasis.
2. Draw more detailed 2D views at a slightly larger scale.
3. Add a second **orthographic projection** (straight on view) to show another face of the object.
4. Draw a 3D view to give a good all-round impression.

Sketching tips

- To draw straight lines freehand, keep your wrist stiff anc move your whole arm. Place the pencil at the start of th line, look at the end point and draw. Just like throwing a ball, look at where you want it to go.

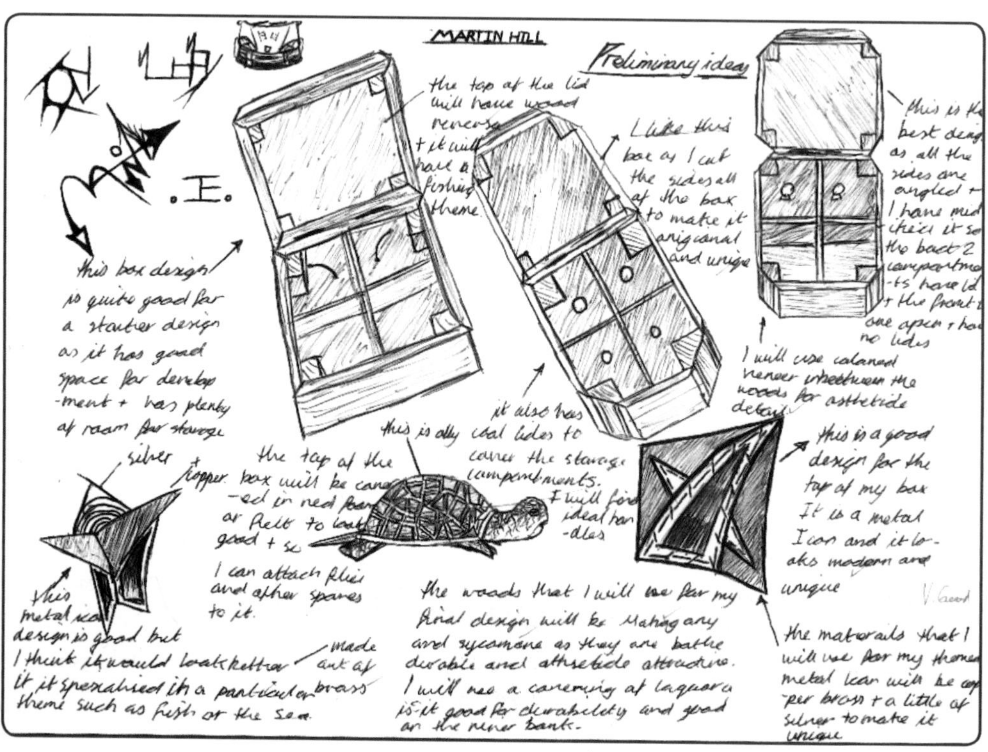

Development wor

To draw curved lines, keep your wrist limp and use the heel of your hand like the point of a compass. Move the paper around to make things easier.

;rating

rawing feint boxes (crates) can be useful to elp position parts of an object. Imagine your esign idea is inside a glass box: draw the box nd then draw the idea inside it. This method an be helpful when drawing in 3D and will elp you to achieve more realistic sketches.

Jsing ICT

omputers can be helpful or visualising design leas. Ideas can be ketched and changed to xplore possibilities. The pportunity to change nd move parts, and vary olours and textures in econds, can make ICT a owerful tool.

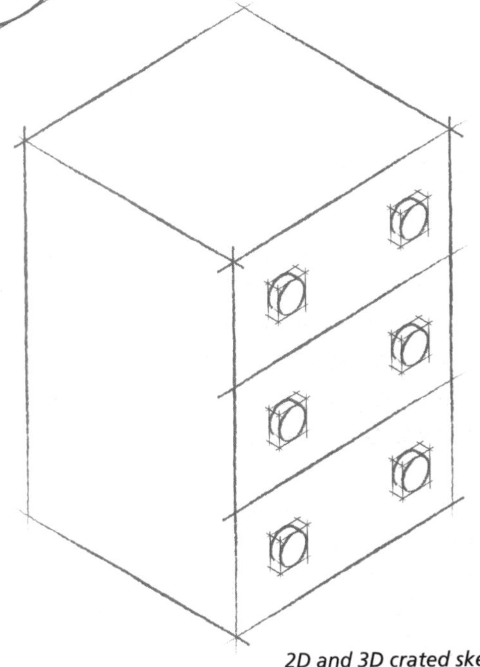

2D and 3D crated sketches

Activity

a Use a biro and produce a series of ten sketches of small objects, such as a computer mouse or a stapler. Spend no more than three minutes on each sketch. Challenge yourself to get the maximum detail in the time allowed.

b Which views capture the most detail?

Coursework

Quick sketching is an excellent way to get ideas out of your head and onto paper, almost like thinking through a pencil point. Use a fine-point marker or a biro and, working without a ruler, produce three five minute ideas sketches for your current project. Quick modelling may be an easier first step for some people.

Summary

★ Developing quick sketching skills will help you to become an effective designer.

Visualising by quick modelling

In this chapter you will learn about:

- ★ **quick modelling as a development tool**
- ★ **using scale modelling to improve and trial designs.**

Visualising by quick modelling

Quick modelling is one way of seeing what an object might be like. Quick models can be put together from scrap card and sticky tape inside five minutes. It enables you to hold a trial version of the design idea in your hand, to be able to look all around it and to make simple changes there and then. This is a great way to move ideas on. Take digital photos of your models and add them to your ideas sketching sheet.

Do not add a finish to your model and leave it in the original colour. The important things to look at are the form and the proportions (balance between width height and depth) of your design.

The scale at which you model is important. As a guide, larger products are often modelled at 1:4 (quarter full size) and smaller products at 1:2 (half full size). If the model is too small it will be fiddly and difficult to make.

Materials and tools

This is a powerful way to develop your design ideas and can save time both at the design and at the making stages. A range of materials, **adhesives** and fixings are needed; for example, paper, card, tubes, straws, lolly sticks, wooden skewers, string and wire. Adhesive tape, hot-melt glue guns, staplers and paper fasteners all enable rapid making. Only basic tools such as scissors, modelling knives and pliers are needed. To do this at home, all you need can be found in most kitchens. It does not matter what the model is made from as long as it allows you to explore and develop your design idea in 3D.

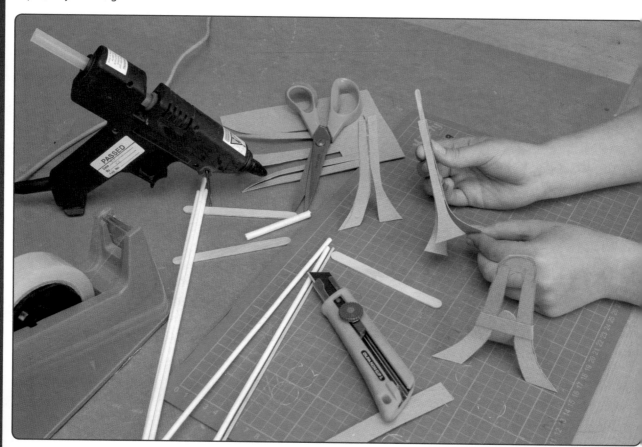

Rapid models, materials and tools

)eveloping your ideas

here is no one way to develop your ideas. Sometimes uick modelling will help you to work out ideas; sometimes ou will be able to draw ideas straight away. All that ıatters is that you have a way that works for you. All the ork you do at this stage is valuable. It may not be as neat s a final design but it is your ideas that count.

Scale modelling

scale model allows you to work out your design at a ıanageable size but looks just like the real thing, so you an make final decisions with confidence.

More elaborate models are an excellent way to explore the final idea

In the final stages of designing, a precise scale model will help to ensure that:

- you have done all you can to think the design through
- you will be able to see what the design will actually look like
- you can trial some aspects of the actual making and assembly.

Safety notes

Cutting knives can be useful but should only be used with care on a cutting mat. Always use a safety rule and cut away from yourself, supporting the work on a firm surface.

Coursework

Quick modelling is a good alternative to drawing, but often the best way of designing is a mixture of drawing and modelling. Many people find that they can model what they cannot draw. If you have time you could produce a model for one of the design ideas for your current project instead of a drawing.

Activities

1 Design a simple free-standing clock based on intersecting triangles. You may only model ideas using a cereal box and Sellotape, and scissors are the only tool available. Drawing is not allowed.

2 Produce a design idea for a small desk tidy to be made from acrylic. You are to use only a panel from a cereal box, Sellotape and scissors. Do not sketch your ideas first, but you may do a rough model first if you wish.

Summary

★ Developing quick modelling skills will help you to become an effective designer.

Inspiring design ideas

> In this chapter you will learn about:
> - ★ how to make your designing more imaginative
> - ★ how to use stimulus material to inspire new ideas
> - ★ the ways in which new design ideas can be created and developed.

Creativity

The very nature of all design is that it is about the unknown. New designs for products are created by designers working to meet the needs of people and using their creativity to do this in new and exciting ways. There are two ways to approach your designing if you want to be creative:

- Use your imagination by playing with ideas in your 'mind's eye' to explore what can be done.
- Focus your thoughts by trying to work out new and exciting ways forward.

These simple approaches will help you to achieve the most difficult thing when designing – being original. Trying to be completely new and different is never easy, but it is always a great thing to aim for.

You need to look at your designs and make careful judgements about what is worth developing at every stage. This is **critical evaluation** and it is important to do this well.

Make a stimulus sheet

Ignore the obvious: start your designing somewhere more exciting than old catalogues! The Internet, library books, magazines and making drawings from life are all valuable sources. Paste up a sheet of pictures and drawings and use this as a starting point.

Using architecture for furniture design

The shapes and forms of modern buildings offer a powerful set of images to use as a starting point for furniture ideas. Use the Internet and get some images of both the interior and the exterior of a selection of modern buildings. Choosing the shapes and adapting them to use at a much smaller scale can be effective.

Using science fiction for storage design

Collect images from fictional future worlds, creatures, machines and structures. Comics, books and movie websites can all be valuable sources. Often the detail can be just as valuable as the main image. Using unusual shapes and fixings developed from sci-fi can give an interesting twist to storage design.

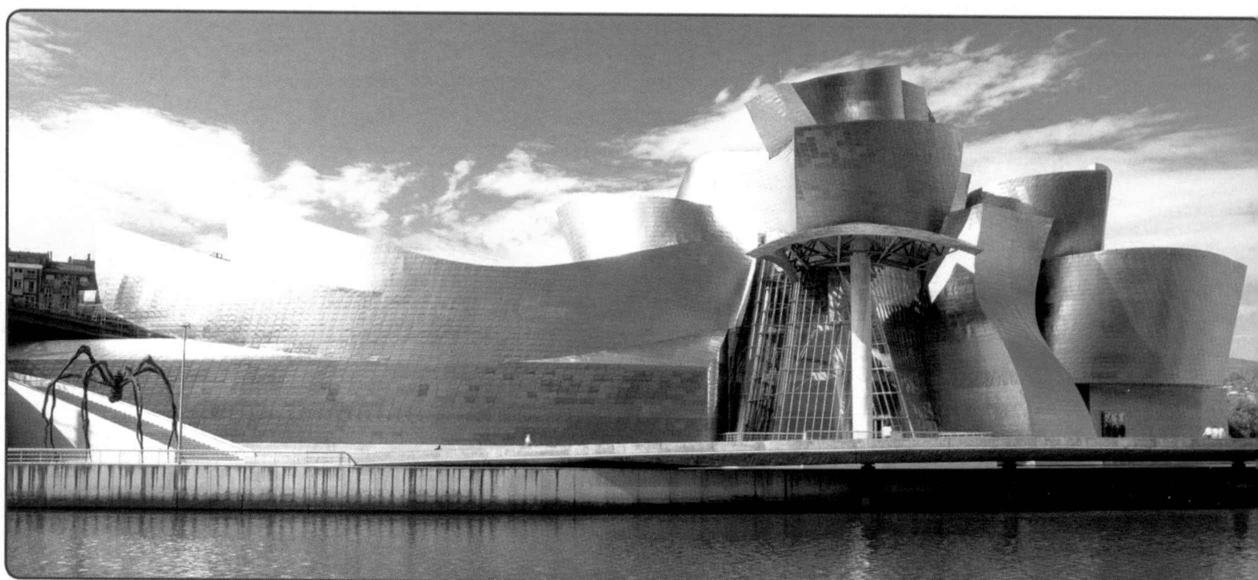

Modern architecture – The Gugennheim Museum in Spain

sing natural forms or jewellery design

owers, seedpods and fruits offer any possibilities for jewellery. ake your own drawings from al life. Choose images with strong apes and plenty of interest. Books drawings of plants are often much tter than photographs for this kind work.

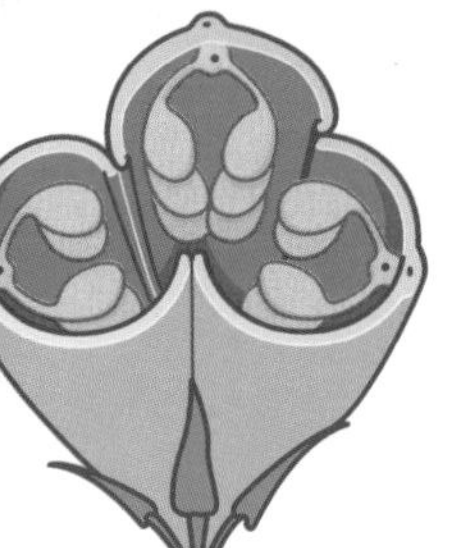

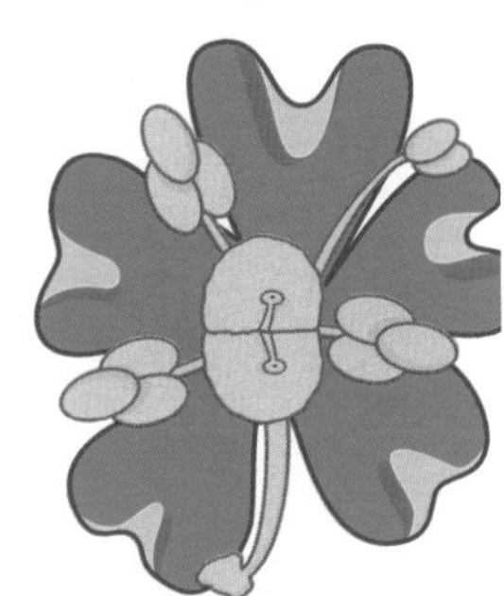

Flowers and seedpods offer many design possibilities

electing, abstracting and dapting

electing

se the basic design principles of shape, pattern, form, olour and texture to look at the images you have collected r your design. Make simple drawings of parts you think ould be useful. Using a card with a small window to select art of an image can work well. Enlarge it and see what ou could use to start a design idea. Similarly, the shapes f large buildings can be reduced in scale and used as the tarting point for smaller designs.

our own drawings are much more valuable than hotographs because, as you draw, you will automatically tart to look for patterns and shapes. Tracing shapes from hotographs can be a great starting point and a photocopier an be used to enlarge small details into workable size.

bstracting

bstracting means taking interesting parts of a picture and sing them in new ways – redrawing and changing them sing your imagination. The way you choose to analyse and select parts is important. Think of it as visually 'filtering out' all but the most interesting parts.

Adapting

Using the parts you have selected and redrawn, adapt them to new purposes by developing new designs that use your drawings as the starting point. Use the shapes, forms and patterns you have abstracted to create your original design.

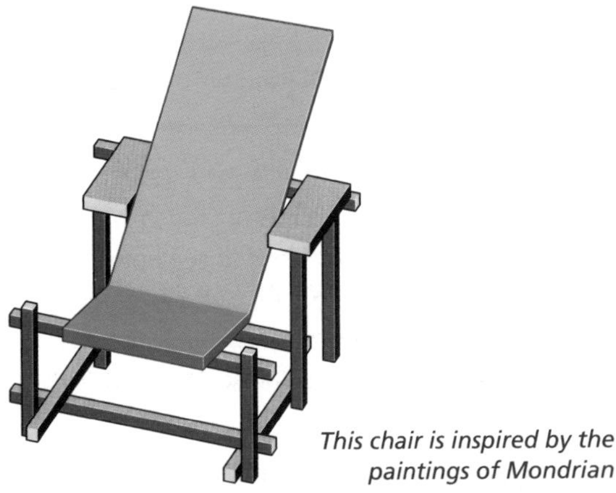

This chair is inspired by the paintings of Mondrian

Coursework

This chapter will help you to develop more creative and original design. What theme could you use to inspire your ideas for your coursework project? Using a theme to help get ideas flowing can be very effective.

Activities

1. Paste up a sheet of pictures and drawings to form a stimulus sheet on one of the themes dealt with in this chapter, such as architecture, the natural world or science fiction.
2. Produce a set of initial ideas for either small furniture, jewellery or storage. Draw in ink, biro or fine-point marker only and add some notes to explain your designs.

Summary

★ To be creative you need to find inspiring material and focus your imagination.

1.6 Using design history as a source of inspiration

In this chapter you will learn about:
- ★ using design history for inspiration
- ★ using design analysis as a starting point.

Using design history

Looking at other designers and styles can be an effective way to inspire your work. Design is evolving constantly and revisiting the works of the past can be a powerful starting point. This type of approach can give rise to new and exciting work.

Use the work to *inspire* your original design ideas; do not just copy them. To use this approach well, you need to analyse carefully the designs to see how designers developed their work. The following examples offer a useful starting point; use a library or the Internet to explore them further. There are many other examples you could look at.

Art Nouveau (1890–1905)

This movement swept though Europe and the USA. It looked to nature as its inspiration and is a decorative and romantic style using subtle colours. Flowing natural forms are typical of this style.

Art Nouveau jewellery

Art Deco (1925–39)

This exciting, decorative style has strong geometric forms. It uses bold images and colours, and rich mixtures of materials, to add impact.

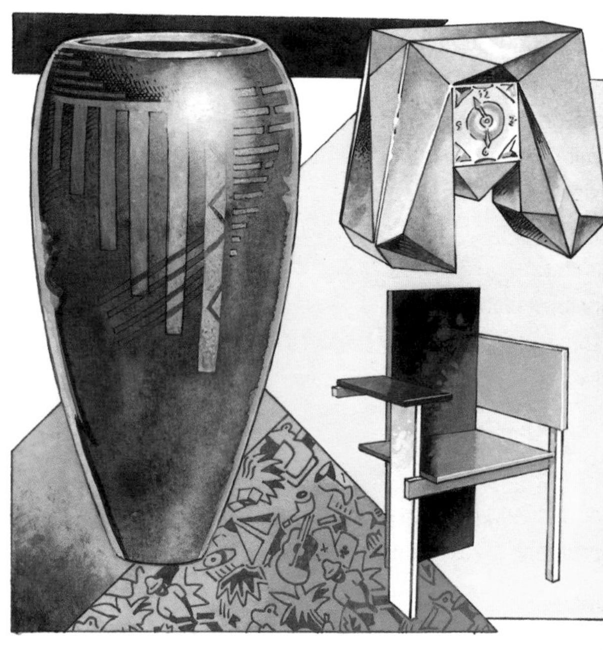

Art Deco furnitu

Memphis (1981–88)

This design style was named after the lyrics of a Bob Dylan song that was playing when a designer was asked to name an exhibition of the work from a group of young designers and architects, Ettore Sottsass put together a collection of objects and furniture that broke all the rules of conventional design. The Memphis objects were like children's toys, with bold patterns, bright colours and playful forms – look at the photo on page 7 for an example.

Alessi (late twentieth century)

Alessi of Milan is the most influential product design company in the late twentieth century, producing many different products. The company designs innovative, colourful, witty and functional objects for the home. A number of maestros (top designers) have worked for the company including Philippe Starck, Richard Sapper and Michael Graves.

hilippe Starck (1949–)

is designer is one of the most famous designers in the orld. His work is everywhere, from interiors to furniture, mps to kitchen tools and even toothbrushes.

esign analysis

detailed analysis of a product is an excellent way of eveloping an understanding of how a designer works. esigning either in that style or in a personal variation the style is an excellent way of achieving different and aginative design. Analysing using the basic design inciples is the best starting point as this will help you focus on each part of the design in turn. Use 1.1 *Basic esign principles* and 2.1 *Product analysis* to help you.

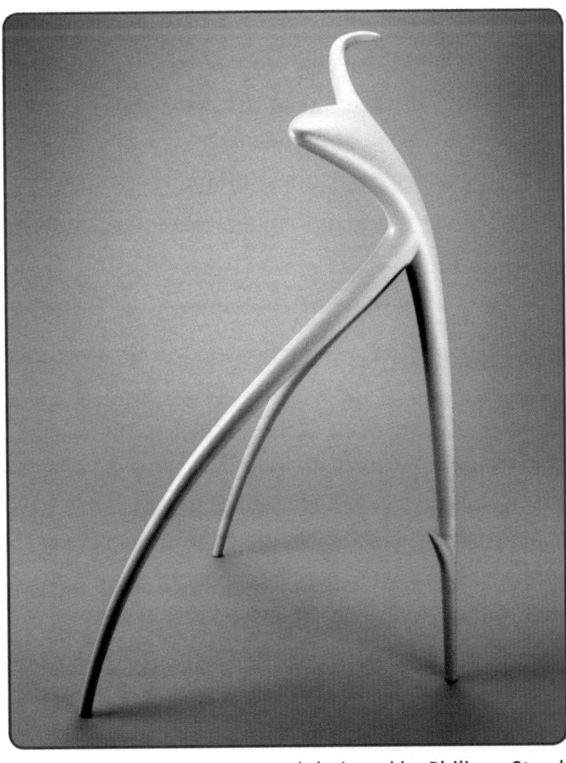

A cast aluminium stool designed by Philippe Starck

esign analysis outline

e following outlines give many headings you will need for our analysis. Not all the headings will apply to all products.

ow has the designer used each of the following?

Line	Shape	Form	Colour	Texture

hat is the product made from? How it has been made and finished?

Materials	Components	Processes	Finish	Decoration

um up the overall design

Mood/feeling	Visual impact	Style	Inspiration	Best features

Coursework

Looking at the work of top designers is a useful piece of research and a great way to get some inspiration for your coursework project. Your research will help you decide on your product specification.

Activity

a Use the Internet and explore both Art Nouveau and Art Deco. Look at jewellery, furniture and architecture.

b Design a mirror frame in one of these styles.

Summary

★ Design history and the work of other designers are valuable resources for designing.

Ergonomics

In this chapter you will learn about:
- ★ **why designers need to have a working knowledge of ergonomics**
- ★ **how designers use anthropometric data**
- ★ **how you can use ergonomics to design better products.**

Ergonomics

Ergonomics is the study of the efficiency of people in their working environment. Designers study how people interact with products and use this information to design better products. Ergonomics is a large area of study and covers every aspect of design for performance. It is about improving performance in many different ways.

Ergonomics helps:
- Formula One racing drivers and Olympic swimmers to win races by designing equipment and accessories to help them perform better
- mobile phone users to text easily and accurately while ensuring the key pad is easy to use and well laid out
- the elderly to get around more easily by designing equipment to aid their mobility.

Understanding and using ergonomics will help you to be a better designer.

Ergonomics at work

Good ergonomics at work can help workers to stay safe and healthy, be happy and make fewer mistakes. This is because the whole **environment** has been ergonomically designed: the machines are well designed, the air is clean, the temperature is comfortable, the light is good and the worker does not need to stretch or strain.

Case Study

computer games controller

The surface of the plastic has a pleasing texture

The weight and balance of the control is carefully arranged to make it feel solid and comfortable in the hand without being too heavy

The control buttons are set in an arrangement that allows a range of movements, with the most frequently used buttons in the easiest places to use

The buttons are 'finger friendly'

The unit has been designed to fit comfortably in a range of hand sizes for both male and female users

Look at this games controller and consider how the designer has used ergonomics to make it

ınthropometrics

ıthropometrics is the comparative study of the sizes and oportions of the human body. Designers use tables of easurements of the human body to help them to design fectively. As people come in a wide range of sizes and apes, the tables of measurements are for both male and male and give three different measurements for each size.

sing anthropometric data

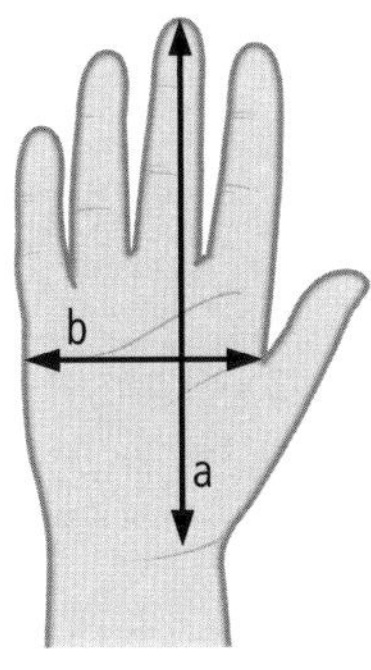

a Hand length: from crease of the wrist to the top of the middle finger

b Hand breadth: the overall breadth of the palm excluding the thumb

	Average hand length	Average hand breadth
Male 12–14	170	80
Female 12–14	170	75
Male 19–65	190	90
Female 19–65	180	85
Male 65+	170	75
Female 65+	160	70

An example of anthropometric hand data

practical example: an artist's case

ook at the photo of the artist's case, which shows a ood example of ergonomic research. Can a small item e grasped and removed from the box by both males nd females with a range of hand sizes? The designer vould need to make a model, take digital photos, take ıeasurements to improve the design and check again to chieve a final solution. This is ergonomics in action.

sing ergonomics to design the internal arrangement of the ase is a vital part in ensuring the case will both be easy to se and hold all the equipment.

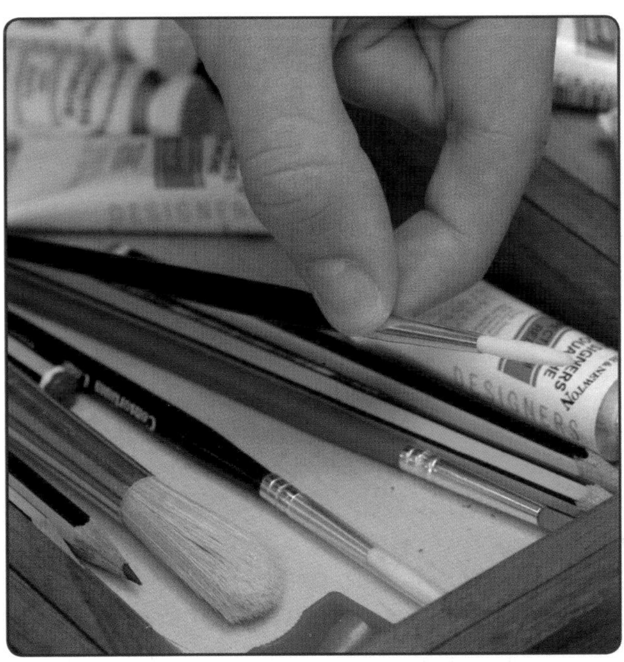

The contents of an artist's case

Coursework

Showing your research through diagrams and digital photography will help you to achieve a quality coursework folder. Ensure you compare different user sizes and preferences and explain how you decided on the final details. Remember that your research should be concise and relvant to the project outline.

Activities

1 Redesign the outside of the artist's case to make it more ergonomic. Produce ideas for both the handle and the opening edge to improve the ergonomics of the design.

2 Take a look at your computer mouse. What evidence can you see that the designer used ergonomics in the design? What do you think needs improving? Draw sketches to show two ways in which the design could be made more ergonomic.

Summary

★ Using ergonomics is a vital part of designing better performing products.

1.8 Presenting design ideas

In this chapter you will learn about:

- ★ how to use a range of graphic techniques to improve the presentation of your drawing
- ★ the materials, media and techniques that can be used to present ideas.

Design techniques

Designers use a variety of presentation techniques to produce realistic drawings to show and explain their designs to **clients**. The most important basic techniques are:

- using tonal effects (light and shade) to capture the form of objects
- applying texture to add realism
- adding backgrounds, shadows and reflections
- presenting your drawings.

Using tonal effects

The way that light falls on the surface of an object varies according to its form. The area nearest the light source will be light and the area furthest away will be dark. Designers add tonal shading to an object to give it the impression of being 3D.

Applying texture

Applying texture to an object helps to increase the feeling of depth in the drawing and gives information about the materials.

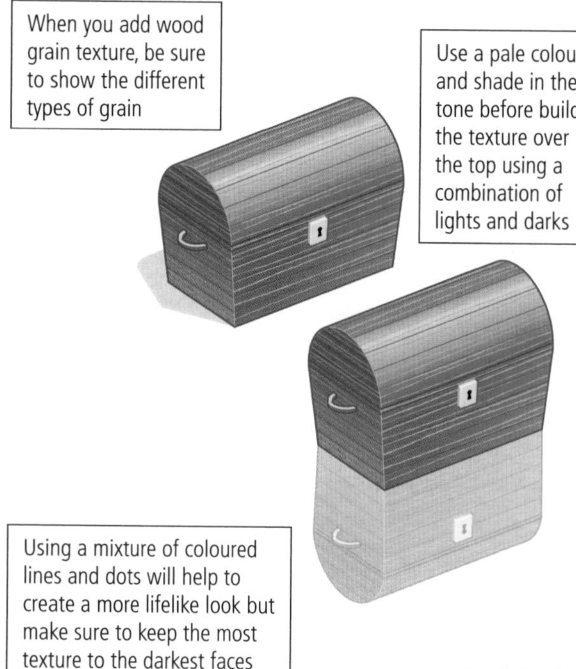

When you add wood grain texture, be sure to show the different types of grain
Use a pale colour and shade in the tone before building the texture over the top using a combination of lights and darks
Using a mixture of coloured lines and dots will help to create a more lifelike look but make sure to keep the most texture to the darkest faces

Applying textur

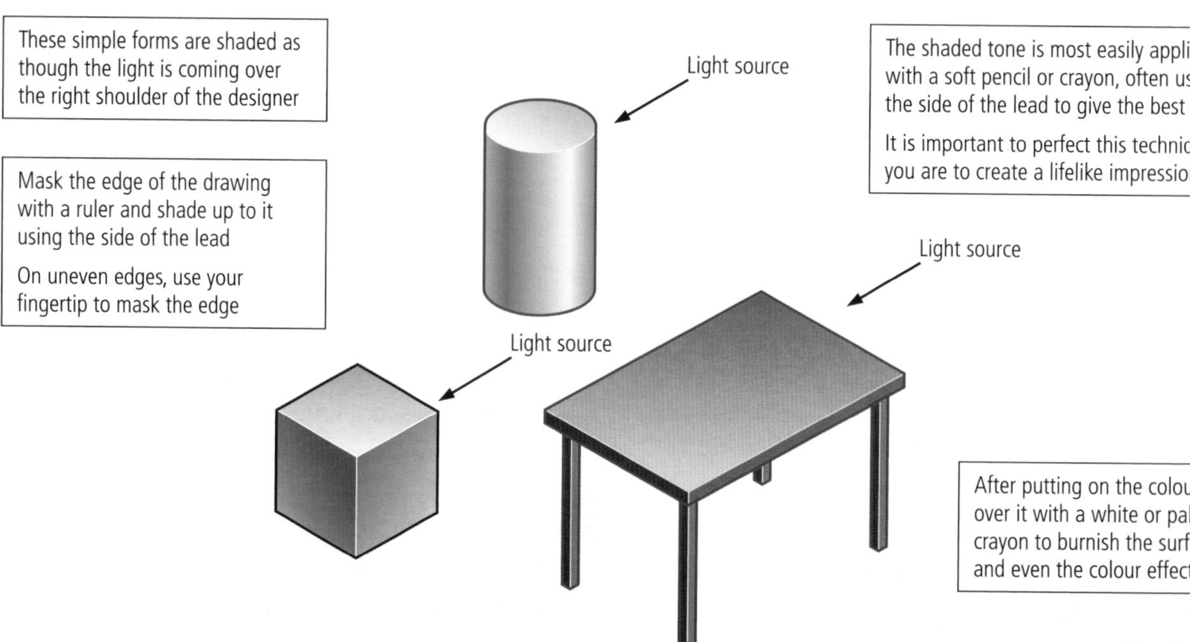

These simple forms are shaded as though the light is coming over the right shoulder of the designer
Mask the edge of the drawing with a ruler and shade up to it using the side of the lead
On uneven edges, use your fingertip to mask the edge
Light source
Light source
Light source
The shaded tone is most easily applied with a soft pencil or crayon, often using the side of the lead to give the best effect
It is important to perfect this technique if you are to create a lifelike impression
After putting on the colour, go over it with a white or pale grey crayon to burnish the surface and even the colour effect

Tonal shading

pplying backgrounds, shadows and eflections

Adding a simple shadow can help to make the object stand out from the background.
Thicken lines around the outside edges of the object and use a thinner line for inside edges.
Adding a slight reflection below an object as though it is on a shiny, wet surface can give an interesting effect.
Carefully cutting out the object and pasting it onto a new colour background can be effective. Mounting onto a photograph can sometimes be dramatic.

Presenting your drawings

A 3D modelling program such as Pro/DESKTOP® can be used to create presentation drawings that are almost photo-real (like a photograph). The drawings can be combined with other special effects such as shadow and backgrounds. Drawings produced this way can be viewed rotating on screen, or printed in colour or black and white.

CorelDRAW® can be used to produce accurate and realistically **rendered** drawings with dimensions, and The Techsoft 2D Design programme can also be used to create similar work.

ietting the best ffects

'epare the 3D view and ake a feint photocopy for e coloured drawing. If you ake a mistake, you can art again. A slightly heavier aper of 120 gsm will take e colour better. Use a good uality pencil crayon to get e best effects and keep sharp. Add highlights to rward-facing edges using white crayon or correction en. Add some final darks nd textures with soft 2B encil.

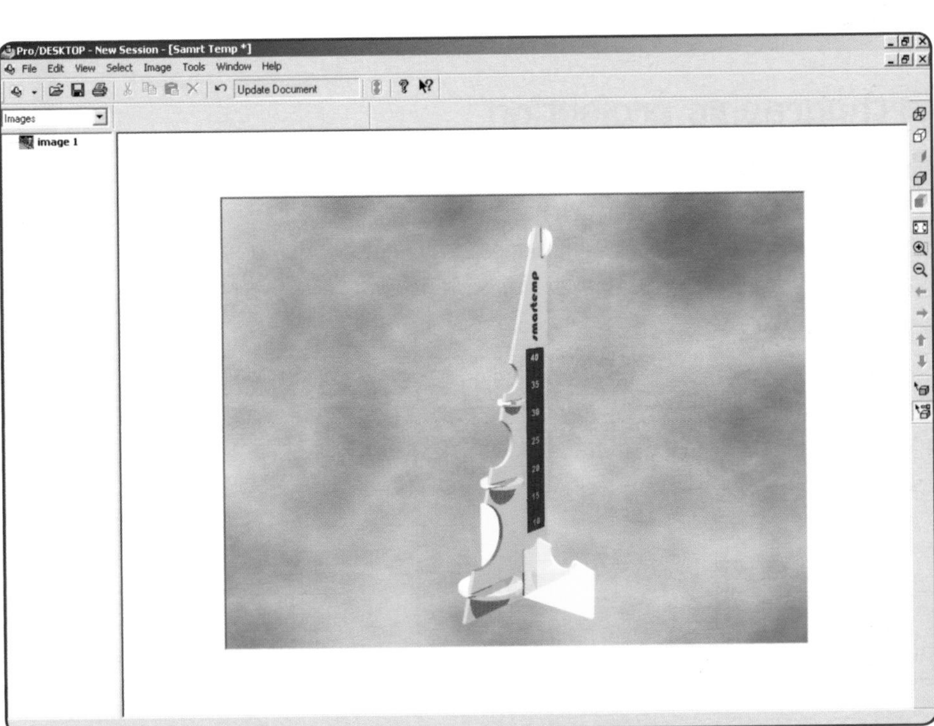

Presentation drawings can be enhanced using ICT

Activity

Draw a colour-rendered view of a product you have recently made, cut it out from the sheet and remount it onto a new background of either a coloured paper or a photo from a magazine.

a How has the drawing changed?

b How could you use this kind of presentation in your project folder?

Coursework

Presenting design ideas in a lifelike form is an important stage in designing. The quality of your drawing is part of the assessment criteria for your coursework project.

Summary

★ Presenting design proposals skilfully can make an important difference to the visual impact.

1.9 Working drawings

In this chapter you will learn about:

- ★ **using orthographic drawing techniques to produce a working drawing**
- ★ **how to communicate design information clearly and accurately.**

Working drawings provide all the information needed to manufacture a product. They are always drawn and set out in a certain way to ensure they can be understood. See 6.1 *Using CAD* for information on producing working drawings using **computer-aided design (CAD)**.

Orthographic projection

This method of drawing is the most commonly used method of communicating all the information needed to make a product. The word 'orthographic' simply means 'straight-on drawing' and refers to the way that each view is drawn looking straight on to the various faces of the object. The main reason why the views are drawn 'straight on' is to ensure all the measurements will be accurate.

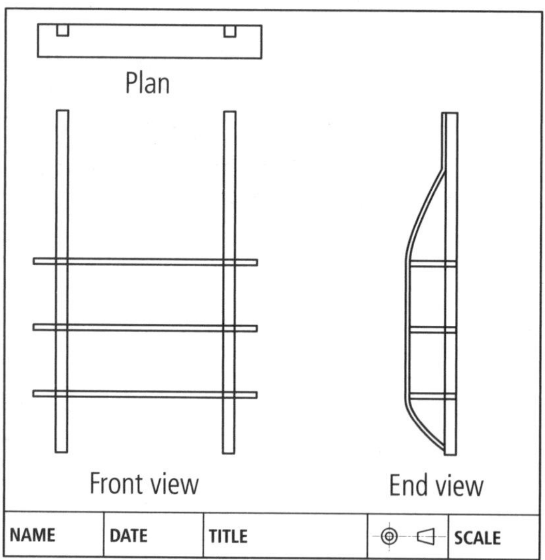

Three views of the product are drawn: a plan, a front and an end view. These are arranged in a way called third angle projection, which helps the viewer to visualise the product in 3D

The best way to start this kind of drawing is with a 3D pictorial sketch of your design. You can use this sketch to work out which views to use and how to lay them out.

Third angle orthographic projection

The simple drawing of a shelf unit shown below makes it easy to see how the views in a working drawing are arranged. The plan view is always as seen from above, the front and end views are always viewed from ground level and are set out next to each other. The end view is the view of the right-hand face of the object and is always drawn to the right-hand side.

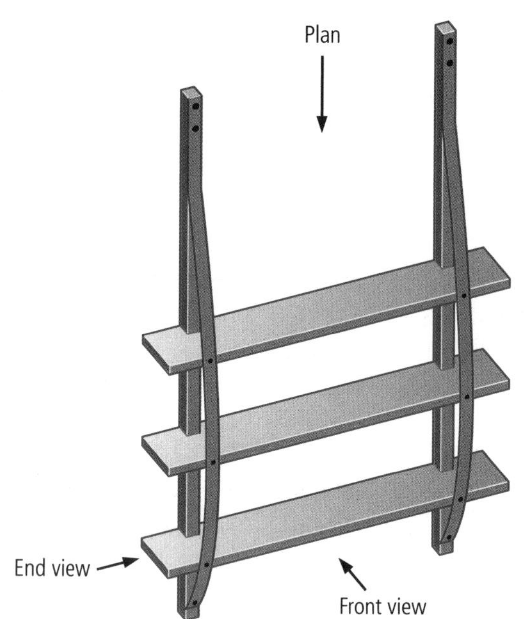

A third angle orthographic projection of a shelf unit

This style of drawing always includes a title block with:

- the drawing name
- the scale used for the drawing, which is always shown as a ratio; for example, an object draw half size has a scale of 1:2
- the units that are used for the dimensions (normally millimetres)
- a symbol to show that it is drawn in third angle orthographic projection.

Layout

The drawing is laid out using construction lines to project the views from one to the other to ensure accuracy and to speed up the drawing process. It is necessary to work out the space needed to lay out a drawing neatly.

ines

e most commonly used lines are shown below:

- continuous thick (0.7 mm) are used for outlines
- continuous thin (0.3 mm) show dimensions and projection lines
- dashed thin (0.5 mm) are used for hidden detail lines
- chain line show centre lines.

ese line types are all shown in the working drawing low.

imensions

e dimensions or sizes for the drawing are added using e following rules:

- always show actual dimensions not scaled ones
- keep dimensions away from the drawing to avoid clutter
- keep it simple: include main dimensions only
- always set out dimensions as described by the **British Standards Institute (BSI)**, which provides a common standard that everyone can follow.

tyle

orking drawings are always laid out in a formal style as is helps to keep everything clear and professional.

British Standards Institute (BSI)

The BSI sets out agreed standard ways of producing a working drawing. These standards ensure that drawings can be understood by everyone who looks at them and helps to prevent misunderstandings. All designers work to these standards. A set of these standards (BS308 Engineering Drawing Practice) should be available for reference in schools and colleges.

Coursework

Accurate working drawings are an essential stage in designing and help making to proceed smoothly. Plan the working drawings you will need for your coursework project by sketching them out freehand. How many views will you need to communicate the design clearly?

Activity

Draw three sketched views in third angle orthographic projection of small items from around your home. Start with a simple object like a stool and progress to something more complex like a table lamp.

Summary

★ Good working drawings will enable you to communicate information accurately and clearly about the design of your project.

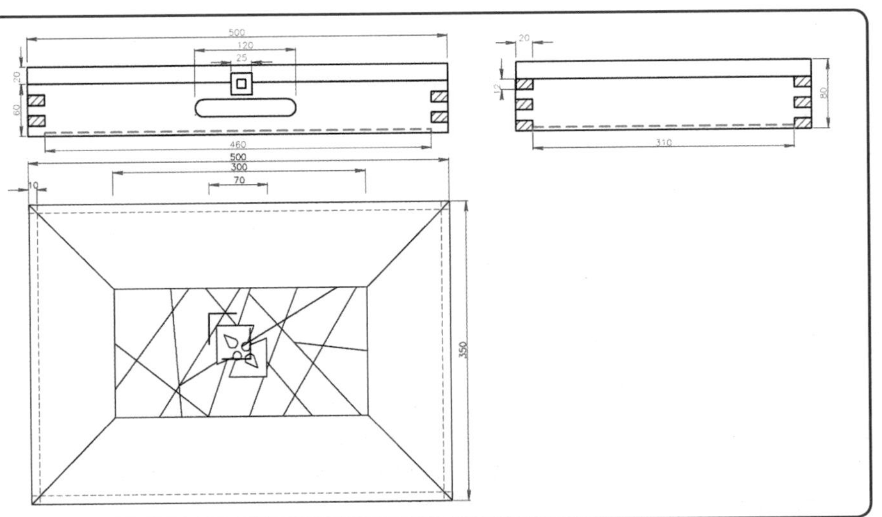

A working drawing should contain all the information needed to make the product

ICT and design

> **In this chapter you will learn about:**
> - ★ using computers to improve the quality and accuracy of your work
> - ★ using computers to research and design more effectively
> - ★ using digital cameras.

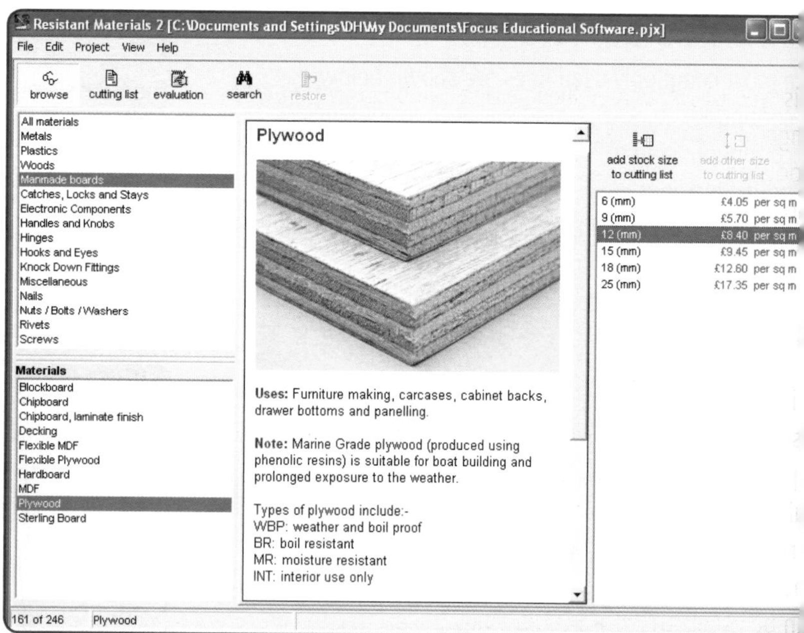

The Focus on Resistant Materials 2 program contains searchable databa

There are many different ways designers use ICT as a tool to improve aspects of designing. They commonly gather information from around the world to help their work. Designs are often sent back around the globe to be made in other countries and then the products are viewed over the Internet. Some large companies design 24 hours a day by having one team in the UK and a second in Australia, both working on the same project and passing it backwards and forwards between them.

Word processing

Using a word processor for specifications allows easy editing and can form the basis of an excellent evaluation. Writing up notes and inserting graphs and photos enable word processing software to be used for many purposes. Microsoft® Word® is a widely used word processor with a number of useful presentation tools.

Spreadsheets

Spreadsheets enable easy handling of data such as the findings from a questionnaire and can be effective for producing charts and graphs to display results. Microsoft® Excel® is a popular spreadsheet program.

Databases

Databases can be used for handing and cataloguing information to allow ease of use. One package, Focus on Resistant Materials 2, gives detailed information on materials, fittings, components and joints, and can formulate cutting lists. Photographs and information are found easily and a project costings section enables a fully costed cutting list to be created with the minimum of effort. The Focus on Plastics database covers the eight mai techniques used to manufacture plastic products.

The Internet

The Internet is a powerful research tool which allows you to obtain information and images from around the world in seconds. You need to be careful in your choice of search words. You also need to choose only relevant information and print just what you need.

A **search engine** like Google (go to www.heinemann.co.uk/hotlinks) will help you to find information and image rapidly. To find images, click on the Images link above the text entry box. Visiting design and technology-related websites can be a useful starting point, providing links to other useful sites.

Sending and receiving e-mails is another invaluable function of the Internet.

raphics software

is type of software is flexible and can be used for a wide ıge of designing tasks. Presentation drawings can be ɔduced and combined with creative text, clipart images d photographs. CorelDRAW®, Pro/DESKTOP® and chsoft 2D Design are all powerful graphics packages.

D modelling programs

is type of software has been available to schools through special free scheme to help young designers. The software powerful and enables 3D drawings to be produced ickly. The drawings can be rendered with lifelike material rfaces and arranged with backgrounds to give almost otographic results. Working drawings with dimensions n be produced from 3D drawings.

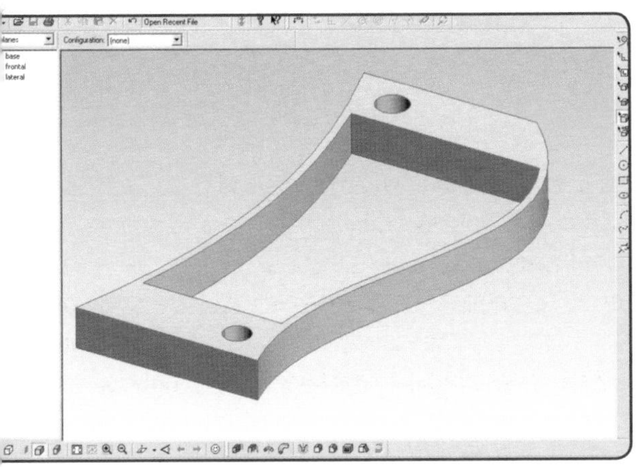
Pro/DESKTOP® is available in many schools

igital cameras

digital camera can be used to:

- photograph development models you have made
- make research more immediate and relevant
- show trials and tests as part of the making processes
- show products in use for evaluations
- print photos in black and white.

igital photos can be edited and merged with other ıotos. Using a photo editing software package such as dobe® Photoshop®, it is possible to combine a photo of ıe product with a different background photo, as well as ɔplying many other interesting techniques.

Digital cameras allow photos to be used in designing

Coursework

Plan where you can make best use of ICT in your project folder. Where will you use:

- word processing
- databases
- Internet research
- digital photography?

Activities

1 Explore a design and technology-related website such as that at www.heinemann.co.uk/hotlinks and follow the links to other sites.

2 Alternatively, use a search engine to find a specific set of search words, such as 'Swedish furniture' and see where the results take you.

Summary

★ Designers can use ICT for research, communication and design.

Exam questions

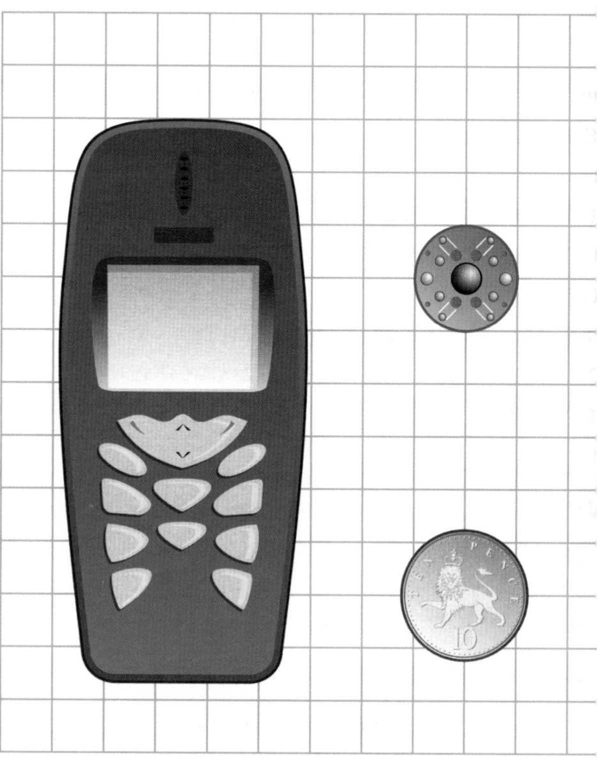

1 A manufacturer of electronic components has produced a flashing unit which will activate when it detects incoming calls to a mobile phone. You have been asked to design a range of mobile phone holders which are suitable for the teenage market and incorporate this flashing unit.

Before attempting this design question you should investigate 'mobile phone holders'. You could search on the Internet or pay a visit to your local mobile phone accessory shop for inspiration.

The picture on the rght shows a mobile phone and a flasher unit. The 10p coin will help you get the size of your idea correct.

Take an A3 sheet of paper and fold it into four. Each section represents the space you will have to work in on the exam paper. Think about your investigation into mobile phone holders, and then have a go at the following exam type question. Keep your eye on the clock!

Use this information to help you sketch **three** ideas for a mobile phone holder.

Remember to:

- incorporate the flashing unit
- design for the teenage market
- add notes to explain your sketches
- evaluate each idea.

Marks will be awarded for:

Three ideas	*(3 × 6 marks)*
Quality of sketches	*(5 marks)*
Quality of notes	*(3 marks)*
Quality of evaluations	*(3 × 2 marks)*
	(Total: 32 marks)

Design and market influences

is section looks at the designer's sponsibilities to society, the environment d the workforce. It looks at the way oducts emerge from different starting ints, such as cultural, historical and chnological. The most beautiful and exciting sign may be manufactured, but unless rkers are kept safe and the consumer otected the designer has failed in his or r duty.

hat's in this section?

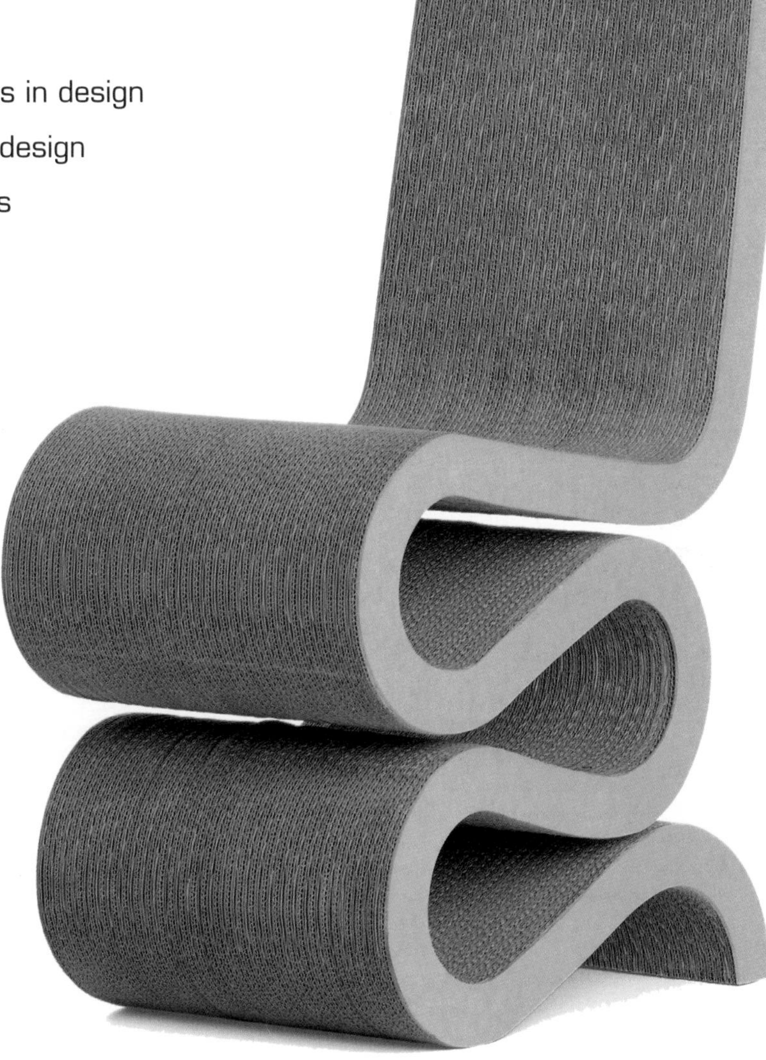

The fat, lazy curves of this Wiggle chair by ank Gehry look like hot poured metal, but actually it is made entirely from the most isposable of modern materials: cardboard

2.1 Product analysis

> **In this chapter you will learn about:**
> ★ **using product analysis as a research tool.**

How to analyse a product

Analysing a real product means you can explore, touch, use and obtain some background information about it. To start your analysis, make some drawings or take digital photographs of the product to show:

- a 3D view: looking at the front corner, add something to show the scale – a ruler or a hand are good ideas
- some details of joints and fittings to show construction.

If the chosen product has instructions on assembly or use, these also give helpful information. If the product is in a catalogue, get a copy and cut out the description and photo. It may also be useful to look at other similar products to compare details such as materials, sizes and costs.

You need to consider the following points in your product analysis.

- Materials and components: identify the materials used and explain why you think they were chosen. Look at which components and fittings have been used in the assembly. How have they been used to develop the design?
- Aesthetics: this is concerned with how we react to the product, how we feel about its style and design feature how the choice of materials and finish affects the appearance and how it feels, what the product is like tc use and how it fits our lifestyles, and whether the overa effect is visually pleasing.
- Style: designers take ideas and inspiration from many sources. Can you identify a style or starting point in the product that has been developed from nature? Does th product show influence from another designer or desig movement? Does it show influences from the past or other cultures?

How have the curved pieces been made?
What fixings have been used?
What sort of room would this be found in?
What kind of wood has been used and why?
Which parts are decorative?

An unusual wall shelf with flowing lin

Function: how well does the product work? Does it do the job it was designed for? How do target consumers react to it?

Ergonomics: how well does the product meet the needs of users? Is it easy and efficient to use? Is it safe? Does it suit a range of different users?

Manufacture: what materials and processes have been used? Was it mass produced? How was it supplied? Was it assembled or supplied as a **flat-pack kit** for the consumer to assemble?

Environmental impact: how environmentally friendly is the product? Is the material it is made from obtained from **sustainable** sources, for example forests that are replanted at the same rate as they are felled? Can the product be **recycled**? How much energy has been used to make and transport it? Were the people who were involved in making the product treated fairly?

A Charles Rennie Mackintosh chair. Where do you think he got his inspiration from?

Coursework

Analysing products that are similar to those you intend to make is an important part of the research for your coursework project and will help you decide what your product will be like.

Activity

a Find two similar products from different times, such as a hand-crafted solid wood product and a mass-produced flat-pack manufactured board product. A small box or storage rack would be ideal.

b Analyse your two products using the following criteria: materials and components, aesthetics, style, function, ergonomics, manufacture, environmental impact.

c Answer the following questions.

- **i** How have the designs developed over time?
- **ii** How have the products been manufactured?
- **iii** How are the pieces joined together?
- **iv** How many similar products are likely to exist?
- **v** How long are these products expected to last?
- **vi** How much are they worth, now and in ten years' time?

Summary

★ Product analysis is an effective and quick way of learning a great deal about how products are designed and made.

2.2 Quality

In this chapter you will learn about:

★ **the difference between quality of design and quality of manufacture**

★ **how you can use quality assurance and quality control in your coursework project**

★ **planning to ensure quality.**

Quality of design

The quality of design is determined by how well the designer has balanced the aesethetic and the functional aspects of the design. When consumers make the decision to purchase a particular product, their choice is initially based on two important design considerations:

- function: how well a product works
- aesthetics: the overall appearance of the product.

They then go on to consider:

- life expectancy: how long is the product likely to last in normal use?
- safety: is the product safe to use?
- ergonomics: how well does the product perform in use?
- trends and fashion: what products are other people choosing to buy?
- value for money: what level of performance will they get for the money they spend?

Quality of manufacture

The quality of a product is determined by how well it has been manufactured. The ability to produce quality products depends on:

- manufacturability: is it possible to make the design well with the available materials, processes and equipment?
- skills: does the workforce have sufficient skills to make the product well?
- time demands: is it possible to make the components and assemble the product in an affordable period of time?
- standards: do the products satisfy the agreed standards? There are national and internationally agreed standards that products have to meet. The British Standards Institute (BSI) and the **International Standards Office (ISO)** set standards for many products.

The Kitemark is t… UK's most recognis… certification mark, is a combination o… from British and S fro… Standards. Can y… spot them

Quality assurance and quality control

Quality assurance (QA) is a whole approach to all aspects of design and manufacture that ensures quality products. All aspects of the process, from designing the product to delivering it safely to the consumer, are include… in a complex plan to ensure a consistent quality product. Staff training and investing in equipment, together with selecting and checking raw materials, are important parts of the QA approach. One part of the process is testing and inspecting the product against the specification as it is being manufactured, which is called **quality control (QC**

QC is concerned with testing, inspecting and checking the product and its components during the manufacturing process. This is a vital part of the overall approach to achieve quality products.

n example of QA and QC

agine you wish to make 20 simple wooden building
cks, all 30 mm cubed, in a school workshop. The
gram below shows a simple plan to make sure you
duce a quality set of bricks.

A Produce a design that is simple and makes effective use of the available skills, equipment and materials

↓

A Select a good hardwood that is non-toxic and hardwearing, e.g. beech

↓

C Check that the wood can be prepared to an accurate 30 mm × 30 mm section

↓

A Set up the mitre saw with a suitable stop to cut accurate lengths

↓

C *Is the wood being machined accurately to 30 mm × 30 mm (check by measuring)?*

↓

A Finish blocks using sanding boards in both medium and fine glass paper

↓

C *Are the blocks well finished and smooth on all faces (visual inspection)?*

↓

C Make a simple jig to test the accuracy of the finished blocks

↓

C *Are the blocks being cut square and to the correct length (check with a jig)?*

Producing a set of bricks

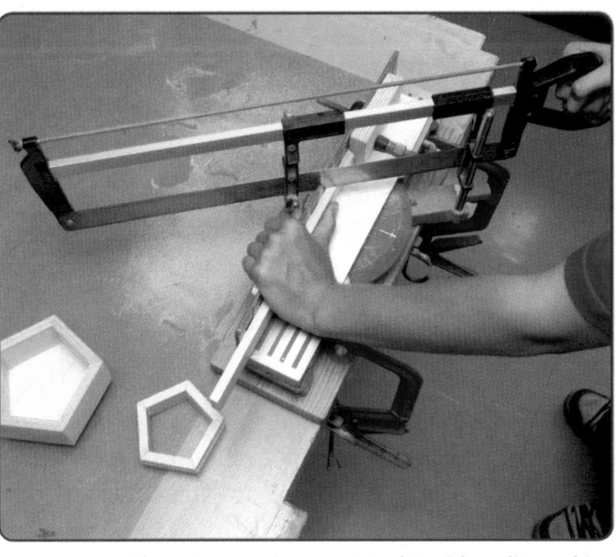

The mitre saw is a great tool to aid quality making

The example flow diagram on the left of this page shows that QA is about planning and preparation to ensure quality before you start making. During making, QC means checking that the plans work out in action to make accurate, well-finished products. Even for one block this would be good practice, but for 20 blocks it is vital to ensure a high quality set.

Coursework

Quality assurance and quality control are the keys to achieving a quality product and you will need to provide evidence that you have considered these for your product.

Activity

Look at four pieces of equipment in your school workshop. Draw a diagram of each item and annotate which features help you to work accurately and efficiently to achieve quality products.

Summary

★ Planning to ensure quality is the secret of successful products.

2.3 Cultural and social issues in design

In this chapter you will learn about:

★ how culture affects the design of products.

The designer's social responsibility

Culture and design

Designers need to consider the attitudes and values of the people who are going to be using the products they design; so they must take into account the culture that exists where the product will be used. People from different cultures have different opportunities. They have different views on the way things should look and the materials they should be made from.

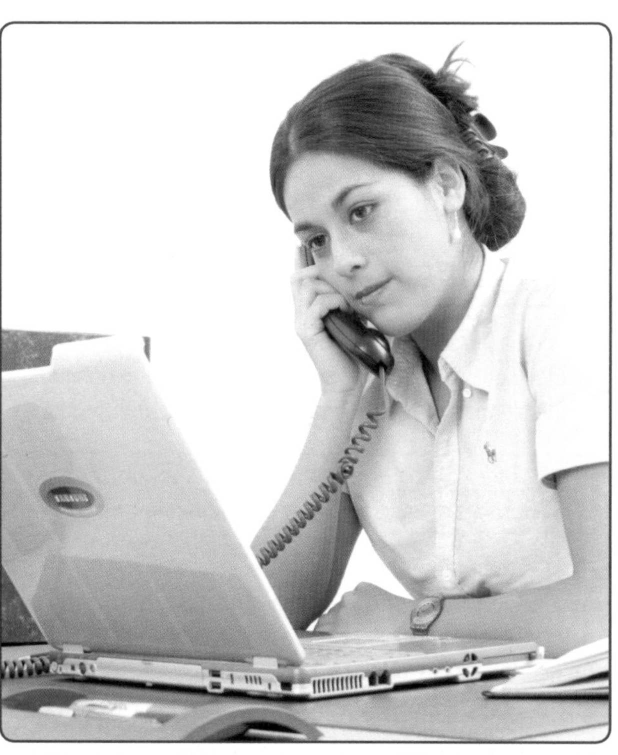

People from different cultures have different opportunities

The way a product looks and how it makes you feel are known as aesthetics; this is often based on historical development and religious views. Different cultures find different things aesthetically pleasing. We are able to put products into groups of fashion and style where the aesthetics are similar.

Handmade papers are produced in Nepal using simple, low-c equipment and labour sk

Designing for society

When designing a product, it is important to think about the people who might use it. If a designer can produce a product that is appealing to more than one group of people it has a greater chance of being successful. Young people tend to be concerned about the style and image that a product portrays. It might be that they like to buy the most up-to-date products available in the range, such as mobile phones or MP3 players, or perhaps they are environmentally aware and prefer to buy only 'green' products. This increases pressure on the designer to keep considering new markets, trends and the latest technolog

Some products are developed because of a demand from the **customer** (**market pull**); others are produced as a result of new technology (**technology push**). For exampl the demand for safer cars led to the development of airbags (a market pull), whereas the microwave oven cam about as a result of developing new radar technology (a technology push).

In 1993, a television programme inspired the British inventor Trevor Bayliss. The programme was about how HI was sweeping Africa largely because the population knew nothing about the disease and how it was transmitted. Across Africa, electricity supplies were limited and batterie expensive. There was a real need (a market pull) to produc a radio available to everyone. His invention, the clockwork radio, was a solution to a real social need.

e BayGen FREEPLAY Radio was the world's first clockwork radio. It was designed for use in countries with scarce energy resources

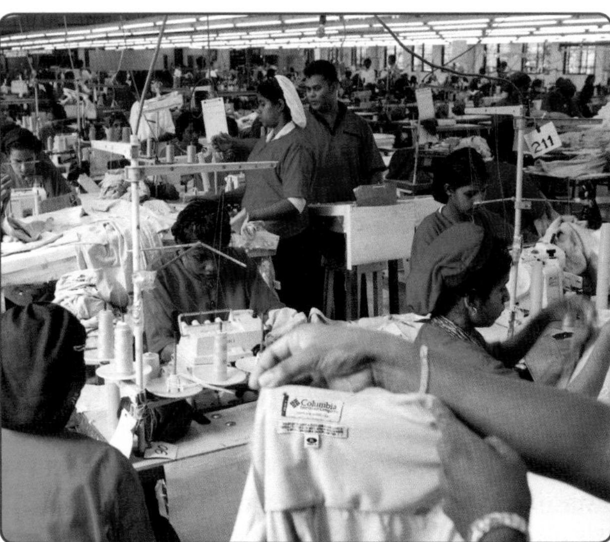

Industrial areas in Asia and South America produce products for US and European markets. These factories are often called 'sweatshops' because of the hard working conditions

signers also have a social responsibility to design oducts that look after people's health and do not damage e environment. This responsibility runs right through the e of the product.

- When making the product, will the workforce be exposed to dangerous conditions (machinery, chemicals), poor working conditions (light, heat, noise) or be treated unfairly (long hours, low pay)? The Fair Trade label helps to identify products that have been made in situations where the workers are treated fairly.
- Will the product offend any social, cultural or religious groups?
- Will the product lead to antisocial behaviour or illegal activities?
- Will the product make someone feel isolated or vulnerable?
- Will the product be effectively and sensibly recycled or reused at the end of its life?

Coursework

During the research and development stage of your project, it is important to show that you have thought about the views of people who may be affected by its production. Modifications can occur during the making of your product to ensure a better outcome and to take into account social and cultural concerns.

Activity

a Use the bullet points listed on the left of this page to analyse a modern hand-held computer game.

b Do you think market pull or technology push was the starting point for its design?

Summary

★ Designers need to consider cultural and social issues. They should take into account the culture of the people who are going to use the product and the social conditions of those making it.

Environmental issues in design

In this chapter you will learn about:

★ the environmental issues that affect the design, manufacture and disposal of products

★ the designer's responsibility for ensuring that the products created minimise potential damage to the environment.

Demand for resources

Everything you have and use, from your alarm clock to the energy used to power it, comes from the resources our planet can provide. There is a limit to the amount of metal ore, oil and gas we can take from the ground: these resources are not endless. We must recycle, reduce and renew the materials we need and find alternatives to make products and create energy. **Sustainable development** means the ability to meet the needs of the present without compromising the needs of the future.

Energy

The manufacture of any product involves using energy. Traditional energy sources such as oil, coal and natural gas are running out and are gradually being replaced with **renewable energy** sources such as wind, solar and tidal power. In the production of steel, aluminium, glass and paper, energy costs are greatly reduced by adding recycled materials to the process. For example, it is 20 times more energy efficient to use recycled aluminium than to use the raw material. Products can also be designed to use less energy. For example, some washing machines now have forward-tilting drums that need less water to get the clothes wet, and sensors that control the exact amount of water used, which means less energy is used to heat up the water.

Recycle

Each year people in the UK throw away over 27 million tonnes of household waste. Local councils now stress the importance of recycling by setting up collections at either the kerbside or places like supermarket car parks. The UK's recycling rate stands at about 11% – about a quarter of some European countries. By 2016, EU law will force the UK to cut down the 80% of its waste going to landfill site to 22% .

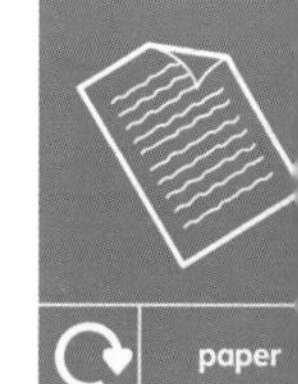

In the future the amount of recycling we do will have increase as European directives come into for

Fleeces can be made from recycled drinks bottl

Many products are now labelled with a symbol that helps identify materials that can be recycled (see 3.3 *Plastics* fo information).

Biodegradable items

Materials that decompose quickly are called **biodegradable** materials. These are being improved all the time. For example, carrier bags and packaging can be ade from 'Biopol', a plastic made from fermenting sugar d vegetables which can be disposed of by composting. 2005, a plant-based plastic made from corn and sweet tatoes was used for the first time by the Japanese ganisation Fujitsu, who used it for the main case of a w computer notebook. This product will biodegrade nen it comes to the end of its useful life.

he Fujitsu notebook – now made from corn and sweet potatoes!

Reduce

- We need to reduce the use of harmful materials and pollutants released into the atmosphere, for example CFCs from packaging, fridges and aerosols.
- A well-designed product has less of an effect on the environment as it uses less material to manufacture and needs less energy to produce.
- Many products are over-packaged, often using several layers unnecessarily. Designers have to compromise between protection, aesthetics and being wasteful.
- Timber has been used to produce energy and products for thousands of years. Although it is a renewable resource, it is not sustainable unless it is managed. The Forest Stewardship Council (FSC) encourages manufacturers to use timber from well-managed forests. The FSC logo is put onto wood products to make consumers aware that the timber has come from sustainable sources.

Forest Stewardship Council logo

Reuse

- Designers need to make it easier for the various useful components of a product to be extracted and reused. They need to consider how easy a product is to repair, replace or upgrade components that will extend the life of the product.
- Refill packs, which are usually made from lighter materials than the original durable container, are one example of how designers encourage products to be reused.

Coursework

Your design specification should state clearly any environmental issues you are going to consider when designing your product.

Activities

1 Produce a wallchart that shows clearly how your home, school and local community recycle waste materials.

2 Make a list of ways to encourage consumers and manufacturers to recycle more of their waste.

Summary

★ Designers and manufacturers have a responsibility to develop products that sustain the environment.

★ Recycling waste conserves non-renewable resources, reduces energy consumption, helps to control pollution and encourages people to think about the effects a product has on the environment.

Designing for consumers

> **In this chapter you will learn about:**
> ★ identifying factors that are involved in consumer choice
> ★ using market research to establish consumer preferences.

Designing and making things can have a huge effect on the world in which we live. Even the smallest product, like a ballpoint pen, makes some impact on people and their environment. Designers, manufacturers and consumers play important roles in product development.

Target market

When designing products it is important to carefully consider who the product is designed for: the **target group**. Consumers are the people who use the product, but they are not always the people it is designed for. For example, Clarks, the shoe manufacturers, recognises that although they design shoes for children, parents must also be targeted because they buy the children's shoes. Clarks has to create a careful balance between making shoes that are appealing to children while satisfying the parents' wishes for a hardwearing, well-fitting, affordable product.

Market surveys

Market surveys are used to find out information that will help designers produce products that consumers want. Market surveys involve:

- using **questionnaires** to gain a better understanding of the needs of the user
- asking questions related to similar products already on the market
- examining pictures and mock-ups of the product
- physically testing the product and collecting opinions
- interviewing experts to collect technical information
- questioning target groups to ensure designs meet the requirements of the intended market
- recording answers and making charts, graphs and displays.

Meeting the needs of the target market

The designer's aim is to design products that a wide range of people want.

- 'Made in Britain': if a product were made outside Britain would you buy it? Many consumers have strong views about 'buying British', so it is often a good idea to point this out.

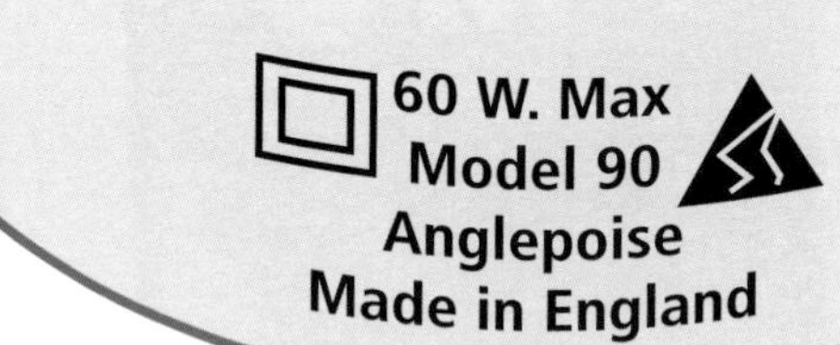

Does it matter where a product is manufactured?

- Range: designers can increase the size of the consumer group by increasing the range of the product available. A common way of doing this is by providing a choice of colours and sizes. 'One size fits all' seems to be true of mobile phones, but the range has increased through the wide choice of covers available.
- The X factor: during the last ten years, the term 'X factor' has been taken up by some modern designers to describe something special in design. In 1995, two British product designers Richard Seymour and Dick Powell used the phrase to highlight products that stand out from the rest. In an electrical store, a row of toasters are practically all alike, but if one is more aesthetically pleasing, more in demand and more sought-after, it could be said to have the X factor.

  Today the term is much more commonplace, with sportsmen and pop stars being described as having the X factor. If you could bottle it, or make it and build it into your designs, it could make you a fortune!

  Peter Birtwhistle has been a designer with car manufacturer Mazda for 15 years. He says 'The X factor is that intangible quality which transforms the ordinary into the extraordinary and the mundane into the must-have'.

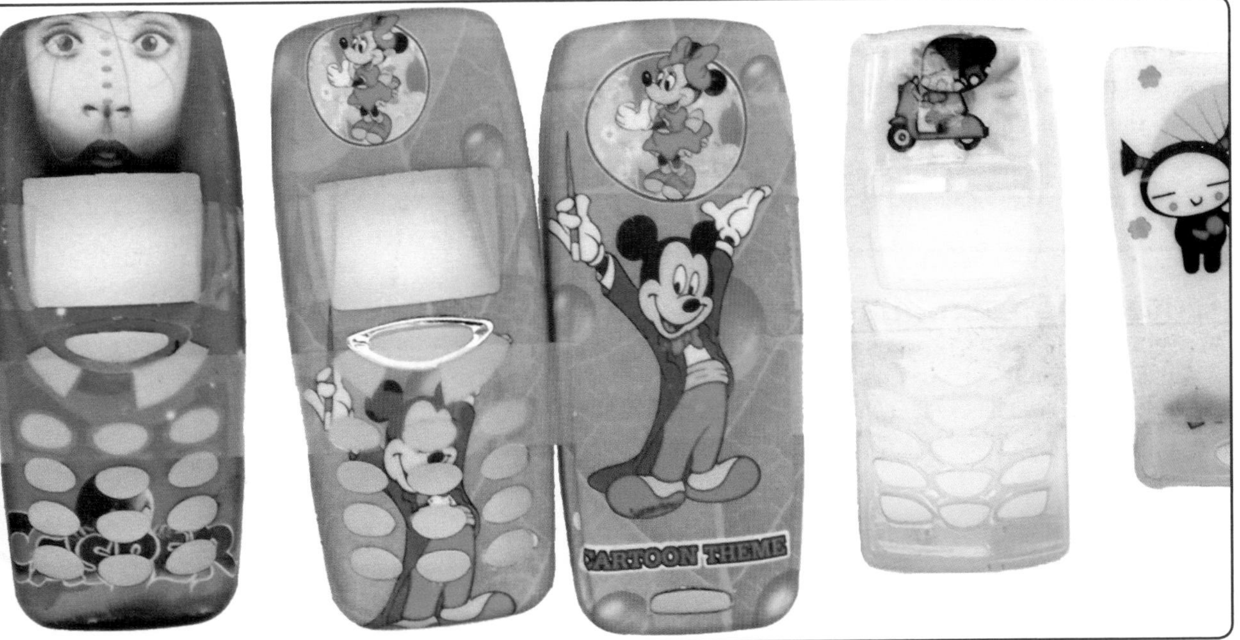

A range of mobile phone covers are available

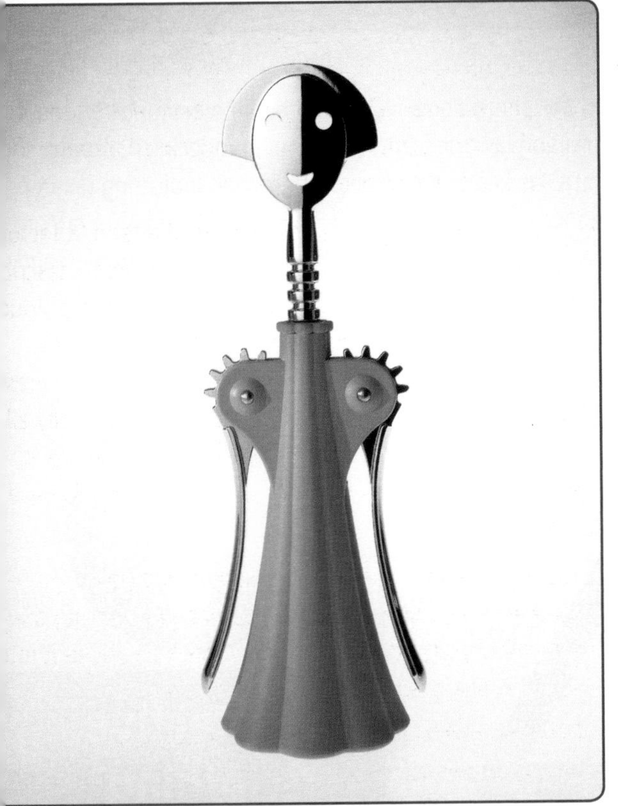

Some products, such as this Alessi corkscrew, have the X factor

Coursework

Always research the type of person or group of people you are going to design for. Find out what consumers like and dislike and use this to help produce your design brief.

Activity

As you can see from the photo above there are lots of different mobile phone cover designs. Do some research on the Internet to find a variety of different phone covers. Who do you think each one has been designed for?

Summary

★ Consumers are the people who will use the product, but they are not always the people the product was designed for.

★ Market surveys are used to get a clear idea about the needs of the target market.

2.6 Legislation in design

In this chapter you will learn about:

- ★ **the various laws and guidelines that affect the design and manufacture of products**
- ★ **the health and safety issues that protect the workforce when making products.**

Protecting manufacturers

Designers and manufacturers should be aware of the various laws and guidelines that control the production and sale of their products. When designing products, it is important to take into account the health and safety laws that protect the manufacturer and the consumer. More information about health and safety, including **risk assessment**, is given in Section 4.

The Health and Safety at Work Act 1974 ensures that factories and workshops are set up to be safe places in which to work. Your school workshop has to follow some of these regulations, so watch out for signs and notices that tell you about your responsibilities, how to behave and what not to do.

Health and safety laws mean that your teacher is responsible for providing a safe working environment, but you are responsible for looking after others and yourself. If you are operating a machine, it is not just you who must be kept safe; others around you must be safe as well.

Safety markings on the floor of a fact

In the photo above you can see white markings on the flc dividing up the factory workshop, producing walkways th must be kept clear of obstruction, and indicating danger zones where machines are operated. If you visit a factory, look at the ways in which the machines are guarded and operated. Make a note of the safety signs and markings you see. Do you understand what they all mean?

Protective clothing must be worn

Eye protection, caution and protective clothing health and safety sig

ontrol of Substances Hazardous to ealth

e UK's **Health and Safety Commission (HSC)** and the ealth and Safety Executive (HSE) produce guidelines r manufacturers. These are designed to protect people's alth and safety in a wide range of jobs from nuclear stallations and mines to hospitals and schools. Part of eir work is to control the use of chemicals for a range of mmon tasks like painting and gluing. These are known as **ntrol of Substances Hazardous to Health (COSHH)** gulations. COSHH regulations are available for everyone read so that manufacturers and users are kept safe. Visit e website at www.heinemann.co.uk/hotlinks to find out ore.

rotecting users

E marking

e letters 'CE' on a product are the manufacturer's claim at it meets the requirements of all relevant European nion Directives, which are compulsory. CE marking dicates to governments that the product can be sold gally within the EU and the European Economic Area EA). This may mean that the product also meets safety andards, for example all toys sold in the EU must meet e Toy Safety Directive and meet the requirements of the ıropean Toy Standard, BS EN 71. It does not mean the oduct has been independently tested. CE marking:

- allows the product to move freely throughout the European single market
- indicates to customers that the product meets EU Directives that may relate to safety standards and therefore offers a minimum level of quality
- promotes public health and safety
- enhances product credibility
- leads to improved sales and greater customer satisfaction.

The CE marking letters show that the product meets relevant European Directives

British Standards Institute

When a new product is ready to be launched into the market and the manufacturer has completed its tests, the product can be independently tested through the British Standards Institute (BSI) and the International Standards Office (ISO).

The British Standards Institution logo

Coursework

When designing and making your product, you should always take great care to follow health and safety requirements. Record any decisions about health and safety in your coursework folder.

Activity

Look around your school workshop and identify the range of safety information available, for example safety information posters, floor markings, guards and safety screens, COSHH regulations and safety clothing. Make a list of all the items you identify and what they mean. Go to the HSE and BSI website at www.heinemann.co.uk/hotlinks to help you.

Summary

★ Designers and manufacturers must be aware of the legislation that controls the production and sale of products.

★ A safe working environment is the responsibility of everyone. Product safety and quality can be identified with CE marking, the Kitemark symbol and BS EN and ISO Standard numbers.

Exam questions

1 Study the pair of secateurs shown below.

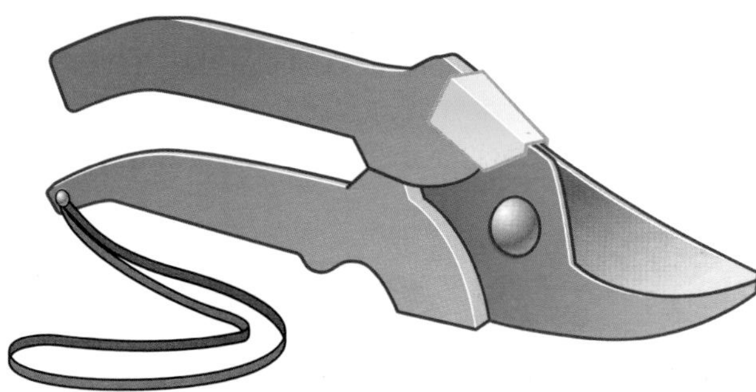

a List **three** ergonomic features of the secateurs.

(3 marks)

b Explain the function of **each** ergonomic feature you have labelled.

(6 marks)

c The designer has chosen to make the blades replaceable. Explain why you think that this is a good idea for the consumer.

(4 marks)

2 a Name a resistant material that you consider to be environmentally friendly and give your reasons why.

Material: *(1 mar*

Reasons: *(4 mark*

b Name a non-environmentally friendly resistant material and explain the harmful effects it causes during its lifecycle.

Material: *(1 mar*

Explanation: *(4 mark*

(AQA 200

Materials and components

his section covers the materials and mponents you will need to be familiar with r your examination and when producing ur coursework.

What's in this section?

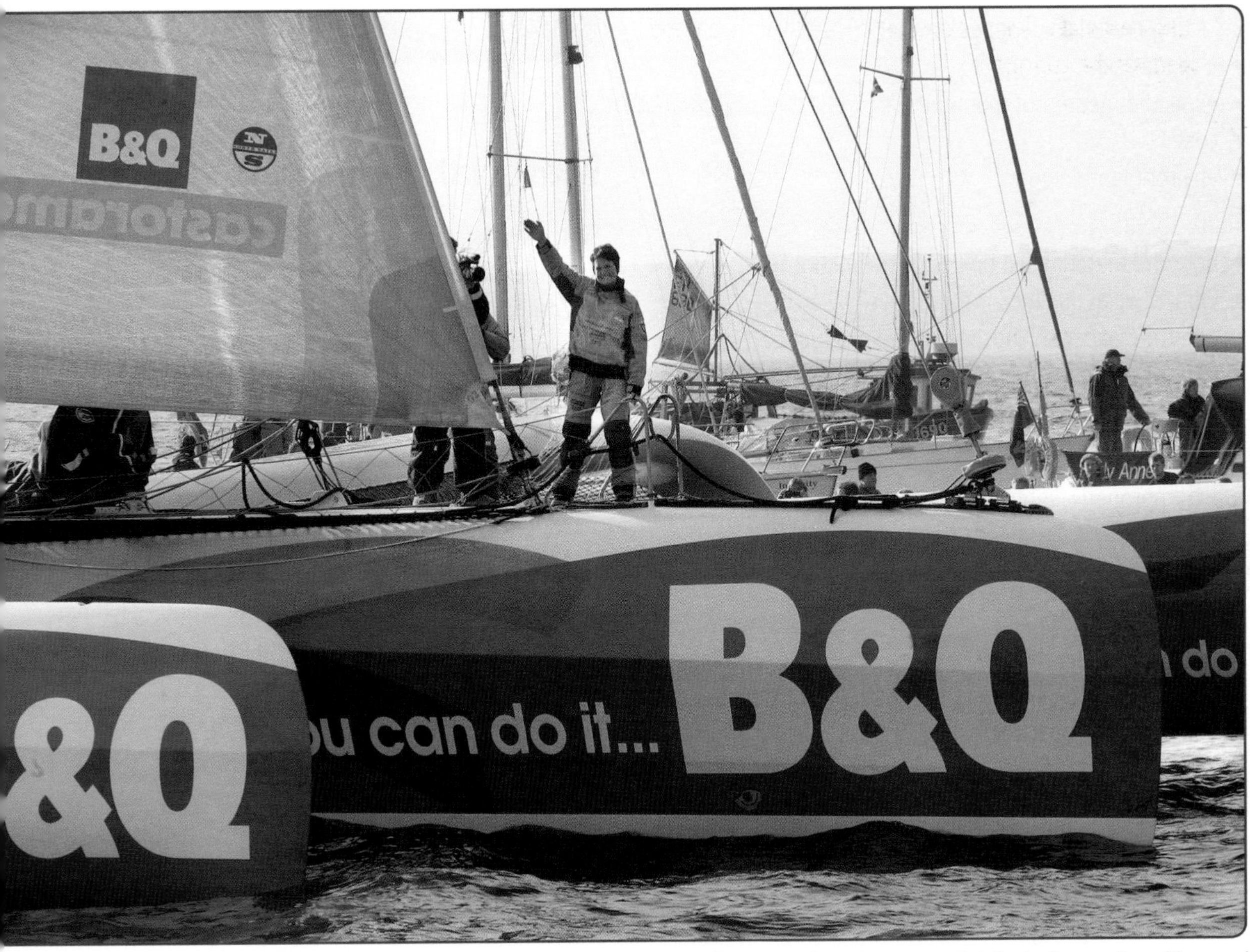

Designers Nigel Irens and Benoit Cabaret used modern materials including carbon fibre and Kevlar® composites in the design of the B&Q Castorama. Ellen MacArthur set a new record in 2005 by sailing around the world in this lightweight but extremely tough trimaran

3.1 Selecting materials

In this chapter you will learn about:

- ★ **choosing suitable materials for a particular project**
- ★ **using the correct technical language to explain the qualities of different materials.**

Choosing materials

Selecting the right material for the right job is important to the designer, maker, engineer and manufacturer. Designers need to choose the right material for each part of the product they are designing. The material must have suitable properties and characteristics for the intended purpose. The manufacturer needs to check that the materials chosen match the making processes available and the needs of the user.

Selecting materials depends on the:

- intended use
- expected method of manufacture
- cost
- environmental impact.

Think about:

- how the material will be used (its function)
- what special qualities it must have
- what the expected lifespan of the product is
- what the visual requirements (aesthetics) of the material are.

For example, a soup spoon needs to be rigid enough to function properly, lightweight and able to be given a suitable finish. It also needs to be hygienic, washable and non-corrosive during its useful life.

The manufacturer's needs also have to be considered. Does the manufacturer have the required skills and experience to work the selected materials? Materials are generally available as standard sections and parts. Does the design match the stock sizes available?

Economic factors including material and labour costs are an important factor in material selection. Where possible, the lowest cost alternatives should be selected without compromising quality. Material costs include the cost of buying stock as well as transport and manufacturing costs.

Consider any environmental issues:

- Is the material scarce and will its use deplete natural resources even further?
- Is the material harmful to persons using it, e.g. lead-based paints or MDF dust?
- What happens to the material after its useful life? Can be recycled? Is it biodegradable?

Materials are chosen for a reas

Material properties

Some words are often used to describe material propertie

- Brittleness: easily broken or snapped, e.g. acrylic.
- Conductivity: the ease at which electricity or heat can pass through the material, e.g. aluminium.
- Density: how heavy a material is in comparison to size, e. low density (expanded polystyrene); high density (lead).
- Ductility: the ability to be stretched, e.g. copper.
- Elasticity: the ability to return to the original shape, e.g. spring steel, rubber, ash.
- Environmental resistance: the ability to resist corrosion and decay, e.g. polypropylene, nylon and polythene.
- Hardness: scratch resistant and usually difficult to cut, e.g. glass, tool steel.
- Malleability: the ability to be deformed, moulded and bent without cracking, e.g. clay and lead.
- Stiffness: the ability to resist bending, e.g. cast iron.
- Strength: the ability to resist pulling (tensile strength), e.g. high-tensile steel cables; pushing (compressive strength), e.g. reinforced concrete; twisting (torsion), e.g. carbon-fibre laminate; and shearing, e.g. tool steel.
- Toughness: the ability to resist impact and shock withou fracture, e.g. willow and mild steel.

laterial characteristics

ese are qualities of the material that are to do with its look d feel, for example colour, grain pattern, surface finish and xture, smell, taste, feel (some plastics feel waxy, metals feel ol), lustre, brightness, and optical and audio qualities (e.g. ood used for a guitar body).

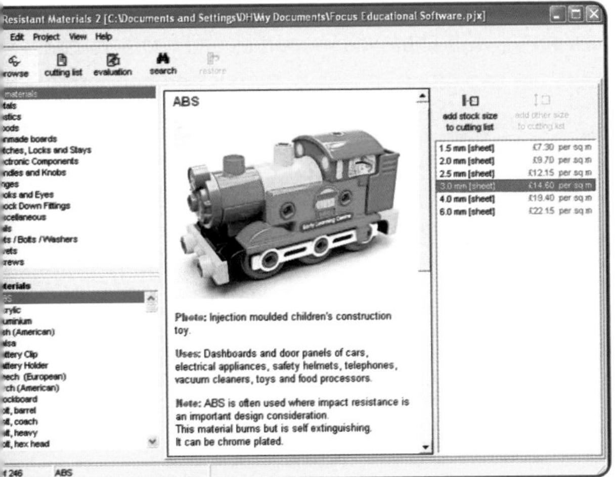

Materials databases such as Focus on Resistant Materials 2 can be used to find out about materials

Activity

Look at the photo showing the ice cream tub on page 44 .

a Explain why each material has been chosen for the items shown.

b The glass dessert bowl manufacturer wishes to produce a 'picnic' version. Suggest a suitable material and explain your choice.

Coursework

Testing materials can provide some useful information to help you with your project, especially at the development stage. Tests do not need to be complicated; for example, testing a range of glues needs a number of samples and a simple test. Make sure tests are relevant to your project and check the choice of materials against your specifications.

There are many databases and CD-ROMs that can give you lots of information about materials. Examples include the Focus databases and TEP's Materials Selection and Processing. However, remember to be selective: if the information is relevant and has helped you make a choice, record it in your coursework folder.

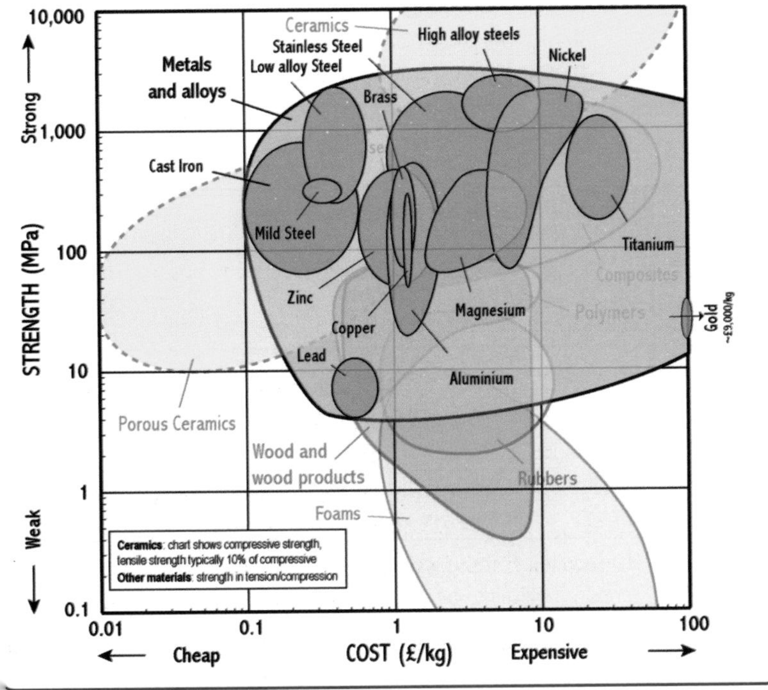

TEP's Materials Selection and Processing CD-ROM can help you to research materials

Summary

- ★ Materials have properties and characteristics.
- ★ When selecting materials for a product, the designer must consider the use, manufacture, cost and environmental impact.
- ★ Testing materials is a good way to make choices.

3.2 Metals

In this chapter you will learn about:

- ★ **the properties, characteristics and uses of pure metals, ferrous and non-ferrous alloys**
- ★ **heat-treating metals to change their properties.**

Steel castings being poured

Metals make up about a quarter of the Earth's crust by weight. All metals, except gold, are found chemically combined with other elements, usually in the form of an oxide or sulphate. These deposits, known as ores, are mined and processed to extract the metals we need. Most metals are produced and supplied in standard stock sizes so products need to be designed to make efficient use of these available sizes. See 5.18 *Finishing* for information on metal finishing techniques.

Pure metals and alloys

Pure metals are often expensive and have poor working properties. Most pure metals have small amounts of other materials added to improve their properties and characteristics. Aluminium, copper and silver are examples of pure metals used in the workshop.

Alloys are mixtures of two or more metals that create a new metal with improved properties and characteristics. There are two groups of alloys: ferrous and non-ferrous.

- **Ferrous** alloys, such as stainless steel and mild steel, ar composed mainly of iron. Properties such as hardness are increased by the addition of carbon and metals like chromium, tungsten and nickel.
- **Non-ferrous** alloys do not contain iron. They include brass (copper and zinc) and duralumin (aluminium and copper).

Heat treatment

Metals can be heat-treated to change their properties. There are three main types of heat treatments.

- Annealing: ferrous metals are softened by heat and then left to cool slowly. Non-ferrous metals should be heated and then plunged into cold water (quenching).
- Hardening: either by work hardening (doing work to the metal, i.e. bending and hammering) or for ferrous metals heating until red and then quenching in cold water. Hardening can leave the metal brittle so another treatment is often needed.

Name	Melting point	Composition	Properties and characteristics	Uses
Cast iron	1200°C	Iron and 3.5% carbon	High compressive strength; not good in tension; brittle; light grey	Car break drums; heavy machine parts
High speed steel	1600°C	Iron and 0.2% carbon plus some tungsten, chromium and vanadium	Very hard; poor torsion and tensile strength; can only be cut by grinding	Lathe-cutting tools; drills; milling cutters
Mild steel	1600°C	Iron and 0.15–0.35% carbon	Tough; ductile; malleable; high tensile strength; easily joined; rusts easily	Car bodies; washing machines; general-purpose engineering
Stainless steel	1600°C	Iron and 18% chromium, 8% nickel and 8% magnesium	Hard and tough; resists wear and corrosion; difficult to cut and file; good appearance	Kitchen sinks; cutlery; teapots; boat fittings

Common ferrous alloys

Name	Melting point	Composition	Properties and characteristics	Uses
Aluminium	660°C	Pure metal	Strong but lightweight; ductile; difficult to join; good conductor of heat and electricity; corrosion resistant; polishes well; silver colour	Scooters; drinks cans; greenhouse frames; kitchen equipment
Copper	1083°C	Pure metal	Malleable; ductile; tough; good conductor of heat and electricity; corrosion resistant; easily joined; polishes well; relatively expensive	Central-heating systems; printed circuit boards; car radiators
Lead	327°C	Pure metal	Heavy; soft; ductile; malleable; corrosion resistant; environmentally unfriendly	Roof flashings; protection against radiation; car batteries
Brass	1000°C	Copper and 35% zinc	Casts well; hard; tough; corrosion resistant; polishes well; good conductor of heat and electricity	Ornaments; musical instruments; water taps; plumbing fittings
Duralumin	660°C	Aluminium and 4% copper plus some manganese and magnesium	Nearly the strength of mild steel but 30% lighter; machines well; work hardens; ductile; stress fractures with age	Aircraft structures; bicycle frames

Pure metals and common non-ferrous alloys

Tempering: this makes the metal tougher and less likely to break. The metal (usually ferrous) is cleaned and then heated carefully. As the metal heats, it changes colour (oxide colours). A tempering chart is used to select the correct colour at which to stop heating and quench the metal in cold water. Metals are usually hardened and tempered. Many tools, such as wood chisels, are hardened and tempered to provide a good combination of hardness and toughness.

The London Eye: architecture with metal

Coursework

If you are going to use metals in your project, you must consider the stock sizes available, the cost, the environmental impact and the manufacturing processes you are going to use.

Activities

1. What is annealing?
2. How would you work harden a piece of silver wire that is to be made into a brooch pin?
3. Why are fizzy drinks cans made from aluminium?
4. The £1 coin is a nickel alloy. Make a list of the properties and characteristics it has.
5. Use the Design InSite website at www.heinemann.co.uk/hotlinks to find out some uses for tin, tungsten and chromium.

Summary

★ Metals can be described as ferrous alloys, non-ferrous alloys and pure metals.

★ Heating can change the properties of a metal.

3.3 Plastics

> **In this chapter you will learn about:**
> ★ the difference between thermoplastics and thermosetting plastics
> ★ the different properties, characteristics and uses of common forms of plastic.

A plastic is a material that can be moulded when 'putty-like', i.e. when it is not solid or liquid but somewhere in between. There are two main sources for plastics.

- Natural plastic materials have been used throughout history. They come in the form of resins such as amber, rubber, bitumen, shellac, animal horn and shell.
- Synthetic (man-made) plastics are the most common forms today. They are manufactured chemically from carbon-based raw materials such as crude oil and coal. Modern technology has produced a number of alternatives that are environmentally friendly and come from sustainable (renewable) sources such as corn and maize. There are two main types of synthetic plastic: **thermosetting plastics** and **thermoplastics**.
  - Thermosetting plastics: once they have been formed into a shape, they cannot be reformed, they are brittle and hard and prone to cracking if twisted and knocked. They are heat resistant.
  - Thermoplastics: sensitive to heat, can be reformed by heating and tend to return to their original shape. If overheated, their chemical structure will be damaged.

As well as chemical changes, various additives can be usec to adjust the properties and characteristics of plastics:

- plasticisers make the plastic more flexible
- antistatics reduce static
- fillers like glass strands or rubber spheres make the plastic stronger or behave in a different way
- pigments change the colour.

With all these combinations, plastics can be designed to suit a specific job. See 5.18 *Finishing* for information on plastic finishing techniques.

Coursework

Before choosing to use a plastic as part of your project, you must find out what plastics and production methods are available. Your research and development should contain alternatives and reasons for your choice.

Activity

a Collect a range of modern plastic products.

b For each product, identify the plastic used and the method of production. Looking for the recycling symbol will help.

c Use the British Plastics Federation website at www. heinemann.co.uk/hotlinks to find out more information about each plastic's properties and characteristics.

Name	Recycling symbol	Production method it is used with	Properties and characteristics	Uses
Polyester resin	7 OTHER	Glass-reinforced plastic (GRP)	Clear; hard; brittle; heat resistant	Canoes; paperweights; sports equipment
Epoxy resins	7 OTHER	Compression moulding	Dark; hard; brittle; heat resistant; good electrical insulator	A liquid two-part glue; electronic components
Urea formaldehyde (UF)	7 OTHER	Compression moulding	White; tough; brittle; good electrical insulator	Electronic fittings; light switches
Phenol formaldehyde (PF)	7 OTHER	Compression moulding	Dark; if overheated gives off toxic fumes; hard; very brittle; heat resistant	Saucepan handles; electrical components

Thermosetting plastics

ame	Recycling symbol	Production method it is used with	Properties and characteristics	Uses
olyethylene rephthalate	1 PET	Blow moulding; calendering	A 'crystal clear' plastic; tough; good resistance to moisture; durable	Drinks bottles; oven-proof film and trays; food packaging; duvet filling
igh-density olyethylene olythene) (HDPE)	2 HDPE	Blow moulding; injection moulding; extrusion; vacuum forming	Clear or coloured; tough when formed; good resistance to household chemicals; stiff	Containers; toys; bottles; buckets; chemical drums; milk crates; gas pipes
olyvinyl chloride VC)	3 PVC	Blow moulding; injection moulding; extrusion; vacuum forming	Very strong and flexible; extremely resistant to household chemicals; weatherproof with a range of colours but affected by UV light, which makes it brittle	Gutters and pipes; window frames; electrical insulation; medical applications; floor coverings; credit cards; cling film
ow-density olyethylene olythene) (LDPE)	4 LDPE	Blow moulding; injection moulding; extrusion; calendering	Wide range of colours; waxy; durable; excellent flexibility; resistant to chemicals; used where heat sealing is needed	Detergent bottles; plastic bags; toys; lids; carrier bags; wrapping films; pipes
olypropylene (PP)	5 PP	Blow moulding; injection moulding; extrusion; calendering; vacuum forming	Excellent chemical resistance; strong; high melting point; tough and durable; very flexible; resists cracking and tearing, even when thin	Crisp packets; lights; chairs; hospital equipment; suitcases; hinges; ketchup bottles
igid polystyrene S)	6 PS	Injection moulding; vacuum forming	Versatile but brittle; clear and in a range of colours	CD cases; model kits; disposal cups; trays; pens
xpanded olystyrene (PS)	6 PS	Hot wire cutting; hand shaping	Low melting point; good insulator and shock absorber; usually white	Buoyancy aids; product models; packaging
crylic polymethylmeth crylate) (PMMA)	7 OTHER	Blow moulding; injection moulding; extrusion; vacuum forming	Good range of bright colours or clear; scratches easily; brittle	Baths; signs; car light lenses; secondary glazing; roof lights; pick 'n' mix sweet dispensers
crylonitrile utadiene styrene ABS)	7 OTHER	Blow moulding; injection moulding; extrusion; vacuum forming	Very strong; tough; scratch resistant; robust; tends to be dark in colour	Household products; cameras; kettles; vacuum cleaners; telephones

Thermoplastics

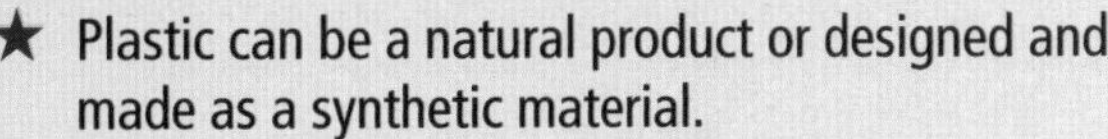

★ Plastic can be a natural product or designed and made as a synthetic material.

★ There are two types of synthetic plastics: thermoplastics and thermosetting plastics. They have different properties and characteristics.

Materials and components

3.4 Woods

In this chapter you will learn about:

- ★ **the three main groups of timber: hardwoods, softwoods and manufactured boards**
- ★ **the properties, characteristics and uses of a number of available timbers.**

Wood is a readily available, easy to use and renewable material. Many woods are able to be worked as soon as the tree is cut down (called 'in the green'), but these products have a high water content and may shrink, distort and split as they dry out. Consequently, nearly all wood used has its moisture content reduced during a process called seasoning. When wood is converted into a useable material, it is known as timber. Timber is supplied to manufacturers in a variety of stock sizes.

There are three main groups of timber: **hardwoods**, **softwoods** and **manufactured boards**.

Hardwoods

Hardwoods come from trees that have broad, open leave[s] and their seeds are contained in fruit. Many of them are deciduous (they lose their leaves in winter). Hardwoods a[re] usually slow growing, which tends to make them hard an[d] expensive. However, not all hardwoods are hard, e.g. bals[a]

Softwoods

Softwoods come from trees that have needles and their seeds are contained in cones. They are usually evergreens. Softwoods grow faster than hardwoods and are mostly softer to work and less expensive. Not all softwoods are evergreen, e.g. larch.

Stock sizes	Name	Properties and characteristics	Uses
• Sold by the metre up to 5 m in length • Planks up to 300 mm × 50 mm • Strips of 50–100 mm • Dowels in diameters of 3–50 mm	Beech	Straight, close grain; fine texture; pinkish-brown colour; hard; tough; polishes well	Furniture; toys; flooring
	Oak	Very strong; durable; light-brown colour; works well with sharp tools; finishes well; contains tannic acid, which corrodes iron and steel fittings causing a permanent blue stain	High-quality furniture; boats; beams and roofing; floors; gateposts; veneers
	Ash	Open grain wood that is easy to work with; pale cream colour often stained black	Tool handles; furniture; sports equipment; ladders; can be laminated
	Mahoganies, e.g. sapele, utile	Easy to work with; pink to reddish-brown colour; good finish	Indoor furniture; shop fittings pub bars; veneers; flooring

Hardwoo

Stock sizes	Name	Properties and characteristics	Uses
• Sold by the metre up to 5 m in length • Planks up to 300 mm × 50 mm • Strips of 50–100 mm • Dowels in diameters of 3–50 mm	Scots pine (red deal, redwood)	Straight grained but knotty; fairly strong; easy to work; inexpensive, cream/pale brown colour	Simple joinery; DIY work; the most popular softwood in the UK
	Parana pine	Works well; fairly strong; durable; available in long, wide boards, often knot-free; expensive; pale yellow colour with red/brown streaks	Best quality interior softwood joinery, especially where grain will show, e.g. staircases
	Spruce (whitewood)	Creamy white softwood with small, hard knots; good resistance to splitting but not durable	Interior joinery; furniture

Softwoo

tock sizes	Name	Properties and characteristics	Uses
Standard size 1220 × 2440 mm Thickness 3, 4, 6, 9, 12, 18, 22 and 25 mm	Medium-density fibreboard (MDF)	Smooth, even surface; available in fire-resistant and water-resistant forms; dust is a hazard; blunts tools quickly	Interior panels and decorative sheets; often veneered or painted
	Plywood	Very strong board made from layers of veneer glued at 90° to each other; interior and exterior grades; strong for its weight and thickness compared to natural timbers	Structural panels; furniture; boat building
	Chipboard	Made from chips of wood glued together; usually veneered or covered with a plastic laminate	Kitchen and bedroom furniture; flooring
	Hardboard	Very inexpensive particle board; sometimes laminated with a plastic surface	Furniture backs; drawer bottoms

Manufactured boards

lanufactured boards

anufactured boards are timber sheets made by gluing rticles or layers of wood fibres together. Manufactured ards were developed mainly for industrial production chniques and they can be made in large sheets of nsistent quality.

MDF
- Fine grain
- Light brown

Hardboard
- One smooth side
- One textured side
- Dark brown

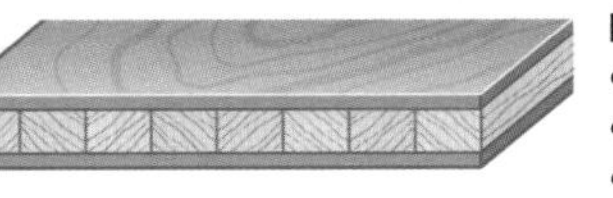

Blockboard
- Veneered top and base
- Light cream centre
- Dark brown veneer

Plywood
- Odd numbers of ply
- Light colour

Chipboard
- Large chips in the middle
- Smaller chips towards the outsides

Manufactured boards

roperties and characteristics

Grain pattern is the growth ring marks visible on the surface of the timber.

A wide variety of colours are available, from the black of ebony to the ginger of iroko.

- The cell structures of different tree species give different textures to the timber surface, described as open grain or close grain.
- How easy the timber is to cut, shape and polish is known as its working characteristics.
- The structural strength of different species helps the designer select the right timber for the right job. For example, ash is able to withstand knocks and blows, which makes it suitable for tool handles.

Coursework

When selecting timbers for your project, you must consider the stock sizes available, the cost, colour, grain and texture as well as the manufacturing processes you are going to use.

Activity

Imagine you have been asked to design and make a high-quality coffee table in a dark-coloured wood. Use the information in this chapter, books from your library and the Internet to decide which wood to choose. Visit the Design and Tech website at www.heinemann.co.uk/hotlinks to help you.

Summary

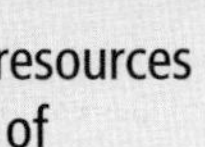

★ Hardwoods and softwoods are natural resources that can be used to make a wide range of products.

★ Some woods are processed into manufactured boards.

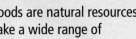

3.5 Composite materials

In this chapter you will learn about:

- ★ some common modern composite materials and their uses
- ★ the different fibres and resins used to make composite materials.

Bonding two or more materials together changes their properties and characteristics. Bonded materials are called **composites**. Designers and engineers use composite materials because of their improved mechanical and working properties.

Composites in action

Many composites are produced by combining a range of fibres (e.g. glass, carbon, Kevlar®, rubber, wood, steel wire, cotton) with a range of matrix materials (e.g. thermoplastics, thermosetting plastics, concrete, aluminium, steel, titanium). Tufnol is a modern composite of woven linen (the fibre) impregnated with a resin (the matrix). It is used for gears, mechanical components and bearings.

Glass-reinforced plastic (GRP) is a composite used for large structural items such as boats and car bodies. The glass fibre is a woven mat of loose strands that are impregnated with a matrix of polyester resin. Together, these materials form a strong, durable composite.

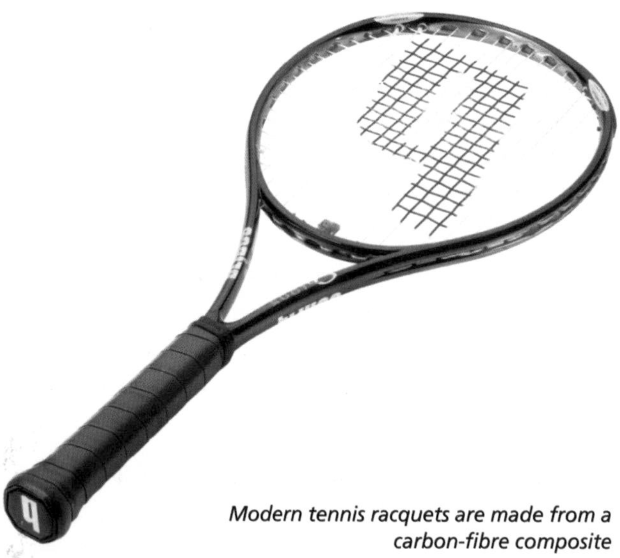

Modern tennis racquets are made from a carbon-fibre composite

More recently, carbon fibres have been developed to be used in the same way as glass in GRP. Carbon fibres combined with an epoxy resin produce a material of high strength and low density. A carbon-fibre composite has better corrosion resistance and fatigue performance than most metal alloys. It is used where products need to be incredibly strong yet very lightweight, such as protective helmets, sports equipment, bullet-resistant vests, racing-ca shells, aircraft structures, artificial legs and sailing yachts.

Reinforced concrete is a composite of steel wire or rods (tł fibre) and concrete (the matrix). This combination produce: a strong material that is widely used in the construction industry for roads, bridges, buildings and dams.

A familiar form of reinforcement: steel rods in concre

Kevlar®

A Kevlar® composite material is used for police vests and military body armour. This gives a tough, light material, with a vest weighing no more than 3 kg and a helmet just 1 kg. Kevlar® composites are also being used in aircraft construction; composite parts are as strong as aluminium but are almost 30% lighter, helping to save fuel.

The Aberfeldy footbridge, on the River Tay in Perth and Kinross, Scotland, is the world's first major advanced composite footbridge. Built in 1992, it uses Kevlar® fibres covered in a protective polyethylene coat to support the bridge.

Kevlar® is used in bullet-resistant vests

'he world's first major advanced composite footbridge over the River Tay

Natural composites

Vood is a natural composite material. It is made up of ellulose fibres in a natural resin known as lignin. It is the ombination of the fibres and the resin that gives timber its pecial properties and characteristics.

Composite manufacture

Plastic composites are time consuming to manufacture. The process is as listed in the bullet points below.

- Layers of the fibre are cut and the resin mixed. The correct health and safety precautions need to be followed; the fibres are small, sharp, lightweight and harmful to touch and breathe in. The resin usually involves mixing chemicals that are irritants, which are flammable and hazardous to health. The correct COSHH regulations should be followed.
- The fibres are placed in a mould and impregnated with the matrix.
- The production of the mould is often difficult and time consuming. Rather like a vacuum-forming mould, it must be easy to remove with a smooth finish.
- When the desired thickness of composite has been achieved, it is left to set (cure) for 6–10 hours in a well-ventilated area. The mould can then be removed.
- Cutting and shaping the composite after it has formed is often difficult because it is so strong.

Coursework

Composites are unlikely to be available for you to use as part of your project, so research the alternatives before making any decisions.

Activity

Research ten products or components made from composite materials. Use the Design InSite and the Design and Tech website at www.heinemann.co.uk/hotlinks to help you.

Summary

★ Combining a fibre and a matrix produces a composite material.

★ Modern composite materials have properties and characteristics that make them better than traditional alternatives.

★ Producing composite plastics is time consuming.

3.6 New materials

In this chapter you will learn about:

★ smart and new materials available to the product designer.

A number of new and **smart materials** are becoming available and finding their way into everyday use:

- Lenticular polypropylene sheet gives the optical illusion. This amazing material, although paper thin, appears to be 6mm thick and any object placed upon it seems to sink below the surface. Turn the sheet over and the same object will seem to float magically above it. It has been used for a number of trick effects, including book covers and CD packaging.
- Polymorph is a tough engineering polymer that can be shaped when warmed with hot water or a hair drier. Its ability to set hard makes it suited to prototyping, including ergonomic handles, vacuum-forming moulds and orthopaedic products.

Polymorph is a new, tough plastic: able to be machined, it fuses and becomes mouldable easily at just 62°C

Smart materials

Any material that responds to external forces such as light, pressure, electric current or temperature and then returns to its original form when the stimulus is removed is called 'smart'. Smart materials can change thousands of times. This technology is now being applied to everyday objects, such as toothbrushes and microwave dishes.

Smart materials can be made of plastic, metal, ceramic or liquid. They can be combined with other materials to form Smart composite materials, often textiles.

- Thermochromic plastics are used to make baby's spoons that change colour to indicate temperature, toothbrushes that change colour the longer you hold them and kettles that warn you when they are hot. Microwave food manufacturers use thermochromic plastic packaging that changes colour when the food is cooked properly.

The Russell Hobbs ThermoColor Kettle: as the water boils, the kettle changes colour from blue to pink

- Thermochromic inks are used in children's medical thermometers, fish-tank temperature sensors and body jewellery. Self-adhesive thermochromic sheet is available in the school workshop. It changes colour from black to bright blue at 27°C.
- Photochromic glass darkens when exposed to a bright light. Used in eyeglasses and welding shields, it is able to repeat the darkening process reliably many thousands of times.
- Shape memory plastics (SMPs) are materials that change shape when heated. Modern mobile phone covers are made from smart material. When warmed to a specific temperature they are designed to come apart to help recycling.

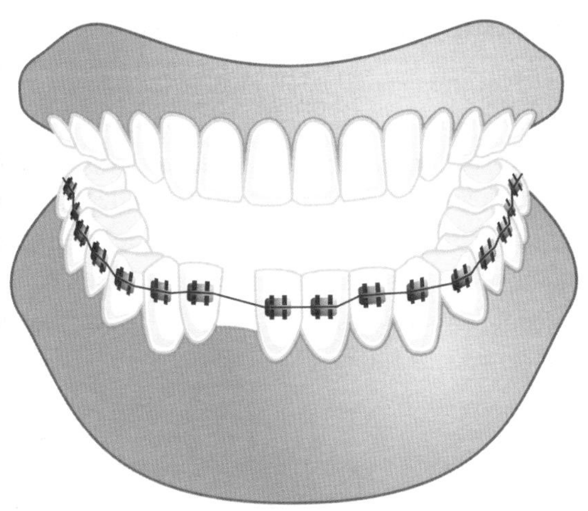

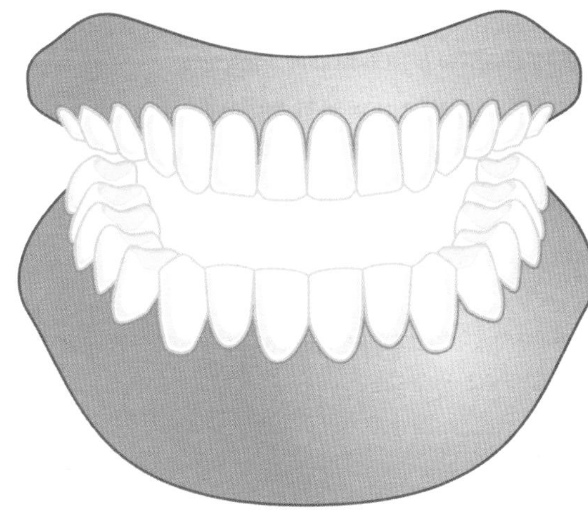

Teeth are gently aligned using an SMA wire brace. After six months the gap between the teeth has become smaller (right)

Shape memory alloys (SMAs) are metals that change their shape when heated. An example is Nitinol, a nickel and titanium alloy. It has lots of uses; in dental work, body temperature is used to shrink wire braces and pull teeth into position. Broken bones can be aligned correctly by fixing a splint of shaped Nitinol. Heat-activated cables adjust greenhouse windows. SMA wire can also be affected by passing an electrical current through it, making it stretch and shrink. One use for this is to operate lightweight **mechanisms**.

Piezo-electric actuators (PZTs) are smart materials used to create an electric current from movement, e.g. musical greeting cards.

Smart steel can 'heal itself' by releasing corrosion-resistant chemicals to seal cracks, cuts, dents and scratches before they corrode. If a colour dye is also released, the area will visibly 'bruise'. One use of this is on trains, because the smart steel makes it obvious where the carriage is damaged.

Coursework

Include research on any smart or new materials you think you may use as part of your project.

Activity

Imagine a new smart material has been developed that produces light in response to a rise in sound levels. You have been asked to design a fun gadget to make the most of this technology. Produce an A3 sheet of initial ideas.

Summary

★ New and smart materials range from colour-changing plastics to self-healing metals.

★ A smart material responds to an external stimulus and then returns to its original condition once the stimulus has been removed.

3.7 Fixtures and fittings

In this chapter you will learn about:

- ★ **the many fixings that are available**
- ★ **a range of knock-down and flat-pack fittings.**

Fixings

Fixings are small components that are used to hold or fix larger materials together.

Hinges

Hinges are available in steel, brass and nylon and can be plated in brass or zinc (galvanised) or painted. The part of the hinge that moves is called the knuckle. There are four main types of hinge.

- Butt hinges are the most common and are used to hang doors. The two parts of the hinge are set into the door and the frame.

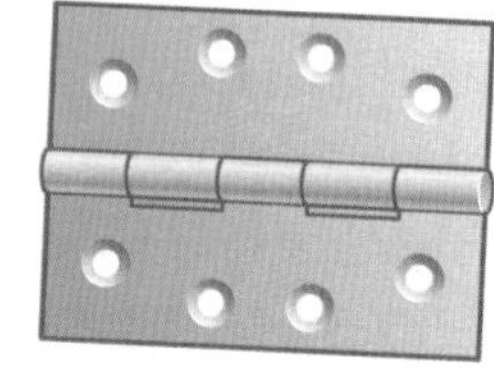

- Tee hinges are often used outside for shed doors and garden gates. The long strap allows the hinge to support a greater weight.

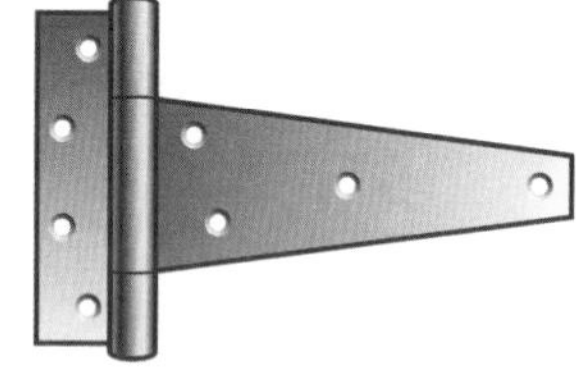

- Butterfly hinges are screwed directly onto the surface of the wood. They are easier to fit than butt hinges and are used for lighter work where the loads they carry are smaller.

- Concealed hinges are used for kitchen and bedroom furniture. They have small adjustment screws to align the door.

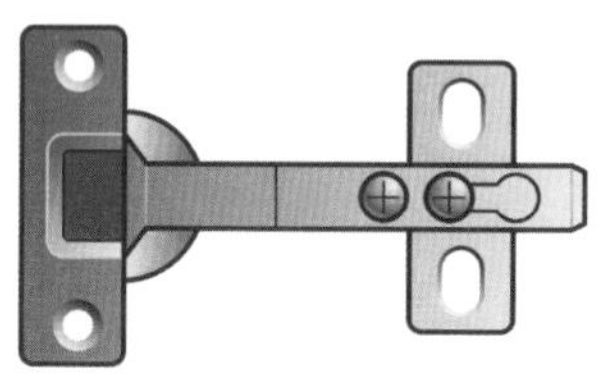

Locks and catches

Locks and catches need to be strong and reliable. They are available in a range of styles and sizes. Cupboard locks ar screwed to the edge of the cupboard door. Mortise latche require fitting into the door and the frame, and a range of handles makes them suitable for a variety of applications around the home. Catches such as the magnetic catch, toggle catch, jewel case catch and nylon roller catch hold the door closed without locking.

Fittings

Knock-down (KD) fittings are commonly used in modern furniture. They allow the product to be taken apart and reassembled. See 7.9 *Case study*: *IKEA* for information.

- Shelving fittings allow a shelf to be placed into a range of positions. A series of holes in the cupboard walls are pre-drilled to allow a choice of shelf positions.

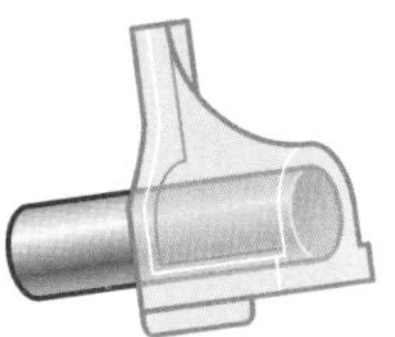

- Plate fittings are used for table legs where the leg need to be removed. Wing nuts are used so that the joints ca be taken apart without tools.

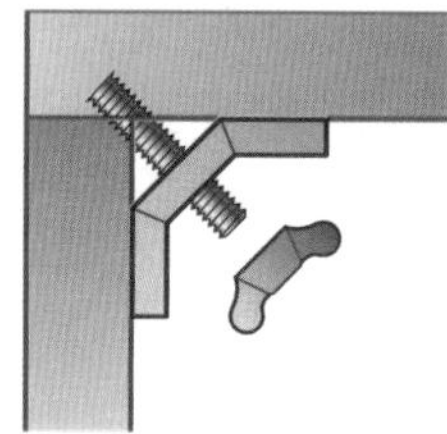

- Bloc-joint fittings are used for butt joints in solid wood ar man-made boards. The fitting has two parts that screw together to make a 90°angle. One half is screwed to eac piece of board and the halves are fitted together using th screw provided with the joint.

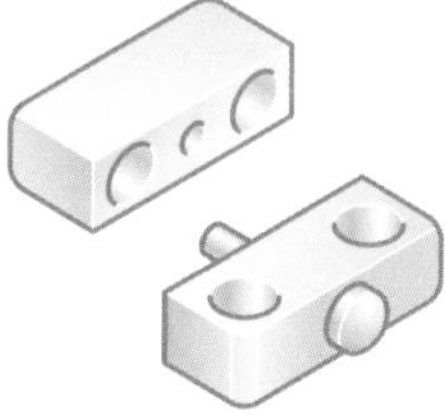

Modesty blocks are plastic blocks with three screw holes, two in one direction and a third at 90°. They are used for light construction and for strengthening joints.

Scan fittings are used for joining frame parts together, e.g. joining legs to table tops. A short length of steel bar with a threaded hole (the nut) is inserted into a hole in one section of the joint. The hexagonal socket-headed screw passes through the leg into the nut. A hexagonal key is used to tighten the screw, pulling the joint together. When this fitting is used as part of self-assembly flat-pack furniture, the correct key is supplied with the pack.

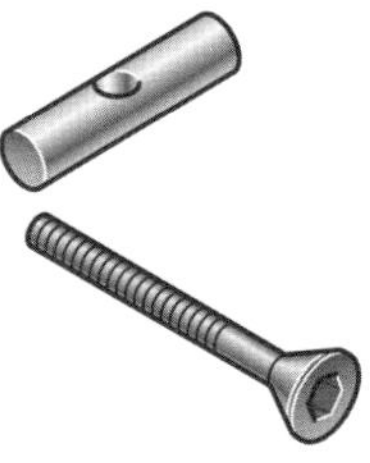

Disc and pegs are likely to be used to butt joint panels together. The disc part is pressed into a pre-drilled hole, the peg is screwed into the other part and then a screwdriver is used to align the disc over the peg. The disc has a slight cam and so tightening the disc pulls the peg and the surfaces together.

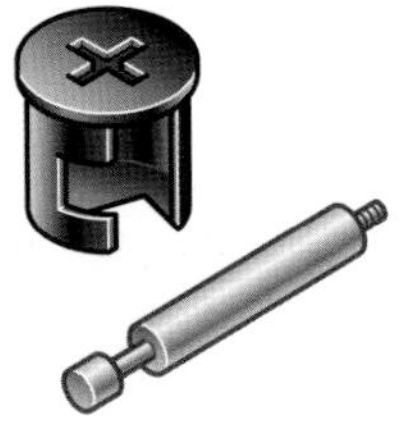

Coursework

Choosing the correct fixtures and fittings for your project should be shown in the development stage of your coursework folder. Making the right selection should be based on the availability of the component, its visual impact, your ability to fit it, and its suitability for the product.

Activities

1 Why are KD fittings used in flat-pack furniture?

2 a Sketch three fittings and three fixtures.

  b Annotate your diagrams to explain how they are used.

Summary

★ Fixings are components that are used to hold or fix larger materials together.

★ KD fittings are used in the construction of flat-pack furniture they allow furniture to be taken apart and reassembled.

3.8 Mechanisms

> **In this chapter you will learn about:**
> - ★ common components used in mechanical systems
> - ★ cams, cranks, levers, gears and pulleys.

A mechanism can be thought of as a **system**, with an input, an output and some kind of control or process going on in between. The input could be human power, wind power, water power or an electric motor. The process could be a cam, crank, lever, pulleys, gears or a combination of these. An example of this is a hand whisk. The input is human power in a rotary motion through the handle, the process is a bevel gear that turns the motion through 90° and changes the speed, and the output is the whisk rotating faster than the input.

Movement in mechanisms

There are four basic types of movement in mechanisms:

- linear, e.g. a drawer sliding in a linear motion
- reciprocating, e.g. a sewing machine needle or a bicycle pump
- rotary, e.g. the sails of a windmill spinning around
- oscillating, e.g. a swing or a clock pendulum

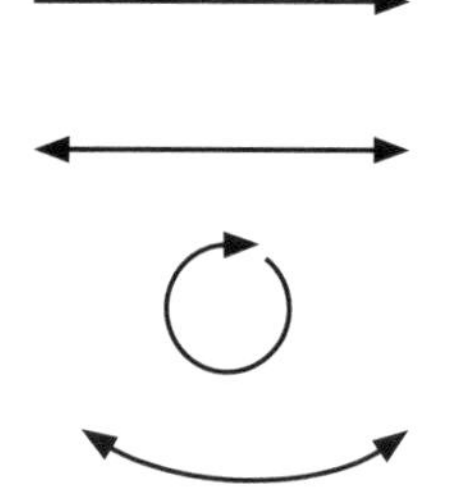

Mechanical systems

Cams

A cam is an odd-shaped wheel that converts one type of movement into another. Different-shaped cams will produce different effects.

Cranks

A crank converts reciprocating motion into rotary motion; for example, the crank pedal on a bicycle. The linear force of a leg pushing down (the input) converts to a rotary motion of the wheel (the output).

Levers

A lever changes the amount of movement and sometimes the direction. Each lever has a point where the effort is applied, a point where the load is attached and a point about which the lever rotates – the pivot or fulcrum. The three types of lever are shown in the diagram.

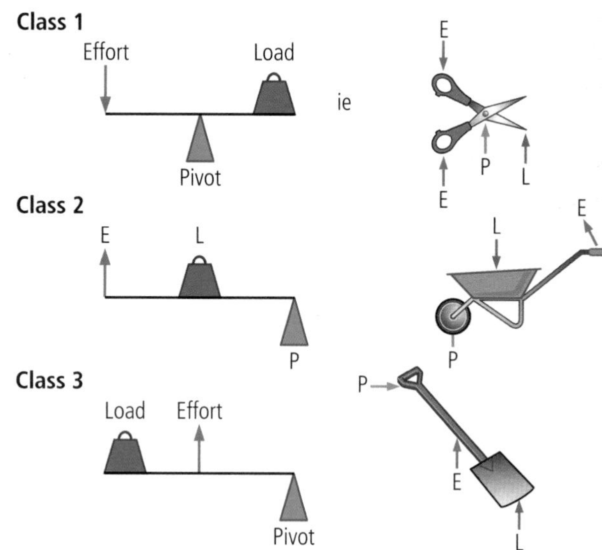

Levers: class 1, class 2 and class

Several levers joined together form a linkage. A linkage can be used to transfer or convert movement. Linkages are found in a number of products such as adjustable lamps, mechanical toys, vehicle jacks and locks.

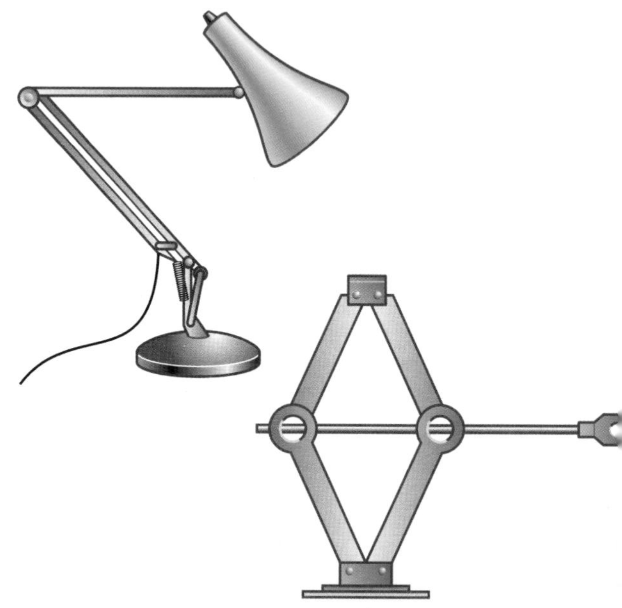

Linkages in a lamp and car jac

ears

ars are used to transfer rotary motion from one place to other. Gears are wheels with teeth around the outside, ich mesh with other gear wheels so that one cannot ate without the other. Chains or belts can also link them. ars are often used to change the speed of a mechanism; example, on a bicycle or hand whisk. They are also ed to reduce the amount of effort put into a mechanism. gear train is a series of gear wheels together in a chanism. An even number of gear wheels changes the ection of the motion, whereas an odd number keeps it in e same direction. Worm gears and bevel gears are used change direction through 90°. To change from rotary linear motion, a rack and pinion are used. Examples e found in toys, corkscrews, drilling machines, lock gate echanisms and car door window winders.

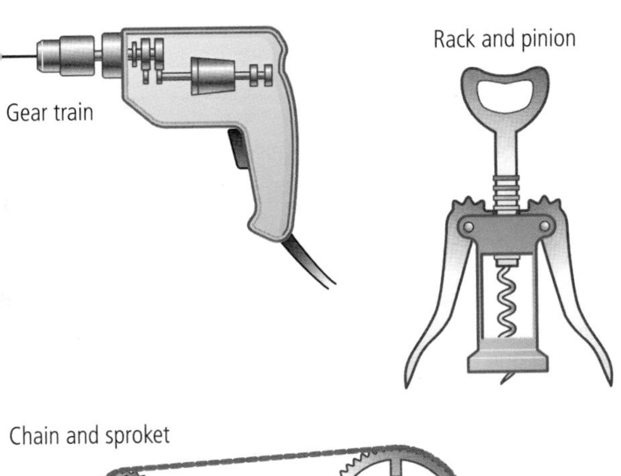

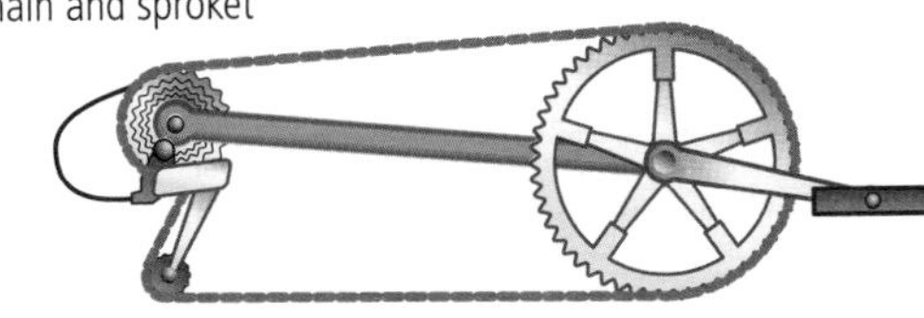

A gear train in a power drill, rack and pinion in a corkscrew, and a chain and sprocket on a bike

ulleys

pulley is a wheel with a groove around it through which ns a belt or rope. Pulleys are used to control the speed nd force by which something turns. They are used in pairs, ften with one pulley larger than the other, and they are ound in cassette recorders, washing machines, pillar drills, ranes and lifting gear. A twist in the belt makes the wheels rn in opposite directions. They can also be used to allow motion to travel greater distances across a mechanism with fewer components, such as on a yacht where a heavy sail can be winched up a tall mast by one person.

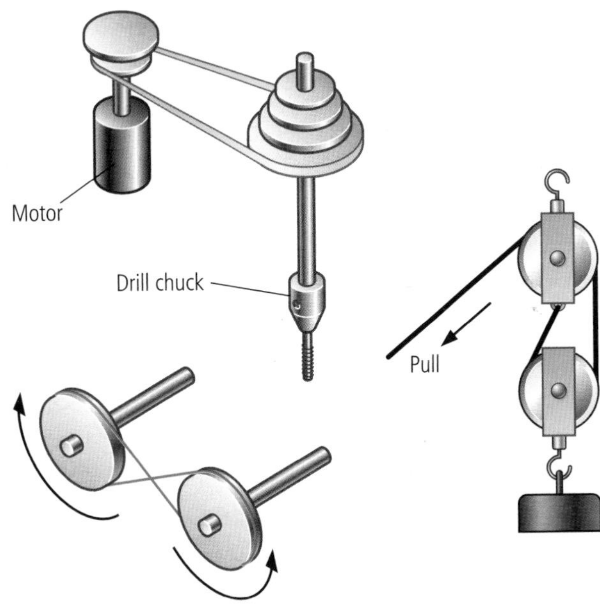

A cone pulley used in a pillar drill to achieve different speeds, a twist belt changes the direction of rotation, and two pulleys make it easier to lift things

Coursework

If your project is going to include a simple mechanism, it is important to develop it thoroughly. Use construction kits like Meccano to help test your ideas.

Activity

a Make a list of everyday objects that use one of the mechanisms above.

b For each object, what alternative mechanism could be used?

Summary

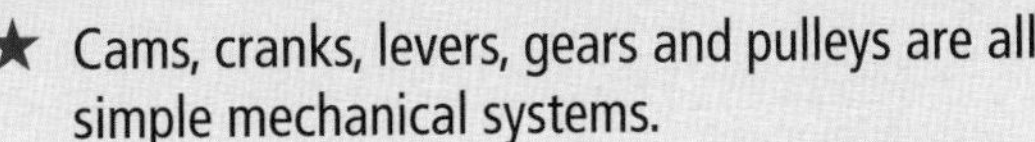

★ Cams, cranks, levers, gears and pulleys are all simple mechanical systems.

★ These mechanisms can be used to achieve different types of motion and increase or decrease the speed of the motion.

3.9 Adhesives

In this chapter you will learn about:

★ **the range and uses of a number of adhesives.**

Using adhesives

Adhesives are used to join (glue) components together and are usually a permanent fixing method. However, some products, such as Post-it® Notes, rely on a temporary adhesive. Some adhesives are rigid and can withstand big forces, whereas others are flexible and can move.

'Gap filling' is the property of the adhesive to fill the space between the areas to be joined. **Solvents** are used on plastics and dissolve the surfaces of the two materials to be joined. When the solvent evaporates the plastic hardens, making a permanent bond. In the school workshop, a range of adhesives are available to use.

Tips on using adhesives

- The surfaces to be joined must be dry, grease free and clean from old paint or varnish. The area to be joined needs to be large enough to give strength to the joint.
- Read the manufacturer's instructions before you start.
- Before the adhesive is applied, a 'dry run' should be used to check the fit of the joint and see if the glued components can be kept together for the drying time.
- Wherever possible, roughen the gluing area to give a 'key' – this helps the glue 'wet' the surface more thoroughly.
- Allow enough time.
- Choose how to apply the adhesive.
- Avoid getting the adhesive on any areas except the contact areas. To prevent marking plastics, cover them with masking tape and paper.
- Remove surplus adhesive as quickly as possible.
- Check for squareness and alignment before leaving to set.
- Some adhesives, such as PVA, require pressure to be applied while drying.

Safety tips

- Risk assessments (see 4.1 *Safety in the workshop* for more details) should be carried out when using any adhesive.
- Hot glue can burn if touched.
- Some adhesives are flammable
- Some adhesives give off harmful fumes: always ensure there is enough ventilation.
- Keep adhesives away from skin as contact can cause irritation.

Coursework

There are no short cuts when applying adhesives. Any mistakes will ruin all the hard work you have done. Before you get started, make sure you read the tips here.

Activities

1. Why do surfaces need to be clean before applying an adhesive?
2. Why is it a good idea to carry out a 'dry run' before starting?
3. Make a table of your own using the same headings as the one on the opposite page. Add any adhesives you have used over the last year.

Summary

★ A wide range of adhesives is available, suitable for use with a variety of materials.

ame	Material	Working time	Application	Waterproof?	Gap filling?	Comments
ot melt glue ick	Most, but best on models and quick mock-ups	Seconds; hardens on cooling	Glue gun	✓	✓	Glue tends to 'string'; poor-quality finish
olyvinyl acetate VA), e.g. vostick, resin	Wood; card	2–3 hours	Brush on; wipe off with a damp cloth	✗	✓	Easy to apply; use clamps to keep the glue under pressure
ynthetic resin Aerolite 306)	Wood	4–6 hours	Spreader	✓	✗	Two parts: resin and hardener; stronger than PVA; very hard when set; colourless
ross-linking VA	Laminating wood	2–3 hours	Brush or roller; wipe off with a damp cloth	✗	✓	A specially formulated PVA to assist with the lamination process using the bag press
ontact (impact) dhesive, e.g. vostick, Dunlop hixofix	Different materials such as plastics, metals, leather and rubber	Instant	Plastic spreader	✓	✓	Apply glue to both surfaces; works on contact, giving no time to reposition parts; good ventilation required
uper glue, e.g. octite	Non-porous rigid materials	Instant	Direct from the nozzle	✗	✓	Super strong; suitable for small, delicate work where clamping is not possible
poxy resin, e.g. raldite	Many materials but not flexible plastics	24 hours, although a more rapid grade is available	Mix equal parts and apply with a spreader	✓	✓	Used for small areas because of cost; does not have a good appearance
iquid solvent ement	Acrylic, ABS, butyrate, rigid polystyrene	2 minutes	Fine brush	✓	✗	Joint is prepared dry and then the solvent applied; water-like consistency allows capillary action to draw the solvent into the joint
Tensol No. 12	A range of thermoplastics including acrylic, ABS and rigid polystyrene	5 minutes	Brush or syringe	✓	✓	Thick, clear liquid solvent that is almost impossible to remove from the surfaces of the plastic if split
Tensol No. 70	Acrylic sheet	15 minutes	Brush or syringe	✓	✓	2-part solvent cement that gives a strong, clear bond
Rigid polystyrene cement	Polystyrene	5 minutes	Fine brush or dropper	✓	✗	Surplus removed with acetone

Adhesives used for joining wood, metal and plastics

Exam questions

1 Study the lamps shown below.

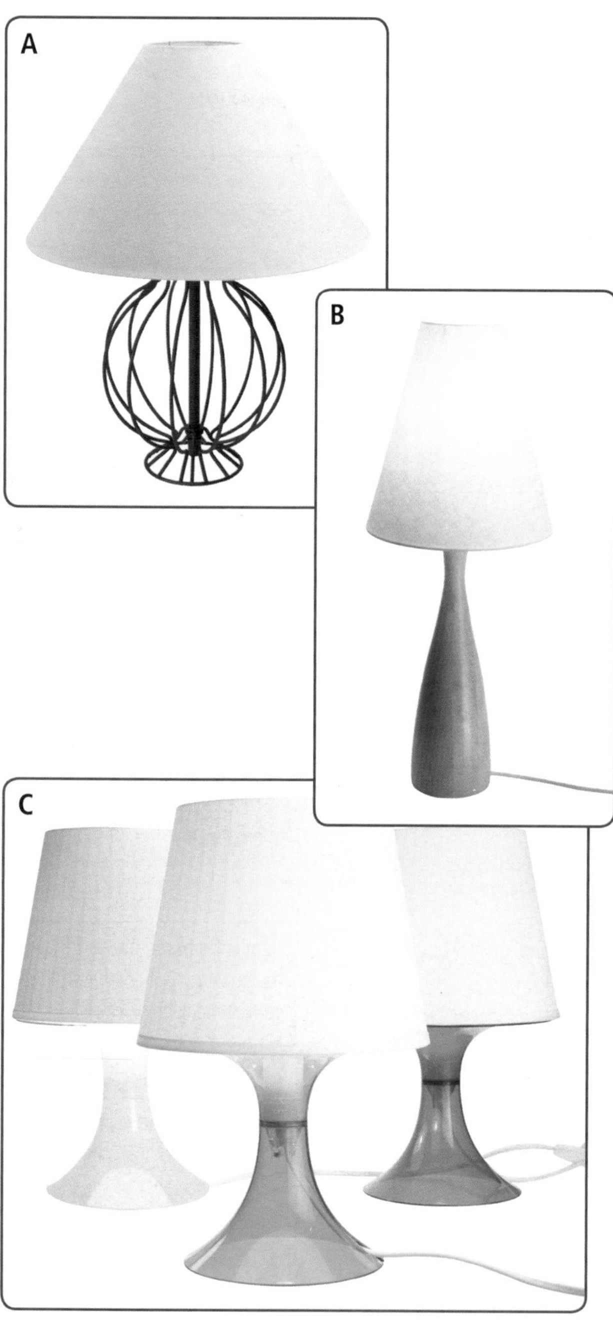

a Name the **main** material which has been used to make the base of **each** lamp. Give one reason for your choice.

(9 marks)

b Name **one** suitable, *specific* finish for each of the materials you have chosen for **lamp A** and **lamp B**.

(4 marks)

2 Study the display cabinet shown below. The display cabinet is being produced by a furniture manufacturer batches of 500.

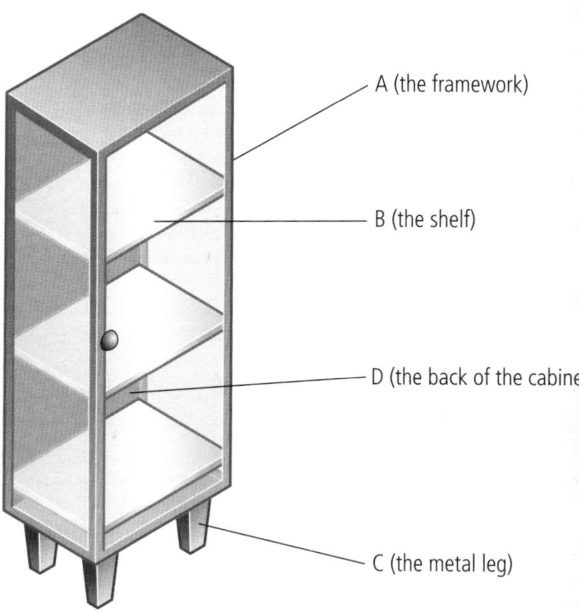

a Choose a suitable, **specific** material from which to make each part and give two reasons for your choice

Part A (the framework) *(3 mark*

Part B (the shelf) *(3 mark*

Part C (the metal leg) *(3 mark*

Part D (the backboard) *(3 mark*

b A cabinet is being made as a 'one off' product in a workshop.

(i) Choose a suitable specific finish for Part C (the metal leg). *(1 mar*

(ii) Describe using notes and sketches the stages in preparing and applying the finish you have namec in part (b)(i) to Part C (the metal leg).

(8 mark

c Explain how the finish would be applied to Part C (the metal leg) if it was being made as part of a batch of 500 in an industrial environment.

(5 mark

(AQA 200

Health and safety

is section is about designing and making fe products safely. Designers are sponsible for the products they design and anufacturers are responsible for the people no will make the designs. You are going design and make your coursework, so u need to consider the safety of yourself, hers around you and those who will finally se your product.

What's in this section?

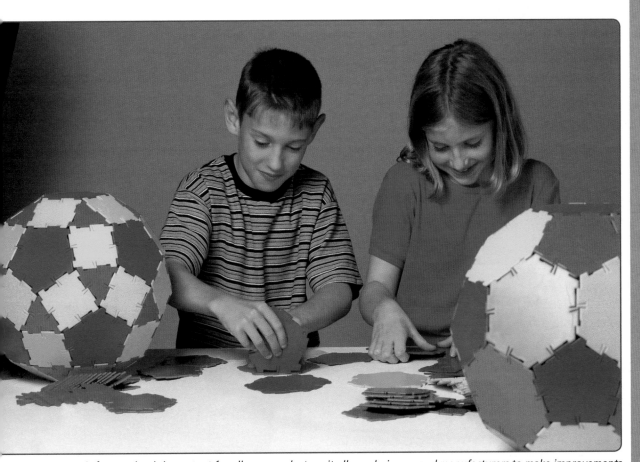

Safety testing is important for all new products as it allows designers and manufacturers to make improvements

4.1 Safety in the workshop

> **In this chapter you will learn about:**
> ★ **the safety rules in a workshop**
> ★ **carrying out a risk assessment.**

Health and safety

It is important to understand that safety for the product manufacturer is an essential part of planning and making a project. It does not matter where you are working, recognising possible **risks** and taking steps to control the **hazards** is everyone's responsibility.

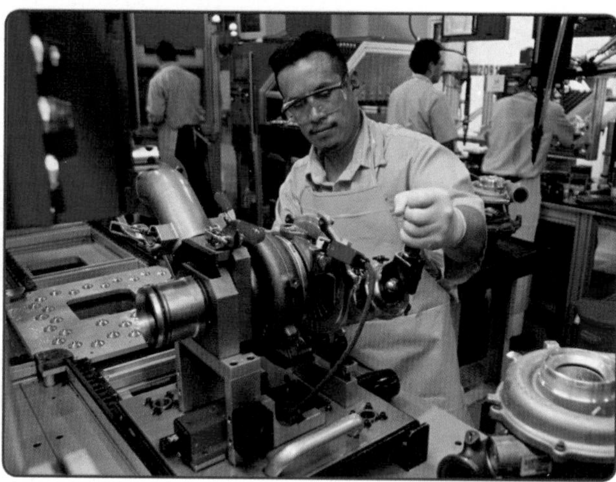

Safety in the factory

Workshop rules are there to help everyone work safely. Safety rules are common sense but you need to learn them.

There are some important things to think about.

- Always check all matters of health and safety with your teacher.
- Carry out a risk assessment and reduce potential dangers.
- Recognise that safety in the workshop is essential. Take responsibility to ensure hazards are minimised and the working environment is safe.
- Look after yourself: use the correct safety clothing, goggles and masks.
- Look after others: always keep a safe space around you and do not disturb others as they work.
- Look after the materials by storing them correctly and safely.
- Look after tools and machines. Never use them for anything except their intended use.
- Do not operate machinery or equipment unless you are allowed to.
- Use guards on machines.
- Hold materials securely. Use the right clamps and fixtur while machining.
- Switch off equipment after use.
- Know where the emergency stop buttons are.
- Use dust and fume extraction.
- Clean brushes or other equipment in accordance with health and safety regulations.
- Handle cut and partially finished components carefully. Watch out for sharp edges, rough burr (the raised area of metal after it has been cut), splinters and sharp swar (produced by drilling, milling and turning).
- Dispose of waste materials in the right way. Consider recycling and reusing where possible.
- Report all faults, problems and accidents.
- Know where the first aid kit is.
- Do not be silly.

A school worksho

isk assessment

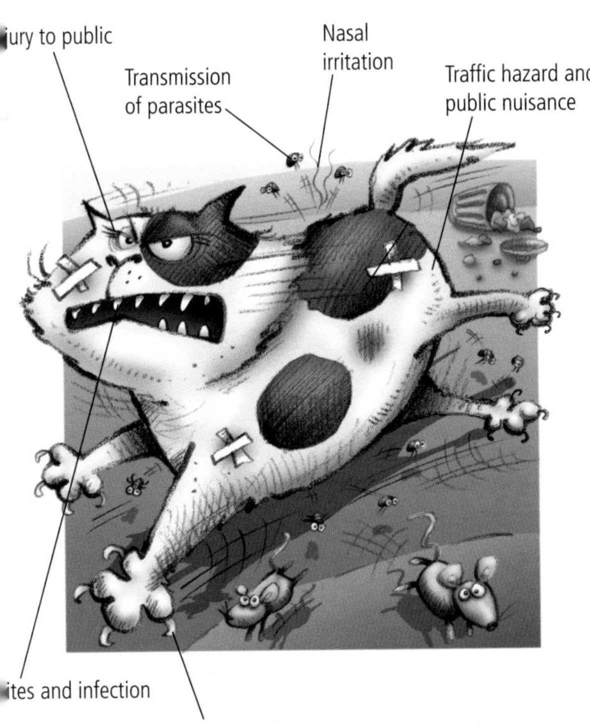

Risk assessment

tecting and reducing hazards or risks when you are signing and manufacturing products is your responsibility. s essential to reduce the number of hazards and safe actions that may occur in the workplace. In lustry, accidents are costly in terms of personal distress, mpensation and loss of production. Steps should be carried t to ensure your safety and the safety of others around u. Identifying potential hazards and doing things to reduce e risk of those hazards is called **risk assessment**.

e table below shows part of a risk assessment for a ıffing machine. This involves looking at the potential ızards and deciding how likely they are to happen, then orking out how to minimise the risk.

Hazard	Likelihood	Consequence	Risk rating	Control action
Polish sprays into operator's face	Very likely	Minor injuries	High	Wear goggles; ensure guards are in position
Clothing or hair gets caught around a mop	Likely	Major injuries	Medium	Ensure all clothing and hair are tied back
Operator is pushed into rotating mop	Highly unlikely	Minor injuries	Low	One person only inside machine zone as marked on the floor

A five-stage risk assessment grid

Coursework

- During the making of your project always follow your school workshop safety rules.
- When producing your plan for manufacture, make sure you include evidence of how you have considered health and safety in the workplace.

Activities

1 **a** In pairs, decide on the ten most important safety rules in your school workshop.

b How can you make sure everyone using the workshop follows these rules?

2 Prepare a short test that can be given to Year 7 pupils to test their knowledge of safety in the school workshop.

3 In small groups:

a Draw a five-stage risk assessment grid on a piece of machinery or equipment. Each group should choose a different item.

b Copy the grids and pass them around to the other groups.

c Discuss your findings.

Summary

★ Plan an efficient and safe working environment.

★ Risk assessment helps to identify and reduce potential hazards.

4.2 Designing and making safe products

> **In this chapter you will learn about:**
> ★ things to consider when designing safe products
> ★ reducing the chance of people hurting themselves on your product.

Safe products

The designer is responsible for designing safe products and reducing the risk to users. Poor design can result in the designer being held responsible for any accidents that occur. The choice and use of materials and components, finishes and packaging is an essential part of safe product design. The designer must always keep relevant safety issues in mind.

- Avoid using toxic paints and materials in products, especially those for children. A range of child-friendly paints is available in good DIY stores.
- Make the product safe from splinters and sharp edges.
- Design rounded corners.
- Avoid areas where small fingers may get trapped.
- Young children often put small parts into their mouths, posing a choking hazard. The Early Learning Centres provide a testing device.
- Design fixtures and fittings that are well secured and unlikely to come off.
- Conform to the relevant safety standards, which must include the standards of other countries in which the product might be sold.
- Analyse the users' requirements at the design stage. Identify who will (and who might) use the product.

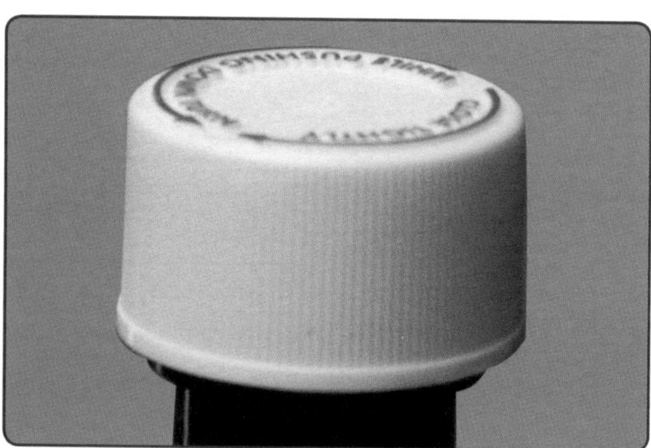

A childproof cap lock

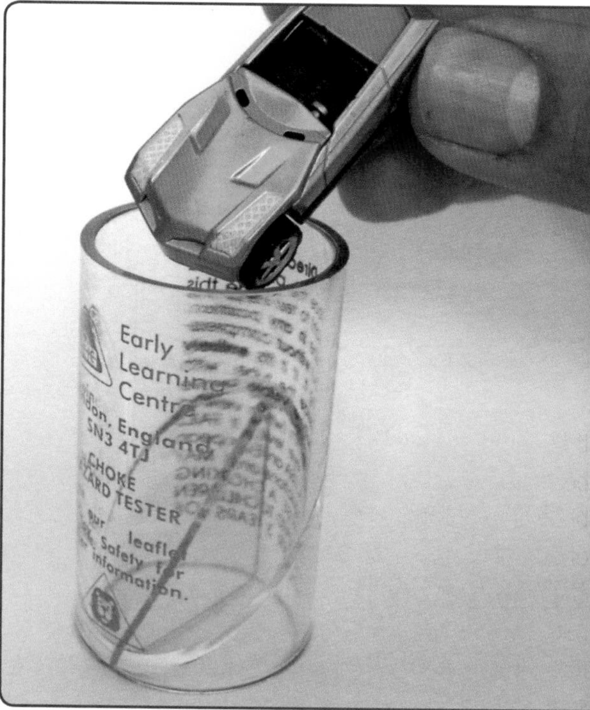

If part of a child's toy fits inside the top section of this cho hazard tester completely, it will fail the European standa for to

Medicine bottle tops are designed so that any adult car undo them no matter how frail, yet they are impossible for children to open.

- Consider ways in which adults and children might misuse the product, and then design any necessary safety devices and warning labels. For example, ballpoir pens have a hole in the top of the lid so that if a child swallows it, they can still breath.
- Design for the whole life of the product: from beginning to end it must be safe.

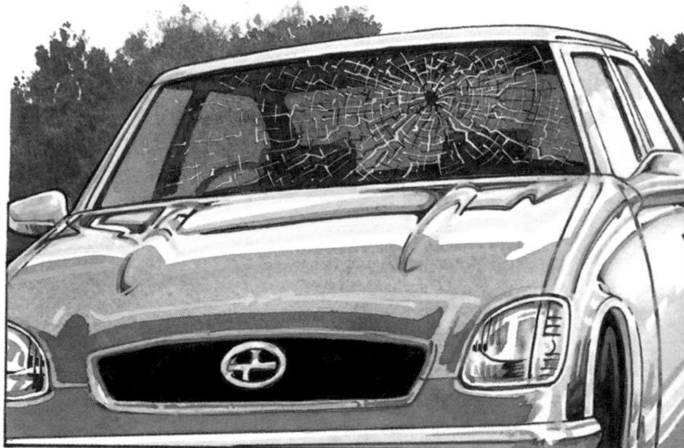

Car windscreens are designed to break into small pieces th are relatively sa

The lid to this pen has a breathing hole

If the product breaks, what would happen? Would there be sharp edges and corners? Safety glass is designed to break into tiny pieces that are safer than the large pieces of normal glass.

The users must be protected from electrical or moving parts. A 13-amp plug is designed so that it cannot be put into a socket without the back on (the pins just pop out), so if it were broken or incomplete it could not be used.

If possible, non-corrosive, non-toxic and non-flammable materials should be used.

ritish Standards Institution

e British Standards Institution (BSI) has developed safety andards and standard guidelines for a wide range of oducts from credit cards to road signs, electrical goods soft toys. Many products carry the **Kitemark**. It is used to indicate that a product has met the required safety standards, and has been independently tested against them.

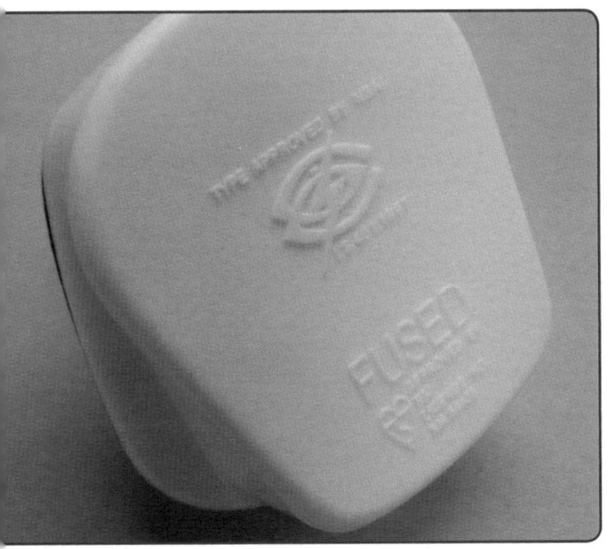

The Kitemark is moulded onto the product

Products with Kitemarks have passed a number of tests. British Standards can be used to help test for correct materials and finishes for a product, as such they are a valuable source of information for any designer. The BSI Education website at www.heinemann.co.uk/hotlinks can be used to access information about product design and testing. See also chapter 2.2 *Quality* and 2.6 *Legislation*.

Coursework

Choices about safety need to be explained in your product development notes. You can research specific information through the BSI at www.heinemann.co.uk/hotlinks.

Activities

1 Make a list of the products around your home and the school workshop that have the Kitemark on them. Can you find two similar products (e.g. electrical plugs), one with and one without the Kitemark? What do you think this means?

2 Produce a list of criteria including suitable materials, components and surface treatments that should be considered when designing children's toys.

Summary

★ The designer is responsible for designing safe products and reducing risks to users.

★ The choice and use of materials and components, finishes and packaging is part of safe product design.

★ The BSI Kitemark is used to indicate that the product has been tested and has met the relevant safety standards.

Exam questions

1 Drilling metals can be a high risk activity.

Copy and complete the table shown below. The first line has been completed for you.

Hazard	Risk to user	Precaution
The metal component can spin with the drill.	*Metal cuts your hand.*	*Make sure the metal component is firmly clamped down.*
Metal cuttings (swarf) can fly off.		
The metal component can become hot.		
Loose clothing can become entangled in the drill bit.		

(6 mark

2 Melamine-covered-chipboard is a sheet material often used in the construction of cabinets, cupboards, tables and shelves.

a Give and explain **three** safety precautions you would take when cutting this board with the jigsaw shown below.

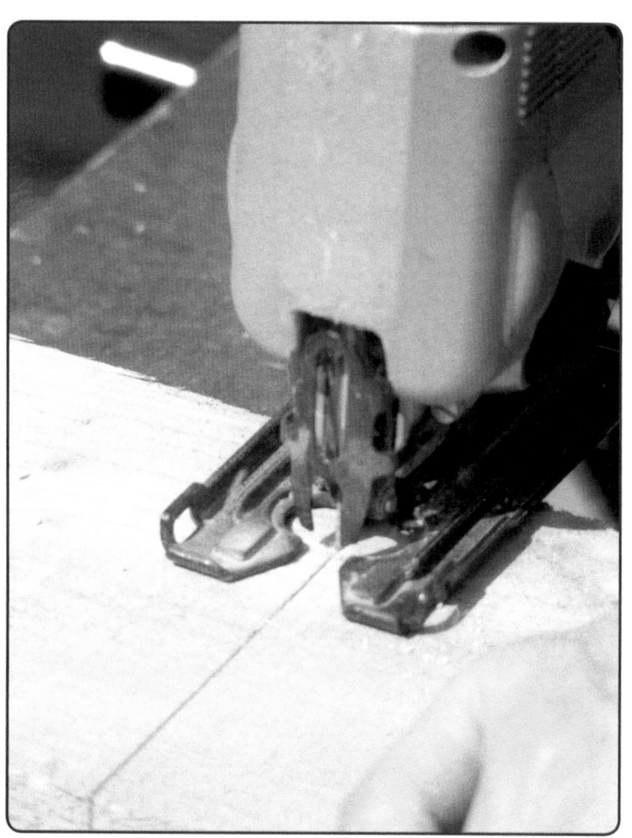

(6 marks)

b It is essential to have a safe environment within the workplace.
Give **four** safe working conditions.

(4 mark

{AQA 20C

Processes and manufacture

ne exciting thing about design and ·chnology is that you make real products. ıis section takes you through a range of ·ols and techniques that are the foundation all the project work you might do in the ture. Skills are developed and refined ırough practice. Good designers, craftsmen, ıanufacturers, builders, engineers, ırpenters and jewellers are always learning ıore about the materials they use.

Vhat's in this section?

Making skills developed through practice

5.1 Measuring and marking out

In this chapter you will learn about:

- ★ quality, tolerance and accuracy
- ★ marking materials to size and shape
- ★ the tools used to measure and mark out woods, metals and plastics.

Quality

Quality products are designed well, produced from the right materials and made accurately. **Tolerance** is the level of accuracy that is acceptable for the product. A working mechanism such as a watch needs to be made within a very fine tolerance, whereas a CD rack can have a wider acceptable tolerance provided that the CDs still fit. Accurate products start with measuring and marking out.

Quality control systems

Working accurately is a skill that needs to be practised. Getting it right first time will save you time, money and extra work. Measuring accurately and marking out materials before cutting improves quality.

To the right there is a **quality control system** (a series of steps) to go through when measuring and marking out. Following the steps given will help you to produce accurate work time after time.

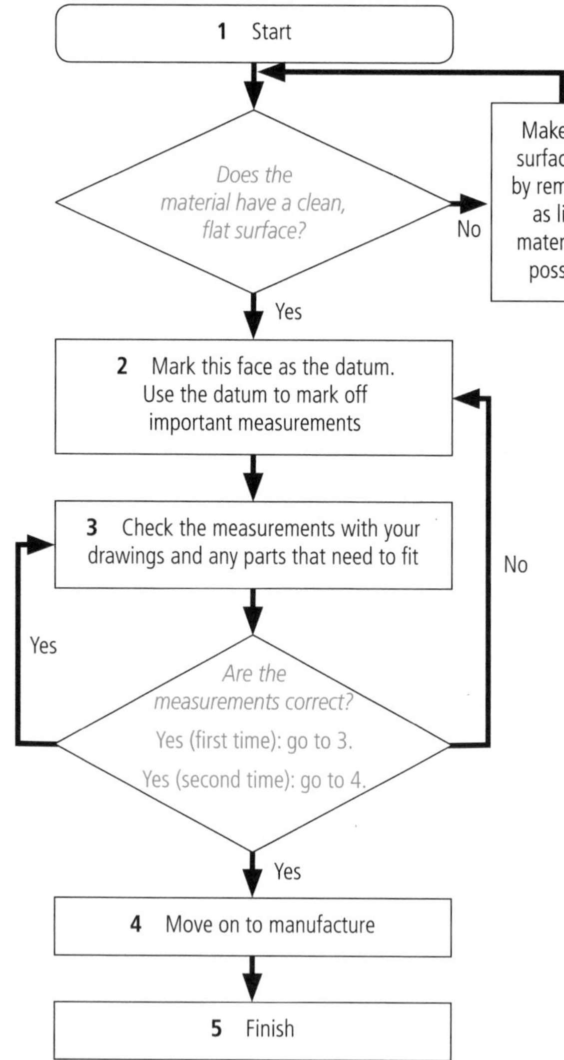

1 Start
Does the material have a clean, flat surface?
No
Make one surface flat by removing as little material as possible
Yes
2 Mark this face as the datum. Use the datum to mark off important measurements
3 Check the measurements with your drawings and any parts that need to fit
Yes
No
Are the measurements correct?
Yes (first time): go to 3.
Yes (second time): go to 4.
Yes
4 Move on to manufacture
5 Finish

Quality control syste

Measuring and marking out

Measuring

In design and technology, millimetres (mm) are the preferred unit of measurement and for most of your work a steel rule should be accurate enough. However, for more accurate work, a micrometer and Vernier callipers may be used.

Marking out

You can mark regular shapes onto a flat surface by selecting a datum to give you a starting point. A datum is a flat surface or line. All measurements should start from the datum.

When working with timber, it is usually necessary to start by making a surface flat. The first surface is usually the fac side; the second surface, at right angles to the first, is the face edge. Mark these surfaces with the symbols as show in the diagram – a loop leading to a V – to make them ea to identify.

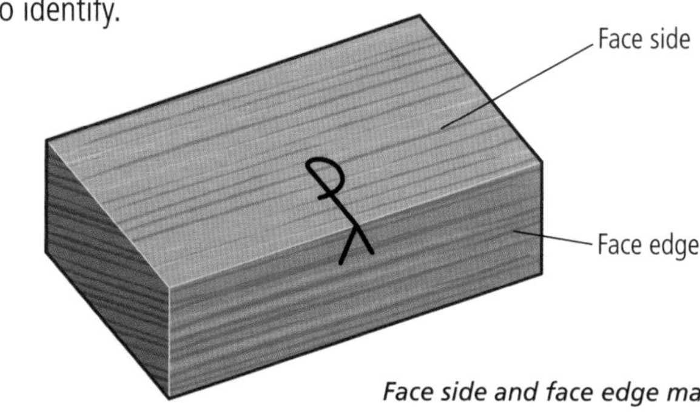

Face side
Face edge

Face side and face edge ma

ferent materials need different marking-out tools:
Many marking-out lines eventually need to be removed, so consider using a light pencil on timber or a fine-line spirit pen for plastics and metals. For more permanent lines, a scriber is used on plastics and metals. On timber, a marking knife is used to cut the surface grain.
A tri square is used to make lines at 90° to an edge. It is also used to check that two edges are square.
A centre square is used to find the centre of a round bar.
A marking gauge and odd-leg callipers are used to mark parallel lines on materials.
Outside and inside callipers may be used to measure complex 3D components.
A pair of compasses, dividers and circle templates are used to mark circles. A centre punch should be used to mark the centre of a hole before drilling. This is particularly useful for metals, woods and some plastics, but it should not be used with brittle materials such as acrylic or they may break.

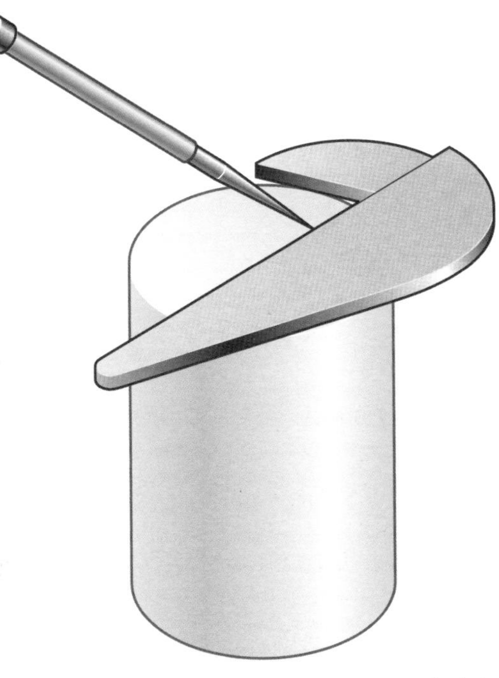

The scriber is used with the centre square to find the centre of the bar

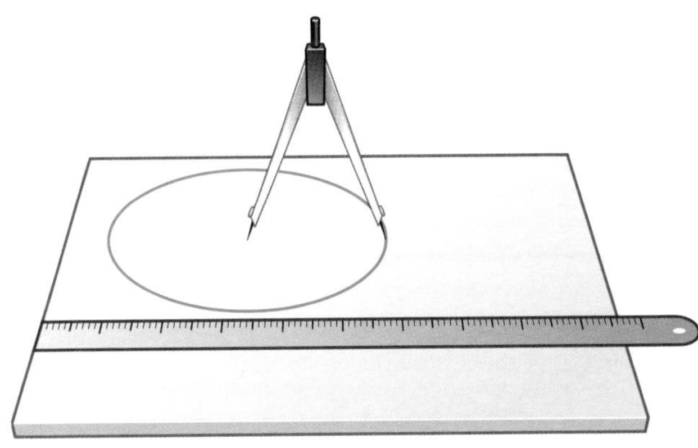

Dividers are used to scribe circles. The steel rule starts to measure from its end

Coursework

Students who check their work carefully produce good products, cutting and shaping with accuracy and within tolerance.

Activity

The letters **D&T** are to be cut from a 100 mm square piece of 3 mm acrylic sheet. Describe how you would prepare accurately the material for cutting.

Summary

- ★ Accurately measuring and marking out materials before cutting improves quality.
- ★ Different materials need different marking-out tools.

Cutting and shaping metals using hand tools

In this chapter you will learn about:

★ **selecting different hand tools to cut and shape metals**

★ **using hand tools efficiently.**

Using hand tools carefully means you can fit the metal parts of your product together accurately.

Saws

Hacksaws are often used for sawing metals and plastics. The teeth face forward and cut on the push stroke. Selecting the correct blade for the correct thickness of material is important.

Material thickness	Pitch (number of teeth per 25 mm)
up to 3 mm	32
3–6 mm	24
above 6 mm	18

Choosing the right saw blade

Abrafiles or tension saws can be used for cutting metals and plastics. The teeth go around the circular blade, mak it easy to cut curves and turn corners.

A piercing saw is used for intricate work, often cutting curves and patterns in jewellery. The work is usually held flat on a bench pin. The saw is kept moving steadily with regular strokes. The very fine blade of the piercing saw is set to cut on the pull stroke, i.e. upward.

Files

Files are classified by their length, shape and cut. They ar made from high-carbon steel that has been hardened an tempered. They need to be treated with care because the are brittle and will snap if dropped or abused. The work needs to be held in a vice, protecting it from the teeth of the vice jaws using aluminium strips or corrugated paper. should be gripped as low down as possible.

The cutting is done by rows of teeth that remove small particles of material, called filings. Pinning happens whe filings clog the teeth of the file. To help prevent pinning, chalk can be rubbed into the face of the file. Pinned files can be cleaned using a file card.

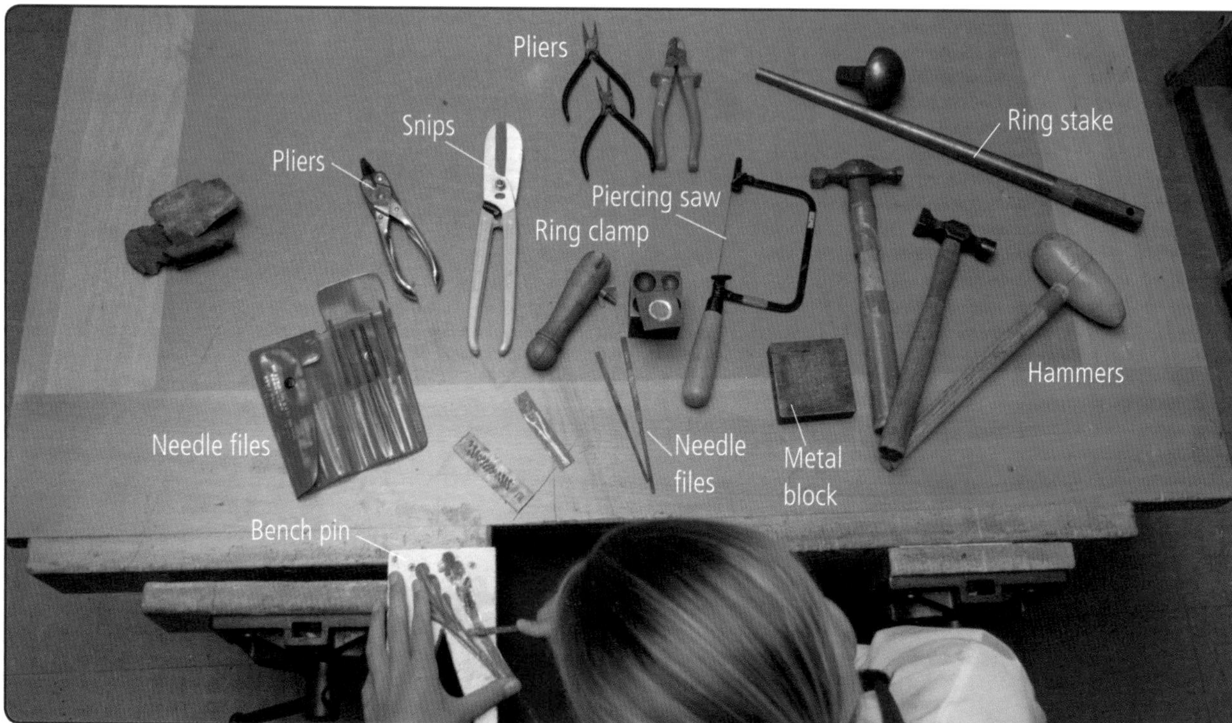

A jeweller's be

oss filing removes material quickly. Draw filing is used to rn all irregular marks into one direction ready for finishing th an **abrasive**. An abrasive such as emery cloth can be apped around the file to produce a fine finish.

ere are many types of files, including:
- rough and bastard cut files, used for coarse work
- general-purpose (double-cut) files, which have two directions of teeth
- single-cut files, used for finishing work
- smooth and dead smooth files, used for fine work
- needle files, used for precision, very fine or intricate work
- warding files, used for thin slots
- dreadnought files, used on soft materials such as aluminium castings.

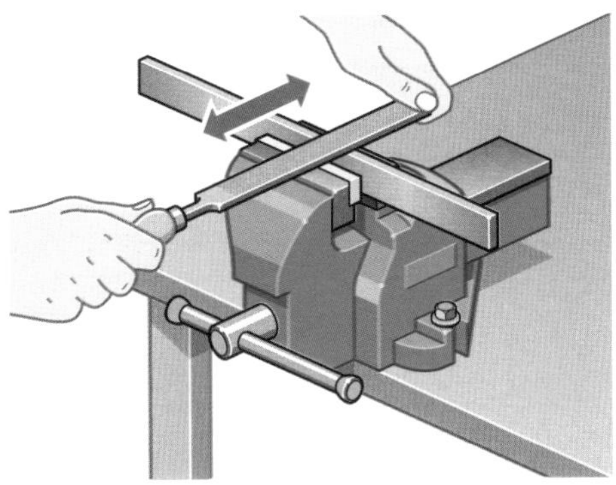

Cross filing

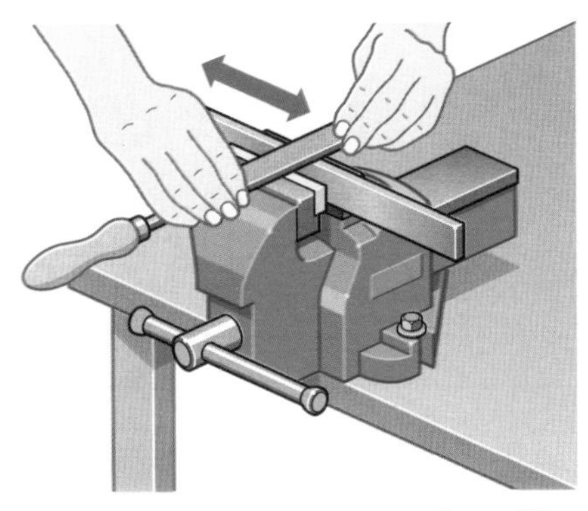

Draw filing

Snips

nips and shears, which can be curved or straight, are sed to trim thin metal sheet. It is best to nibble away the aterial with short cuts.

A guillotine can be used for cutting straight lines in metal. This is a dangerous machine, so make sure you position the guards carefully and ask for help. A risk assessment should be carried out before using a guillotine.

Hammers

A variety of hammers and mallets are available for shaping metals.

- A ball pein hammer is used for rounding, general shaping and riveting. It is available in large sizes for heavy-duty work.
- A bossing mallet has an egg-shaped boxwood head. It is used with a sand bag or wooden block for hollowing and dishing sheet metal.
- A planishing hammer has a highly polished head and should not be used for general work. It is used with a polished metal stake to create accurate contours and decorative surfaces. Planishing helps to close the pores on the metal surface ready for polishing.
- A rubber- or nylon-headed mallet is used for bending metals without marking the surface.

Pliers

A variety of sizes and shapes are available for holding, twisting, bending and forming thin metal strips and wires.

Activities

1. Why would a piece of metal be draw filed?
2. Which way do the teeth face on a piercing saw. Explain your answer.
3. Give five top tips for cutting a 4 mm piece of mild steel bar.
4. Explain how you would cut out a copper heart shape for a pendant.

Summary

★ Selecting the correct tool allows metal components to be cut and shaped accurately.

5.3 Cutting and shaping plastics using hand tools

In this chapter you will learn about:

- ★ marking plastics ready for shaping
- ★ shaping, joining and finishing plastics by hand.

Marking out

Plastics are usually soft and care should be taken when handling them. Acrylic comes with its own protective sheet that should be kept on as long as possible. A ballpoint pen can be used to mark out the protective sheet. Mark out bare plastics with a chinagraph pencil, a spirit-based pen or clear tape. Areas to be drilled or cut with a scroll (Hegner) saw can benefit from an additional layer of clear tape, which helps prevent the build-up of heat that can friction-weld a cut back together. The tape also helps to stop the drill skidding on the smooth surface.

Shaping

- Plastic sheets and blocks can be drilled, sawn and filed with the same hand tools and processes used for wood and metal. See chapters 5.2 and 5.4 on cutting and shaping using hand tools.
- Thin sheets can often be cut using a paper guillotine, but a risk assessment should be carried out before using one.
- Drilling plastic sheet is best done with a twist drill whose tip has been reground to 140° rather than 118°. This helps to reduce the stress at the bottom of the drill hole and so reduces cracking.
- Some plastics, such as polypropylene, can be punched with the appropriate size-hand or scissor-type punch.
- Plastics can be planed and finished with abrasives.
- Many plastics can be snapped along a straight line. The plastic sheet and cutting guide are secured firmly to the bench. Apply three or four cutting strokes before attempting to snap. The finish is often rough and this method works best with thin sheet polystyrene, ABS and acrylic.
- Vacuum-formed and blow-moulded shapes can be trimmed with a special trimming machine. This machine has an adjustable fibrous disc that spins at high speed. Gently pushing the moulding against the disc cuts a parallel and even line, removing the waste.

Tools used with polypropyle

A trimming machi

Joining

Permanent joining can be achieved by using adhesives or hot air welding. It is important to use the correct adhesive for example, Tensol 12 is a solvent-based adhesive used tc join acrylic. See 3.9 *Adhesives* for information on adhesive A solvent-based adhesive melts the surfaces of plastic to be joined and evaporates, leaving a permanent bond. The strength of the joint depends on the areas bonded. The tw

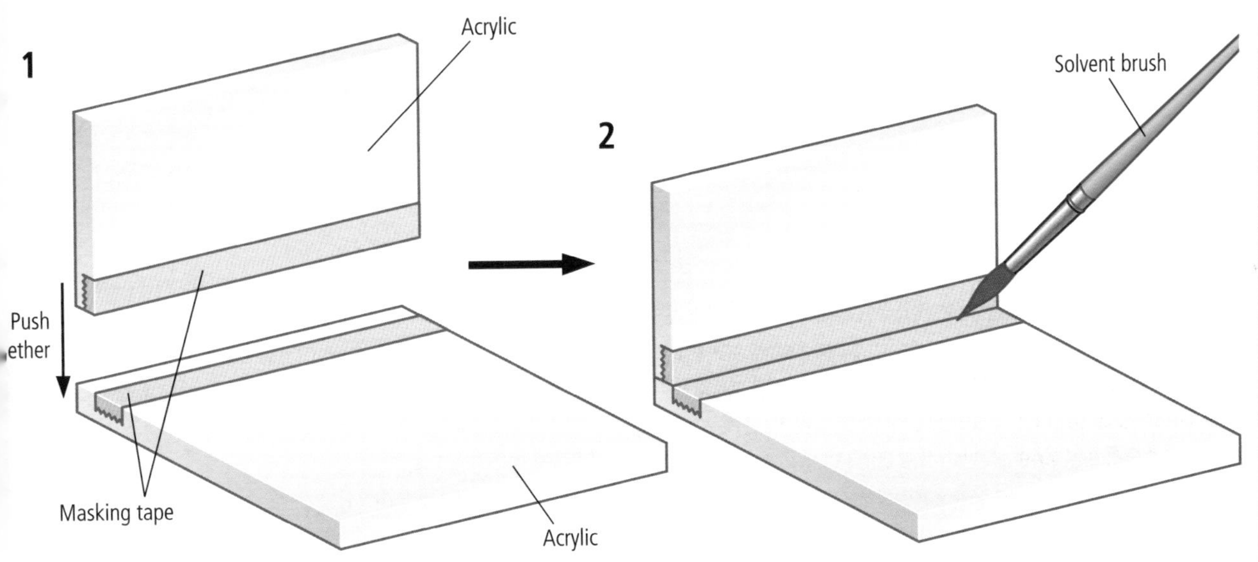

Prepare the surfaces with wet and dry paper. Bring together and apply solvent with a brush

rfaces must be held under pressure during the bonding ocess. Eye protection and fume extraction are important hen using solvents.

hot air gun and a filler rod of matching plastic can be ed to join plastic materials in a similar way to metal elding. The plastics are heated until soft and then the filler astic rod is introduced.

emi-permanent joining

echanical fixings like nuts and bolts are easy to use, but r more decorative features you can be creative. Think bout press-studs, brass fastenings, coloured cords, hook d eye strips, leather laces, cable ties and the vast array f metal and plastic rivets. Some plastic rivets come in two arts and can be joined only once. They have a serrated haft that allows movement in one direction.

inishing

Vhen finishing plastics, the process may be quick because ey often have a moulded or formed finish that is cceptable. The only part that may need attention is the dge where the waste has been removed. Filing, draw filing and then using wet and dry paper (silicon carbide) can make the edges suitable for polishing. Using a liquid polish or a polishing compound used on the buffing wheel produces a shiny, high-quality finish. See 5.18 *Finishing* for information on these techniques.

Coursework

Always protect the surfaces of plastic sheet as you work. This saves time during the finishing stages of your project.

Activities

1 Start a collection of different fastenings and fittings that could be used to join plastic sheet.

2 Experiment by snapping a piece of 3 mm acrylic sheet. Examine the pieces closely – what do you notice about the quality of the snapped edge?

Summary

★ Plastics can be cut, shaped and joined using simple hand tools, but accurate work starts with careful accurate marking out.

5.4 Cutting and shaping woods using hand tools

In this chapter you will learn about:

★ **selecting hand tools to cut and shape woods**

★ **using hand tools efficiently and safely.**

Saws

Saws are used to cut materials to size. All saws cut a gap wider than the blade to prevent it becoming stuck – this is known as the kerf. The sharp teeth of the saw are set by being bent alternately to create the width of the kerf. The pitch is the number of teeth per 25 mm. The finer the pitch, the more delicate and precise the cut. When making a cut, always cut on the waste side of the line. Wood saws have sharp teeth and should be used with care.

- Tenon saws are used for sawing all kinds of wood found in a school workshop. Tenon saws are typically 250 mm long and have a pitch of 12–14 teeth. Many of the general wood joints can be cut with this type of saw.
- Dovetail saws are used for small, accurate work such as dovetail joints. The saw is smaller than the tenon saw and has 20–25 teeth per 25 mm.
- Hand saws are used for the fast cutting of larger work. These saws are usually 550 mm long and have a pitch of 8 teeth.
- Mitre saws are widely used as they enable accurate cutting of set lengths at a variety of angles. They are excellent for cutting simple joints like picture frame mitres. Adjustable length and depth stops enable mitre saws to be used for accurate repetitive work. The main advantage of this type of saw is the accuracy of the cu even with an unskilled user. Mitre saws are popular fo many DIY jobs.
- Coping saws are used to cut curves in wood and plasti They have a thin replaceable blade held in a frame, wh can be rotated to cut complex shapes. Unlike other wo saws, this saw cuts on the pull stroke as the teeth poin towards the user.

Planes

Planes are used to prepare and smooth the surface of wo They use a sharp adjustable blade to remove fine shavings Planes can produce quickly an accurate and smooth surfa

- Jack planes are used to plane wood to size. The length this plane (350 mm) helps to produce a flat surface.
- Smoothing planes are a smaller version of the jack pla measuring 250 mm long. They are used for fine finishin
- Spokeshaves are versatile planes used to smooth curve There are two types: concave for inside and convex for outside.

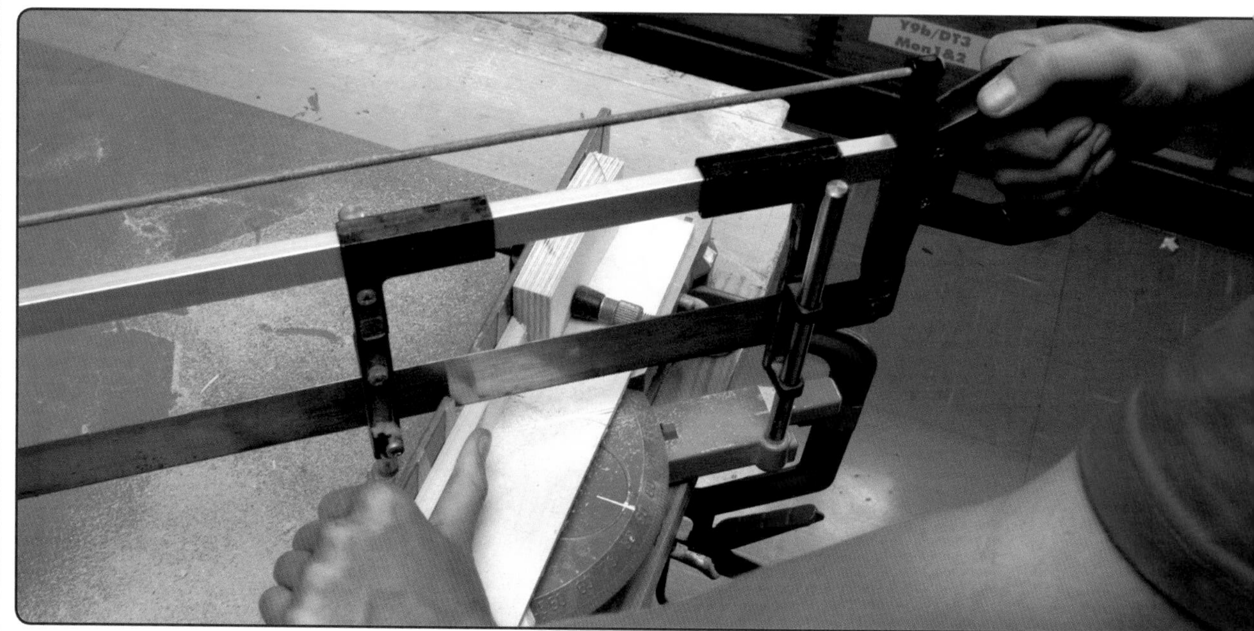

The mitre saw enables materials to be cut very accurately with ea

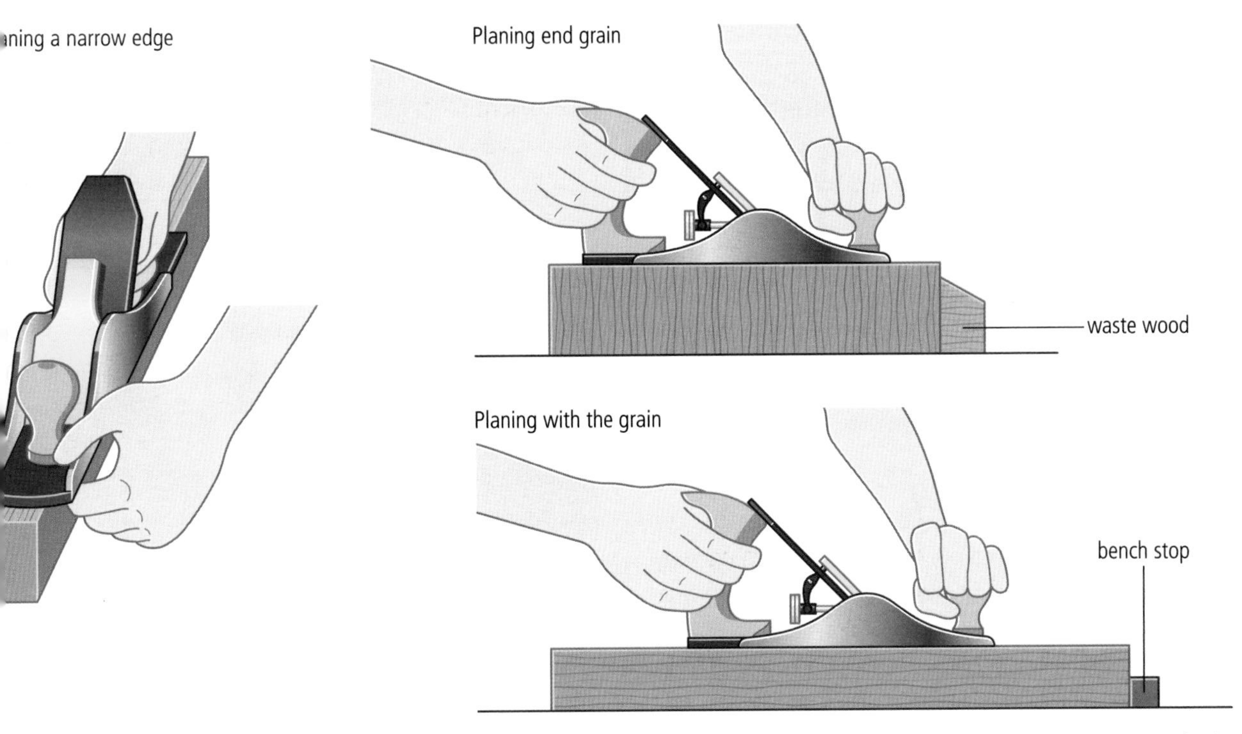

Planing

hen using a plane:

- keep it sharp to make sure it works well
- always rest it on its side to protect the sharp blade from damage
- use a light smear of candle wax on the sole (underside) to help it run smoothly.

hisels

isels are used for many cutting purposes. The sharp blade either pushed through the wood or driven with a wooden allet. Chisels come in a variety of widths from 6 mm up to mm.

- Firmer chisels are general purpose tools with a square edge.
- Bevel edge chisels are lighter chisels with a bevel on the blade, allowing them to cut accurately into corners such as dovetails.
- Mortise chisels are thicker, heavy duty chisels used with a mallet for chopping mortise joints and levering out waste.
- Gouges have curved blades and are used for carving.

When using a chisel:

- handle it with care
- keep it sharp to make sure it will cut without undue force
- keep both hands behind the cutting edge.

Coursework

It is important to know the correct tools and techniques to use for each part of the making process. Tools that enable accurate working can make a difference to the quality of your coursework project.

Activity

a In detail, describe how you would cut four identical sides for a box with simple mitre joints using a mitre saw.

b How can you minimise the chance of any inaccuracy?

Summary

★ There are many fast and effective hand tools for cutting and shaping wood.

5.5 Using power tools for cutting wood

In this chapter you will learn about:

- ★ **the health and safety issues concerned with using power tools**
- ★ **the range of power tools available to cut, shape and finish materials.**

Power tools can be used to cut, shape and finish materials. You need to be aware of what they are capable of, when to use them and how to use them safely.

Health and safety

It is important to use machine tools and portable power tools safely. There are many rules and laws that deal with how to use them properly. Some machines can be used only by qualified adults. Always check with your teacher before you use a power tool and take the following precautions.

- Standard personal protection is always required: wear an apron and the right eye protection, and if you have long hair tie it back.
- Portable tools need dust masks as the dust created when cutting wood is hazardous.
- Treat all power tools with respect and keep clear of anyone using them.
- Ensure the machine is set correctly and the work piece is secure.
- Ensure all guards are in position before starting the machine.

Power tools

Belt sanding machines

These machines allow flat and curved surfaces to be finished quickly, including the end grain of wood which can otherwise be difficult to finish well. Usually a belt sanding machine is fitted with a coarse belt for rapid working but this will need further finishing.

Pillar drills

Pillar drills enable accurate drilling of both large and small diameter holes using a variety of drill bits. The main

The belt sanding machine is a very versatile machi

feature of this machine is that it enables holes to be drille accurately and perpendicular (at right angles) to the table It also has a depth stop to enable holes to be drilled to a precise depth.

Small work needs to be held securely in a hand vice. Larg work is often cramped to the machine with G cramps.

Mortising machines

These are rather like drilling machines but have a hollow square chisel in place of the drill bit. A drill runs inside the square chisel to remove the waste. This machine can drill square holes to create mortise joints. Mortise machines need to be set up carefully but will cut accurate holes to make precise joints.

Scroll saws

Scroll saws are sometimes known as a power jigsaws or Hegner saws and cut complex shapes in thin woods, meta and plastics. The saw produces a clean and smooth edge but needs practice to use accurately.

Band saws

These saws have a continuous band of blade that runs ov large wheels in the machine. The blades can be varied to enable woods, metals and plastics to be cut. Curves and larger circles can be cut accurately.

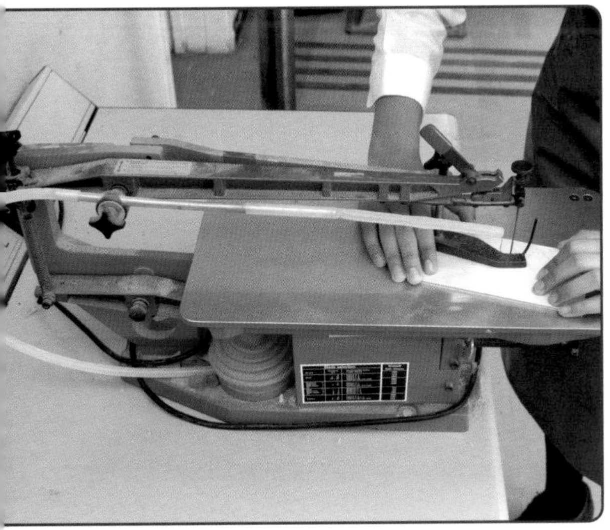

A scroll (hegner) saw in use

ortable power tools

igsaws

ese hand-held power tools can be used to cut curves in oods, plastics and metals. This tool can be used to cut rge shapes that would not fit into fixed machines.

ower drills

ower drills are a versatile tool. They can be used for many illing tasks but must be held upright to achieve accuracy. ften drills of this type are used at low speeds to drive in oodscrews.

rbital finishing sanders

ese portable hand-held sanders have a sheet of abrasive aper stuck or clipped to a pad. The pad moves at high eed in small rotations and rapidly smoothes a surface ady for finishing.

outers

outers are versatile machines. They have a high-speed otating cutter that moves out from the base of the achine. The machine can be used to cut wood to shape, ften using templates for the router to follow for accuracy. outers can also cut grooves, rebates and produce ecorative moulding to edges with special cutters.

Using the router to create a decorative edge profile

Activity

a What are the advantages of using a pillar drill over a portable power drill?

b When would you have to use a portable power drill?

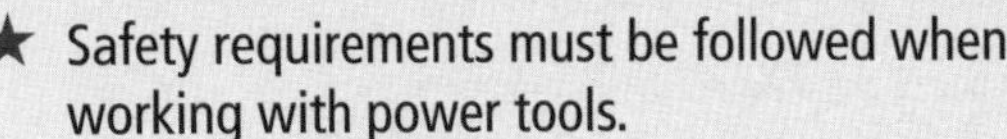

Summary

★ Safety requirements must be followed when working with power tools.

★ They enable materials to be worked with great accuracy, ease and speed.

5.6 Using mechanical methods to join metals

In this chapter you will learn about:

★ **the permanent and temporary joining methods for metals using mechanical fastenings.**

Metals can be joined using heat or mechanical methods. Mechanical methods of joining metals have a number of advantages over the use of heat:

- they can join dissimilar materials together
- they can be permanent or temporary
- they are available in a wide range of shapes and sizes, materials and finishes.

Nuts and bolts

Using nuts and bolts (thread fastenings) is seen as a temporary joining method, even though many are never intended to be undone. There is a wide variety of nuts, bolts, studs, machine screws and washers to choose from. When you select this type of fastening, think about its length and thread size (diameter), the shape of the head, the material it is made from and the finish it has.

Cutting threads

Sometimes you need to make your own threads as part of other components. Most metals, some plastics and occasionally some woods can have a thread cut into them.

Tapping is the process of cutting a screw thread into a piece of material. Internal (female) threads are cut using a tap made from very hard steel. The tap is twisted into a drilled hole in the material using a tap wrench. A split die is used to cut an external (male) thread on the outside of round material. The die is held in a die stock, which is carefully twisted around the material so that the thread is cut accurately.

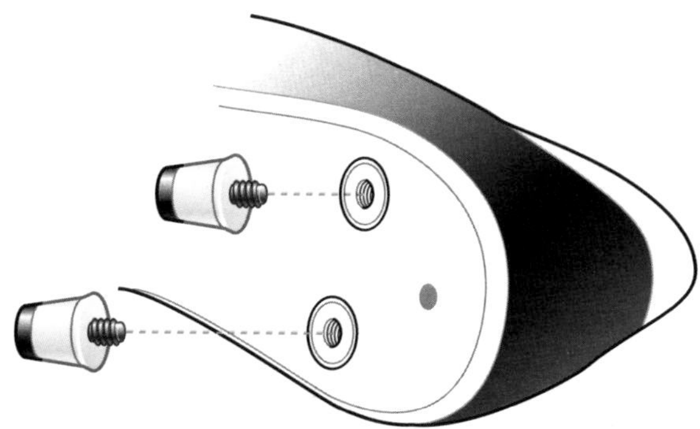

Football studs have threads cut into them

Rivets

Rivets are small metal pins used to fasten sheets of material. They are cheaper and often less visible than nuts and bolts. Rivets can be used to join materials permanentl[y].
There are two methods of riveting to consider.

- Plain riveting: a soft steel or aluminium rivet is pushed through a pre-drilled hole in the sheet materials to be joined. The second end is then hammered into the shap[e] of the rivet head; this pinches together the sheets and prevents them from separating. Plain rivets are used as decorative features in metalwork and as pivoting joints on tools such as snips and pliers.
- Pop riveting: quicker than plain riveting and can be done from one side. A pre-formed aluminium rivet has a steel pin trapped inside. The rivet is pushed through a pre-drilled hole in the materials to be joined. A special tool is used to pull the steel pin, which swells the rivet and finally the pin 'pops' off, leaving a neat joint. Pop riveting is used in the furniture and upholstery industrie[s] to provide a fast joint between sheet materials. Some plastic materials such as polypropylene can also be pop riveted together.

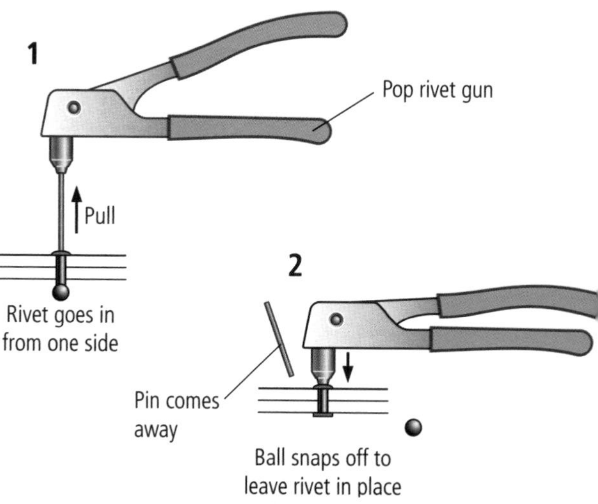

Pop riveting – the rivet goes in from one side an[d] the ball snaps off to leave the rivet in plac[e]

ame	Pictorial view	Assembled view	Notes
ut and bolt			• Hexagonal head to fit standard spanners and socket sets • Used for holding two or more materials together
tud			• Bolt with no head • Threads on both ends • Often used in machinery and engine assembly
exagonal ocket screw			• Engineering components • Used with self-assembly furniture • Easy adjustment and removal with specialist tool
rub screw			• Screwdriver slot • Used to hold wheels and pulleys on a shaft • Used on areas where outer surface should remain flush
Ving nut			• Tightened using fingers rather than a tool • Often used for self-assembly furniture • Quick release • Allows for easy maintenance
lain washer			• Helps to spread the force of the nut or bolt head • Used in most nut and bolt applications
pring washer			• Helps to keep the nut tight • Used where temperature and vibration occur, e.g. car engines
li-lock nut			• Nylon inset helps prevent vibration loosening nut
elf-tapping screw			• Round head • Used to hold sheet materials together • Screw cuts its own thread into material
Machine screw			• Cheese head, often made from stainless steel • Found in precise, small mechanisms and components • Brass machine screws are used in electrical plugs and fittings

Mechanical fastenings

Activity

Think about a piece of equipment or machinery in the school workshop.

a Identify the different fastenings that have been used in its construction.

b Why is it important that some of the fastenings are temporary and some are permanent?

Coursework

Cutting a thread is a skilled process. If your project needs you to cut a thread, you will need to practise. Record all your experiments.

Summary

★ There are a large number of mechanical fastenings available for the designer to choose from, both temporary and permanent.

5.7 Using heat to join metals

In this chapter you will learn about:
★ **permanent joining methods for metals using heat**
★ **health and safety issues to do with these processes.**

Metals can be joined using heat to form a permanent joint.

For all joining methods, it is important that the pieces are clean and fit well together.

Soldering

Soldering makes a permanent joint between two pieces of metal using an alloy (see 3.2 *Metals*) with a lower melting point (MP) than the metals being joined. It is used as glue; when it is melted, it bonds to the surface of the two pieces to be joined and sets (cools) to hold them together. Bonding can only take place if the surfaces do not contain any metal oxide, so a flux is used to prevent this from forming. Fluxes are available in liquids, powders and pastes.

There are two types of soldering: hard and soft.

- Hard soldering has two common forms: silver soldering and brazing. The diagram below shows a simple silver ring being silver soldered (MP 625–800°C). The edges are covered in flux. The flux keeps the metal surface clean as the temperature rises. The solder melts and runs across the joint. Heating is stopped, the solder sets and the ring is quenched in cold water.

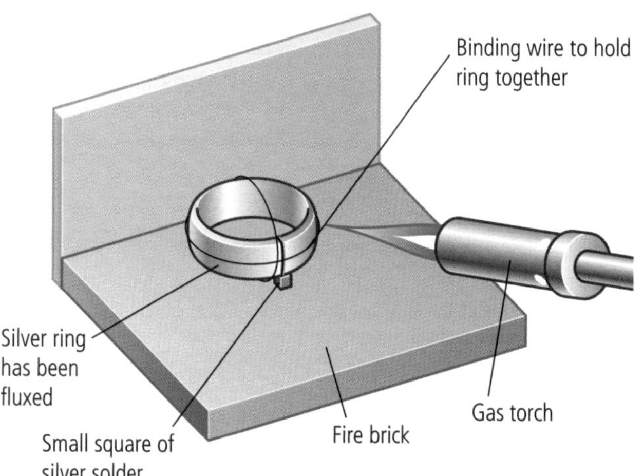

A silver ring being silver soldered

- Soft soldering requires less heat (MP 180–250°C) and used for light work, electrical connections and plumbin joints. Often solder (a lead-based alloy) is applied as a wire or stick. The two surfaces to be joined are given a thin coat of solder. This is called tinning. Soft-soldered joints should not be quenched but left to cool slowly.

Welding

Welding works by melting the edges of the metals to be joined so that they fuse together. On cooling, they solidify and form a joint that is as strong as the metal around it. A filler rod is melted at the same time into the joint to fill the gap. The filler rod is made from the same metal as the metals being welded. Welding is mostly used to join mild steel, stainless steel and aluminium, such as in furniture and architectural features. There are four main types of welding available in the school workshop.

- Gas welding (oxy-acetylene welding): a mixture of oxygen and acetylene is used to create a very hot flame (around 3500°C). This heat is used to melt the joint while the filler rod is introduced. Gas welding equipme is potentially very dangerous.
- MIG welding: more commonly used in schools. The filler rod is in the form of a reel that continually feeds the weld. An electric arc (a very bright spark) is struck between the work and the filler rod. The rod melts and fills the joint. An inert gas flows over the arc to keep th welding area free from oxidisation. The bead of weld that is formed fuses with the base metals to form an extremely strong and permanent joint.
- Arc welding: similar to MIG welding but individual rods coated in flux are used. The arc glare is potentially dangerous so proper eye protection must always be worn.
- Spot welding: a common industrial process. A pair of electrodes pinch two thin sheets of steel together and produces a high charge of electricity. This creates enoug heat to melt the metal surfaces together. The result is a permanent spot of weld. Spot welding is often part of a robot production line. It is a quick, clean, efficient and cost-effective joining method. See 7.7 *Case study: Clare Merchandise Handling Equipment Ltd* for information o this technique.

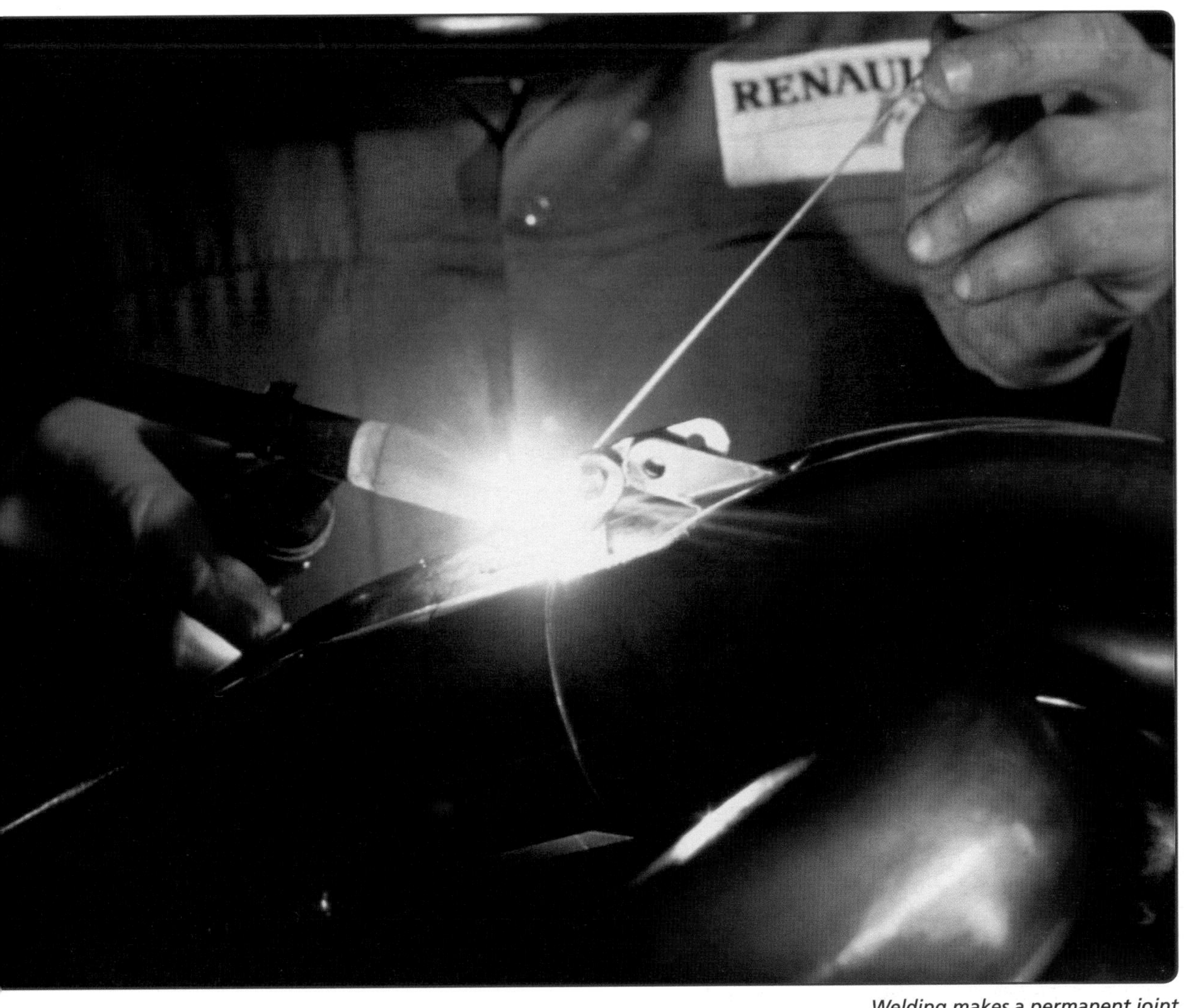

Welding makes a permanent joint

Coursework

You must be able to choose the right joining method for your product. Use notes in your folder to explain your choices.

Activity

- **a** Identify three metal products (e.g. a school stool, an aluminium micro-scooter) that have been joined using heat.
- **b** Draw simple diagrams of each product.
- **c** Add annotations to each diagram to identify the metals and explain the joining process used.

Summary

- ★ Metals can be joined in several ways using heat.
- ★ The metals to be joined should be clean and fit together accurately.

Joining wood: frame joints

> **In this chapter you will learn about:**
> ★ **the different types of frame joints.**

Wood frame constructions are the basis of many wooden products. Chairs, doors and tables are all frame constructions.

The choice of joint for a frame is important as it often has a load to support. As a natural material, wood continues t move even after joining, so joints must be flexible if they are to last. Many frame joints are so strong that they hard need gluing.

Name of joint	Picture of joint	Advantages	Disadvantages	Uses
Mortise and tenon		Very strong and versatile	Time consuming to make and needs skill	Strong, hidden furniture joints
Dowel		Quick to make and very strong	Needs a jig to be used to drill parts accurately	Strong, hidden furniture joints; often combined with a single barrel bolt to give a simple, strong joint that can be easily assembled
Butt		Easy to make, especially with a mitre saw	Unsightly and weak unless reinforced with nails or screws	Rough work such as fencing
Mitre		Neat, attractive joint	Weak unless reinforced; needs mitre saw to make accurately	Picture frames, small boxes, decorative trimming
Corner halving		Quick and easy to cut with saw; fairly strong	Can be unsightly; best if reinforced with screws or dowels	Simple frames for basic work

Types of frame joint

raditional frame joints

tural wood has been joined to make frames since the rliest times when frames were lashed together with cord. mboo furniture is still made in this way.

nock-down fittings

ock-down (KD) fittings are the basis of almost all self-sembly furniture. They allow the product to be delivered t-packed in a box and assembled by the consumer. This akes the furniture much cheaper to buy. This is the basis almost all IKEA furniture. The main disadvantage with ock-down frame joints is that you can often see part of e bolts that hold furniture together.

owel joints are often combined with a single barrel bolt to ve a simple, strong joint which can be easily assembled.

A dowel joint combined with a single barrel bolt

nconventional frame joints

is sometimes necessary to design a different joint a part of a new product. Simple butt joints can be ansformed after gluing by drilling and inserting exposed owels of various sizes and colours. Interesting joints can so be created by layering thin sections to create joints.

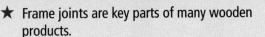

Pedastal tables with knock-down joints

Coursework

Strong joints can be time consuming to make. There are many ways to create frames for products. Sometimes it is possible to develop unusual ways of constructing frames, experiment to see what alternative joints could be used in your coursework project.

Activities

1. Name three types of frame joint and sketch each one.
2. Sketch two different products that use frame joints and name the joints used.
3. Name a joint suitable for making a simple stool frame from natural hardwood.
4. a What joint would you use to make a mirror frame?
   b How can the joint be made stronger?

Summary

★ Frame joints are key parts of many wooden products.

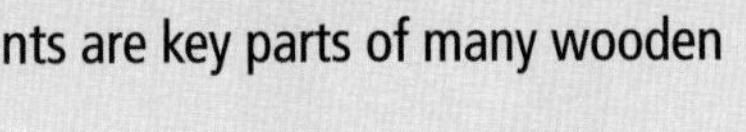

★ There are many effective ways to create frames for different purposes.

5.9 Joining wood: carcase joints

In this chapter you will learn about:

★ **how to construct strong box structures using carcase joints**

★ **different techniques to join wood to create boxes.**

Carcase joints are an important form of basic construction. Boxes, drawers and cupboards are all carcase constructions. Carcase construction involves joining together wide panels of wood at the corners to create a box.

Complex joints have developed for joining natural wood to allow the wood to move and to maximise the gluing area, thus increasing strength. Manufactured board is mu more stable and more simple joining methods can be use including knock-down (KD) joints for flat-pack furniture.

Traditional carcase joints

Wood has been joined to make carcases since the earliest times when wide boards were pegged together to make storage chests.

Name of joint	Picture of joint	Notes
Comb (finger)		This joint simply uses alternate fingers of wood to create an interlocking edge with a good surface area for strong gluing.
Dovetail		This joint is used on many quality carcases and drawers. The joint ensures a strong joint in natural timber which is always moving. Several forms of dovetail joint can be found in fine work. The simplest is the through dovetail. This has shaped tails that interlock with smaller pins to create a strong joint which resists pulling apart in one direction. This joint requires accurate working and can be time consuming to cut. Jigs are available to enable these joints to be cut using a portable power router.
Housing		This joint is used to insert shelves or divisions in a box. A groove is cut into the side of the box to allow the shelf to fit (or become housed) inside it.
Dowelled butt		This joint is an effective way of joining manufactured boards. A simple jig needs to be made to allow accurate drilling. The jig ensures any small errors are repeated in the matching sets of drilled holes. The dowels reinforce the joint and increase the gluing area. As the dowel holes are stopped, they are invisible after assembly.
Butt		Butt joints are the simplest form of joint but need reinforcing with nails or an internal wooden block. They are weak and can be unsightly. It is possible to glue the joint and then add reinforcement to it by nailing or drilling the edge and inserting dowels, but these will be visible. One of these joints has been reinforced with triangular plates.

Types of carcase join

Simple dowel jigs are easily made and ensure accuracy

nock-down fittings

ıumber of joints can be used for knock-down (KD) ings. The simplest, but most unsightly, is the plastic ıdesty block, which is screwed to the inside of each rner. Often a mixture of dowels and scan bolts are used achieve good strength and improved appearance.

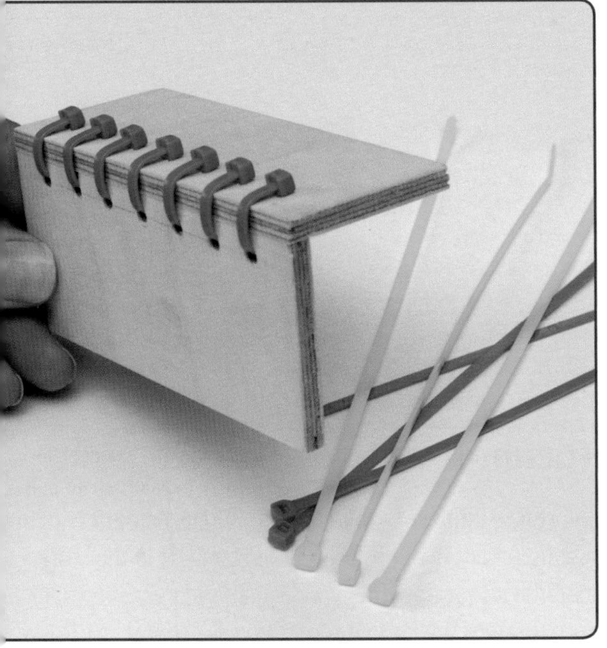

Unusual joints can be very effective and have a fun aspect

Unconventional carcase joints

There are no limits to what can be achieved through an imaginative approach. For example, coloured cable ties inserted through drilled holes offer an unusual fixing for plywood panels.

Backs, bottoms and tops

All carcases are weak without a back panel. The panel prevents the box being strained and completes an effective structure. The top and bottom panels of a box do the same job. These panels are either pinned and glued to the surface or fitted into a rebate or groove, as strength and appearance demands.

Coursework

Investigating how other products that use carcase joints are constructed can give you some valuable ideas to use in your own designing. Look at carcases that are made from the same materials as you plan to use for your project, how are they joined?

Activities

1. How many different kinds of carcases can you find in your home? List them and the materials they are made from.
2. How many different ways of supporting shelves inside the carcases can you find?

Summary

★ Carcase joints are an important part of the structure of many products.

★ There are many effective ways to create carcases for different purposes.

5.10 Cutting metals by machine

In this chapter you will learn about:

★ **different machines for cutting metal components**

★ **the safe use of metal machining tools.**

Before machining any metal, it is essential to carry out quality control and safety checks. This risk assessment (see 4.1 *Safety in the workshop*) is essential and should be recorded as part of your project development.

- Is the machining area clear of swarf, dirt and dust?
- Has the correct cutting tool, drill bit or blade been selected?
- Is the work held securely and accurately in place?
- Have the guards been placed correctly to protect the operator?
- Has a test cut or hole been made?
- Has the correct cutting speed been selected?
- Are you wearing an apron and eye protection?
- Has your teacher made a final check before you start machining?

Drilling

The pillar drill, sometimes known as the drill press or pedestal drill, can be floor or bench mounted. It provides an accurate and easy way of drilling perpendicular (at right angles) holes into materials that fit onto the machine's table. Twist drills are used for drilling metals as well as woods and plastics. Always hold your work securely using hand vice or mole grips.

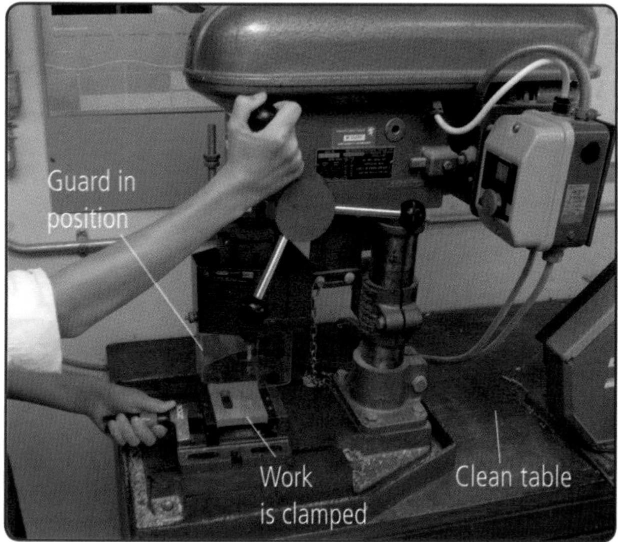

A guarded twist drill

Milling

Milling machines involve clamping the material to a movi table. The work can then be moved either manually or via computer control along three axes: vertically (z-axis), horizontally (y-axis) and front-to-back (x-axis). A milling cutter removes material along its path. Surfaces, slots and holes can be milled with great accuracy creating complex shapes and forms. Milling machines are robust and powerful. Great care must be taken to clamp the wor securely and guards should be set to protect you.

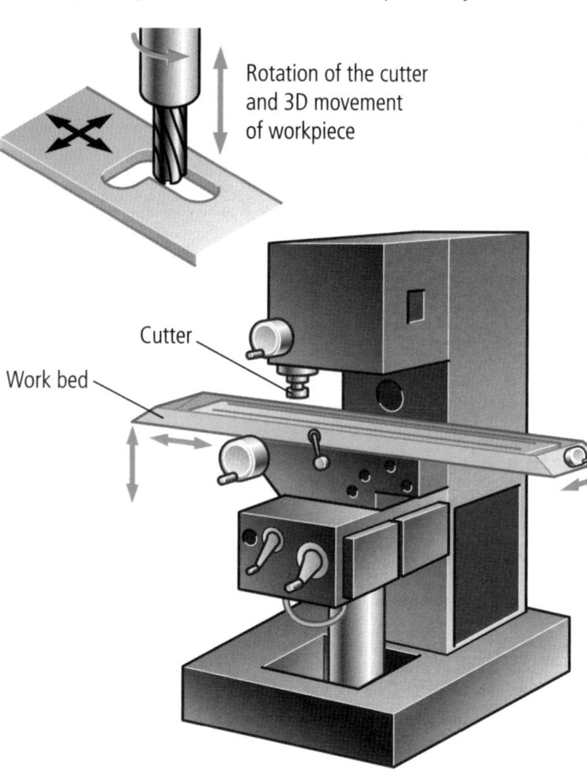

Vertical milling machi

Turning

The centre lathe is used to turn cylindrical components fro metals. A variety of tools are used to machine the stock material into shape. The work is held securely in a chuck ar then rotated. The cutting tool is positioned against the wor

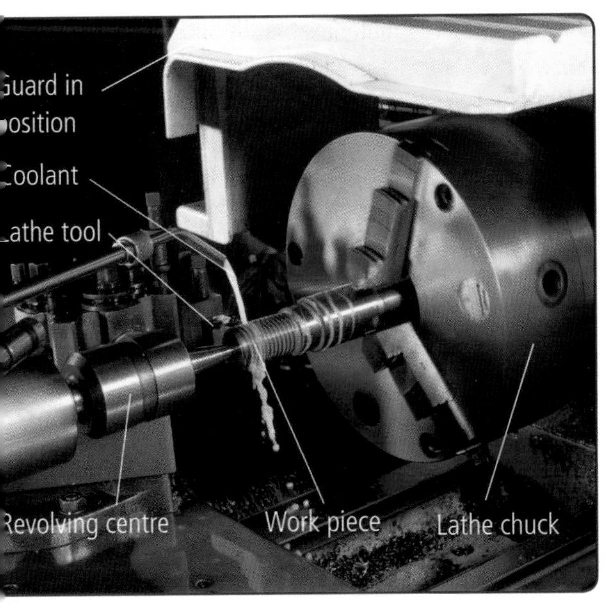

A centre lathe turning a brass bar

d cuts away the waste. The correct tool and cutting speed ed to be selected for each machining operation. Turning oduces accurate surfaces, holes and screw threads.

Scroll saws

roll (Hegner) saws can be used to cut thin gauge metal eet. To prevent bending, use double-sided tape to ld metal blanks onto a thin wooden backing such as rdboard. Use a high-speed cut and a blade with lots teeth. Let the saw do the work and use gentle, steady ntrol.

Polishing machines

lishing machines have a mop or buffing wheel that tates at high speed. Metal polish is available in a wax rm, which is then applied to the mop. The product is refully pressed against the mop. Metal polish is always ghtly abrasive as it relies on cutting away the surface of e metal until it is smooth. It is important that the work kept within the safe working area of the wheel and no ose clothing comes into contact with the moving parts. e protection must always be worn. Typical cutting and lishing would include using a stitched calico mop dressed ith tripoli compound and then finished with rouge mpound on a soft swansdown mop.

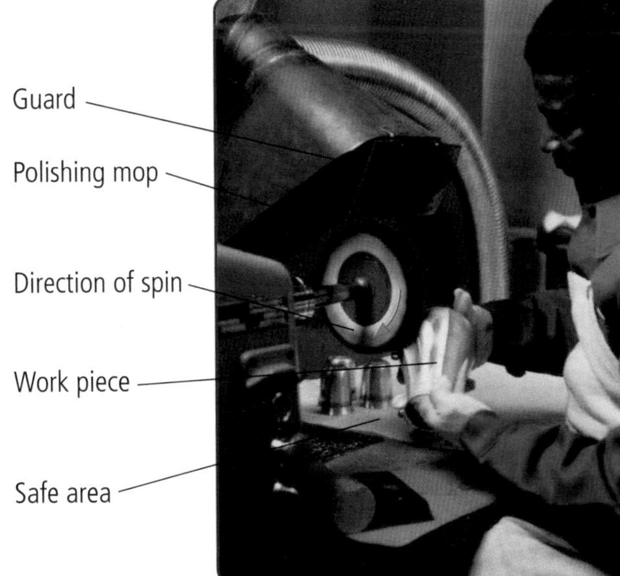

A polishing machine

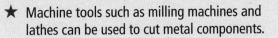

Activities

1 Identify a turned component that has been made on a lathe and investigate the method of manufacture of each detail.

2 Outline the safety precautions necessary when using a lathe or milling machine.

3 In small groups:

   a Carry out a five-stage risk assessment for drilling a hole using a pillar drill.

   b Discuss your results.

Summary

★ Machine tools such as milling machines and lathes can be used to cut metal components.

★ In most cases, the operation is complicated and potentially dangerous.

Deforming metals

In this chapter you will learn about:
- ★ the different methods of deforming metals
- ★ press forming metals in the school workshop.

Deforming means changing the shape of a material. Most metals need to be annealed (made softer and less likely to crack) before deforming because as you work them their properties change, making them hard and brittle. Annealing changes the distorted grains back to their original shape, re-softening the metal so work can be carried out. Allow plenty of time to deform metal components. It is often difficult to get exactly the right results the first time you try.

Forging

Forging is associated with the manufacture of strong metal components. It improves the structure of the metal by refining the grain. Traditional blacksmiths used a hearth, hammers and anvil to shape and modify hot iron and steel. Some products can be worked cold, but when a cold metal is squeezed during forging or rolling it becomes work hardened and brittle. It might then need to be annealed c tempered. Forging and rolling steel today is a sophisticate computer-controlled process.

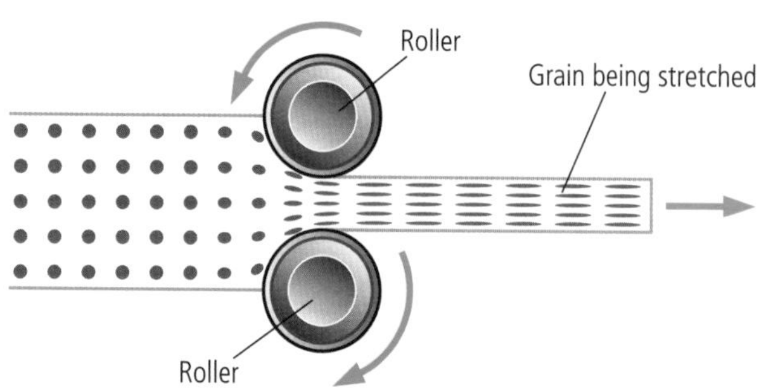

Grains within the metal are distorted after rolling

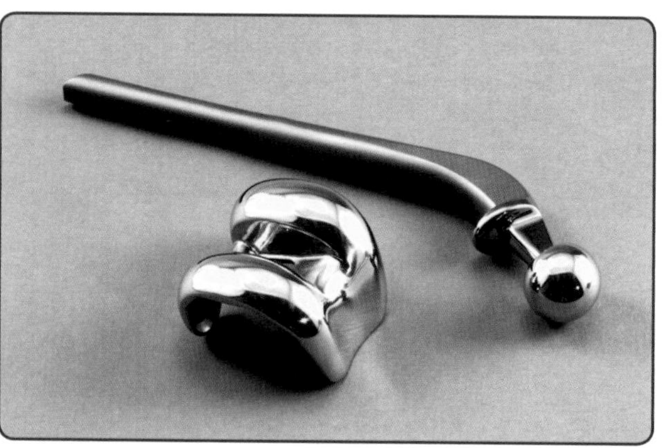

Hip implants are forged from titanium

Bending

Annealed metals can be easily bent using a simple former (a wooden block) or jig and a nylon-headed mallet. Sheet metal folding machines are often available in schools. The are excellent at performing sharp, crisp bends at a range of angles including 90°. Thicker or harder ferrous metals have to be heated to red heat before bending as this mak them more malleable.

A sheet-folding machi

Beaten metalwork

Beaten metalwork is a traditional deforming process more commonly used for working non-ferrous metals. A blank o copper, brass or silver needs to be annealed before it can b worked. A variety of hammers, mallets, stakes and sandbag are used to bend, hollow, raise and planish the metal into shape.

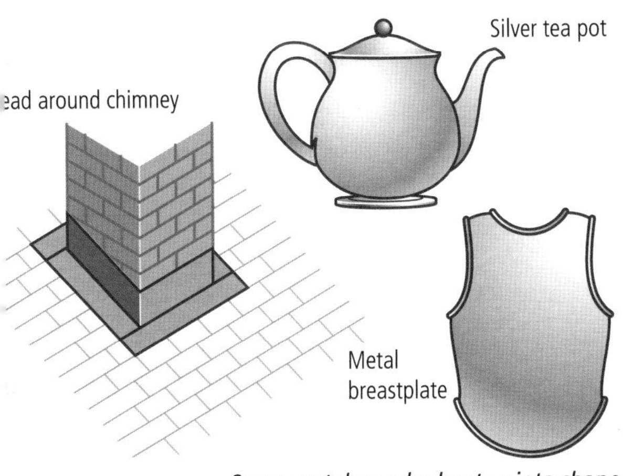

Some metals can be beaten into shape

tamping

mping is the industrial process of cutting shapes in tals. Products such as cutlery and washers are made in s way.

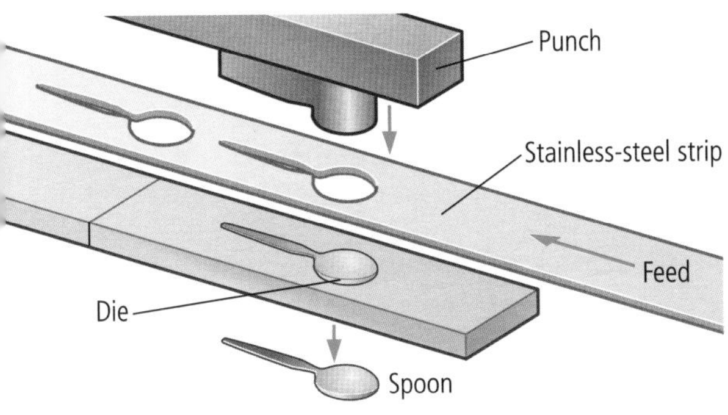

Stamping stainless steel spoons

ress forming or cold pressing

s often necessary to form thin sheet metals into complex ells or panels. Industrial presses are used to contour e sheet into shape with enormous force. The thin metal eets are placed into a hardened metal die. This die is in o parts, shaped top and bottom to match the panel to pressed. The press can pierce holes, indent and bend as forms the panel into shape. Examples of products made this way are car body panels, toasters, washing machine ells, heating radiator panels, baking trays and 'up and er' garage doors.

a small scale, it is possible to press form simple shapes in hool by following the stages in the diagram on the right.

Start with an annealed copper shape

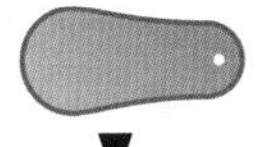

Use a hard metal wire like a paper clip and bend it into the required shape

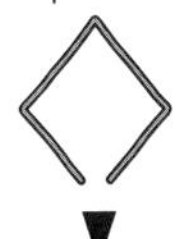

Use some tape to hold the wire securely onto a steel block, then place the copper shape on top

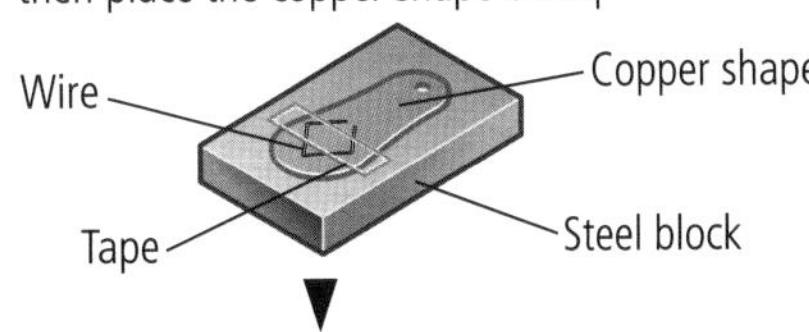

Use a planishing hammer to hammer the copper shape onto the wire until the wire becomes visible from the back

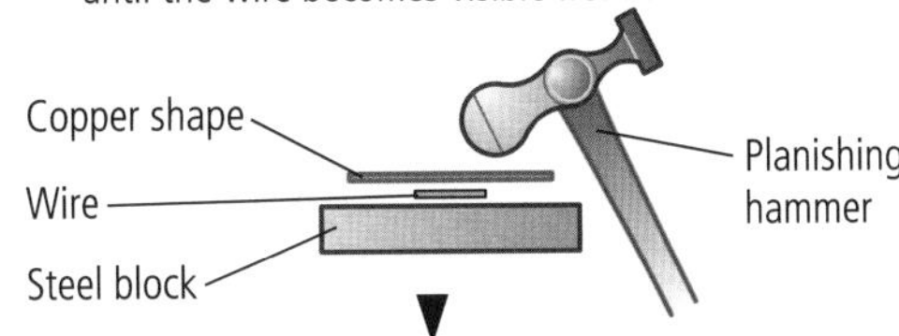

Remove the copper shape. Lightly clean the surface with wet and dry paper to reveal the shape of the wire

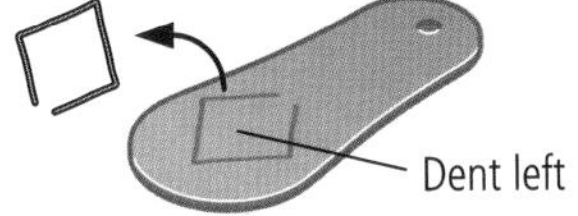

Press forming

Activity

a Try press forming by following the stages in the diagram on the left of this page.

b When you have finished, examine the metal. Can you feel that it is now harder than before you started hammering?

c Explain what has happened to the grain.

Summary

★ Most metals need to be annealed before deforming.

★ There are a variety of ways to deform metals.

5.12 Reforming metals

In this chapter you will learn about:

★ **reforming metals by sand casting**

★ **industrial die casting.**

Reforming is when metal changes state during the manufacturing process. Metal reforming methods include sand casting and die casting. Casting is a more efficient way of using metal than machining a component from a solid block. It also provides a stronger product because the grain of the metal has not been cut but flows around the contours of the component.

1 Mould, metal casting box and wooden pegs

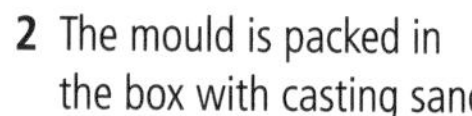

2 The mould is packed in the box with casting sand

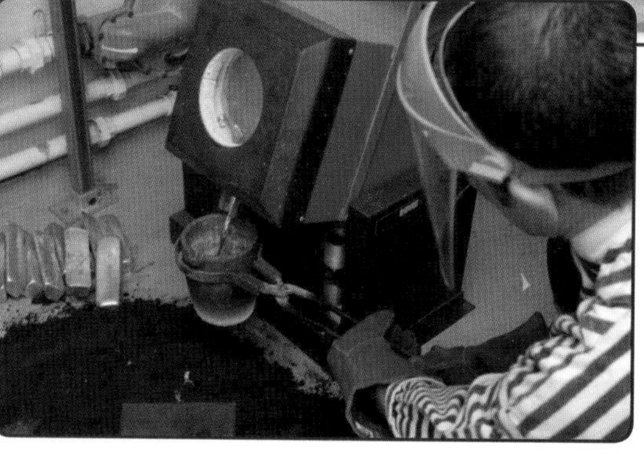

3 Mould and pegs are taken out, and aluminium poured in

Sand casting

Casting metal in sand is a cheap and simple process. It i used in industrial foundries for unit, small and medium **batch production**. You'll learn more about this produc method in chapter 7.4 *Manufacturing in quantity*. The sand is special oil-bonded sand that holds the detail of the pattern and is porous, allowing steam and gases to escape. The pattern is usually made from wood, with a smooth lacquer finish. The sand, with the pattern remov becomes the mould. Typical uses of sand casting include engine blocks, gearboxes, church bells and sculptural for

Casting in school is usually restricted to aluminium. The photograph below explains this process.

4 When the aluminium is cold the sand is broken open to reveal the casting

5 Unwanted material is removed and the mould can be re

Sand casting in the school worksh

important to be aware that casting is a potentially gerous process. Protective clothing and facemasks uld be worn at all times. Casting should only be carried under strict supervision.

e casting

high-volume industrial production process is similar to ction moulding. It is widely used in industry to produce ll-scale metal products. Low melting alloys such as :, pewter and aluminium are used to make handles on equipment, toy cars, toy soldiers, kitchen equipment, orative items and mechanical components. The die is etal block with a cavity cut away to match exactly the pe required. The components are then ejected from the and the process repeated.

simple forms it is possible to replicate the die casting cess in school. Using MDF blocks cut to create the uld, possibly using **computer-aided manufacture AM)**, a low-melting metal alloy like lead-free pewter is ated with a blowtorch and then poured into the mould. od air extraction should be used to quickly remove any nes from burning MDF.

Coursework

Simple aluminium and pewter castings can add depth and complexity to your project, but this process can take a long time. Some cast components to consider are furniture feet, decorative panels and lamp bases from aluminium, and jewellery from pewter.

Activity

a Identify three products that have been made by casting.

b Draw a simple diagram of each product and add labels to explain why the product was made in this way, where the mould lines are, and where the runner and riser marks are.

c Have any areas of the products been machined?

Summary

★ Casting involves pouring molten metal into a mould or injecting it into a die, and then allowing it to cool.

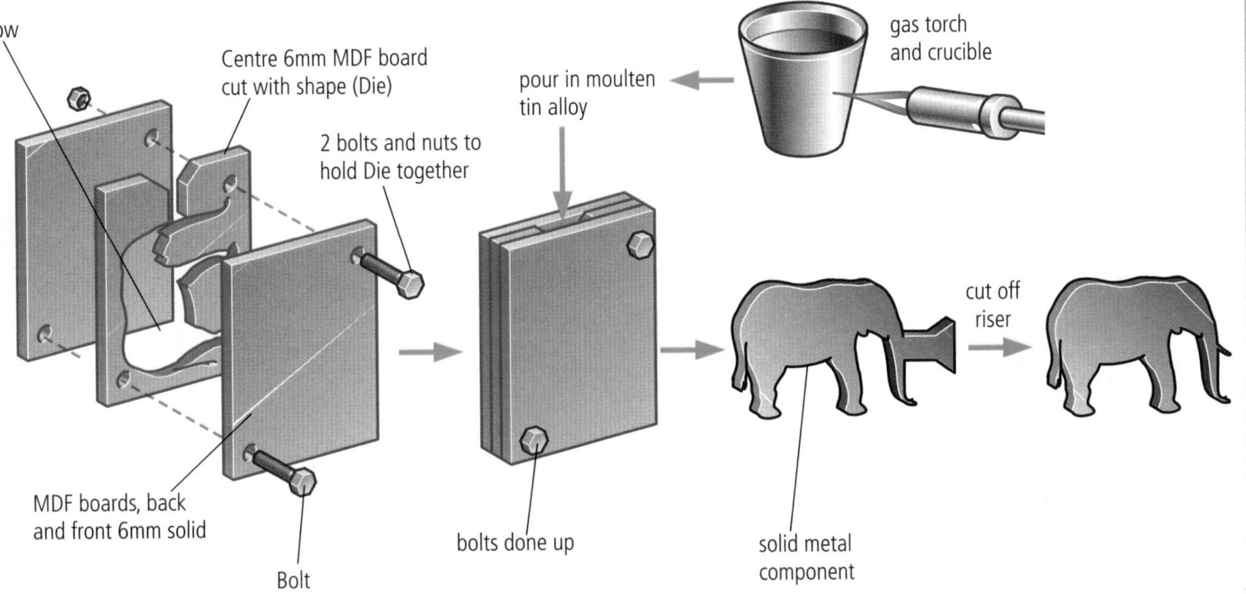

Die casting in school

5.13 Deforming thermoplastics using heat

In this chapter you will learn about:
- ★ **how to bend and shape plastics using heat**
- ★ **how some plastics have memories.**

Deforming means producing a change in shape without the loss of any material. Acrylic is a popular thermoplastic material that deforms easily. It is available in sheets, blocks, tubes and granules. When it is heated, acrylic becomes pliable enough to be pressed, bent and curved.

Thermoplastic	Deform temperature (°C)
Polystyrene	120
Polyethylene	120
PVC	130
ABS	159
Acrylic	165
Polypropylene	180
Polycarbonate	200

Thermoplastics and their deform temperatu

Heating

A special plastics fan oven can be used to heat different plastic material. This equipment is often found in the school workshop and has a built-in thermostat. Different plastics need to be heated to different temperatures before they become flexible enough to deform.

It is important to understand the characteristics of plastics as they heat up. A rigid sheet of plastic becomes flexible as it passes through two stages.

- First is the elastic condition where it is springy and behaves like an elastic band. It has to be pulled into shape.
- After further heating the plastic changes into its plastic condition. Here its characteristics are more like clay, and it can be deformed easily.

Line bending

Bending along a straight line can be done using a strip heater. The plastic sheet is placed over the straight heating element. As the sheet warms it should be turned occasionally to provide an even heat. It can be bent wher it has become flexible. A former can be used to hold the plastic in place while it cools. It is helpful to make a template and to test the bending sequence and the position of the curves. It is not a good idea to produce ve sharp curves as this can cause the plastic to become thin and weak.

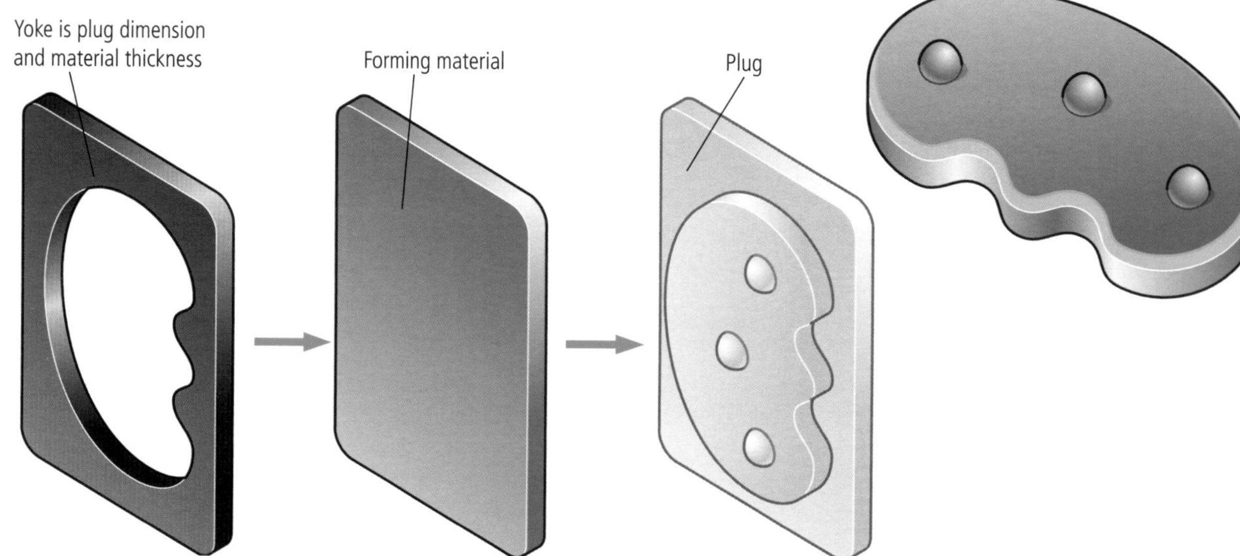

Plug and yoke formers are used to press form thermoplastic sheet into three dimensional objects like these 'po

·ress forming

·ss forming is a quick but not accurate way of producing ·ves. The plastic sheet is heated in an oven and then ·dwiched between the two halves of a mould called the ·g and yoke. Pressure is applied through clamping and · plastic is left to cool. Acrylic and expanded PVC foam · both suitable materials for this process.

·cuum forming makes use of the fact that plastics become ·t when heated. See 5.14 *Manufacturing plastics in ·antity* for details of this process.

·lastic memory

·hen thermoplastics become warm and elastic, they try to ·urn to their original shape. This plastic 'memory' can be ·ed to produce some interesting effects. Acrylic's memory ·aracteristics can be used to make decorative patterns ·at stick up above the surface.

Coursework

Deciding to use a plastic material as part of your GCSE project allows you to explore different manufacturing processes. The more creative your projects, the more testing and experimenting you will need to do.

Activity

Imagine you are a manufacturer planning to supply clear acrylic display stands for A5 information cards.

a Design a suitable stand and use a flow diagram to explain how a prototype could be made.

b Do you think the process might change if the company decides to produce 500 stands?

Summary

★ Heat can be used to deform different thermoplastics and so create bends and hollows.

★ Plastics change their characteristics as they heat up.

★ Some plastics, like acrylic, have a memory and return to their original shape when heated.

1 Use Tensol cement to join two colours of acrylic sheet. Heat in oven until soft

2 Press a wire shape into the top of the acrylic, then remove it once the acrylic has cooled

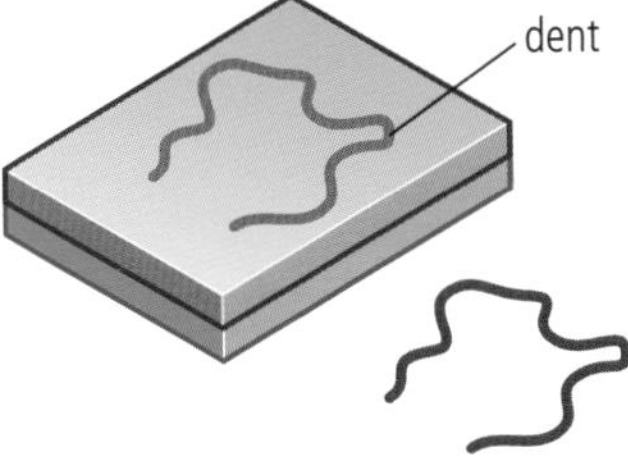

3 File away the top colour

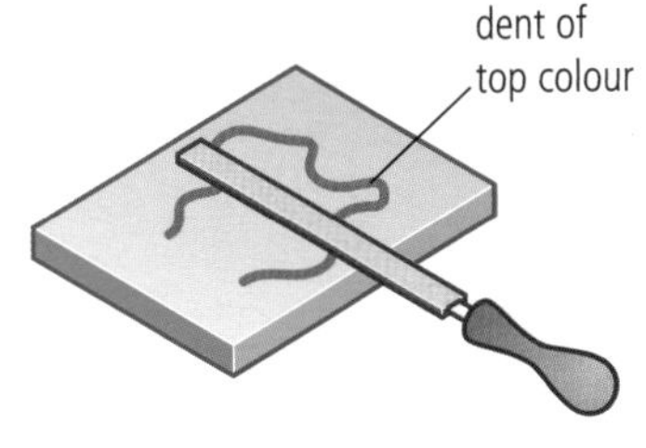

4 Polish

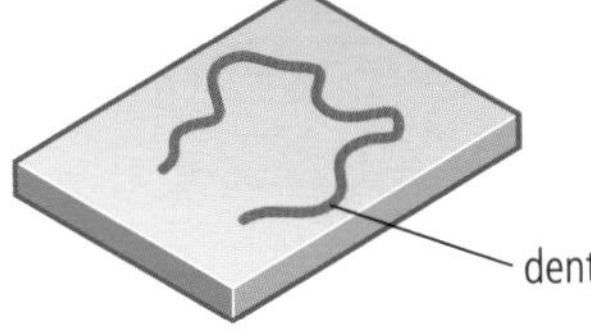

5 Return to the oven at 160°C and watch the wire shape rise from the surface

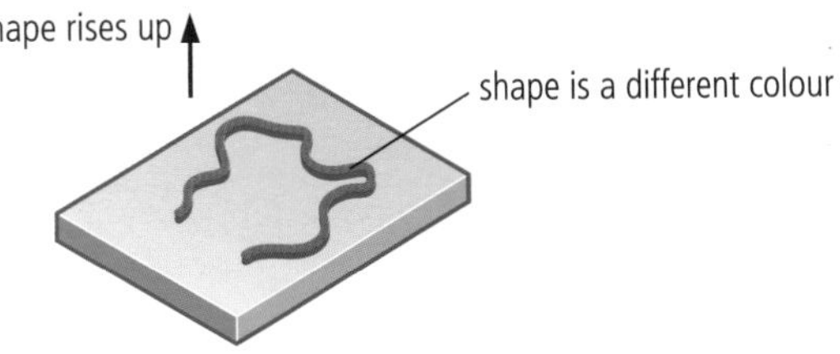

Acrylic's plastic memory

5.14 Manufacturing plastics in quantity

In this chapter you will learn about:

- ★ **the different ways of producing plastic components in large numbers using machines**
- ★ **formers, dies and moulds used with plastic machines.**

Reforming plastics includes compression moulding, vacuum forming, extrusion moulding, free-blow moulding, die casting and injection moulding. Reforming processes are used in industry to produce a range of plastic products on a large scale.

Compression moulding

A measured amount of plastic powder is placed in a highly polished and accurate steel mould held in the lower part of the moulding machine. A high pressure ram closes the mould, compressing the plastic material. Pressure and heat cause a chemical reaction in the plastic, which sets it into the shape of the mould. The mould is then opened and the item removed by an ejector mechanism. This process is used to shape thermosetting plastics such as urea and phenol formaldehydes. It produces items that resist temperature changes such as electrical fittings and saucepan handles. This process is not available in the school workshop.

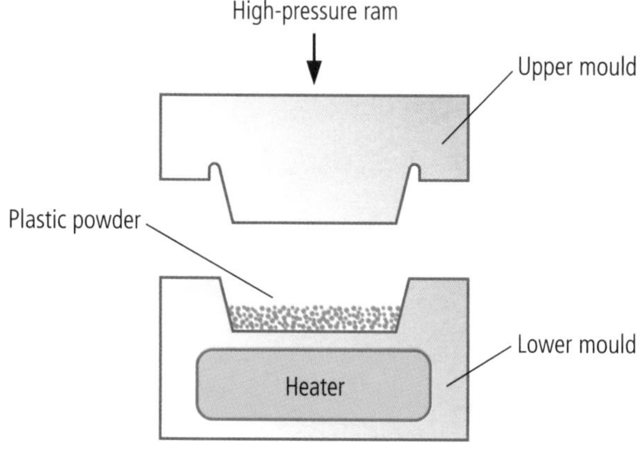

Compression moulding

Vacuum forming

This process works by removing air and creating a vacuum underneath a heated thermoplastic sheet. Atmospheric pressure pushes the soft, flexible plastic down onto the former. The quality of the former is shown in the final product; often made from wood, it should have tapered sides and no sharp corners. Air vents and fillets help it to separate from the plastic. Various products are made in thi way including polystyrene packaging (e.g. chocolate box trays), fancy-dress masks and acrylic baths. One advantage of this process is that because of the low pressures involve moulds are inexpensive and can be easily modified, makin the process suitable for **prototype** production. In the schc workshop this is a common and simple plastic reforming process that can be used as part of your GCSE project.

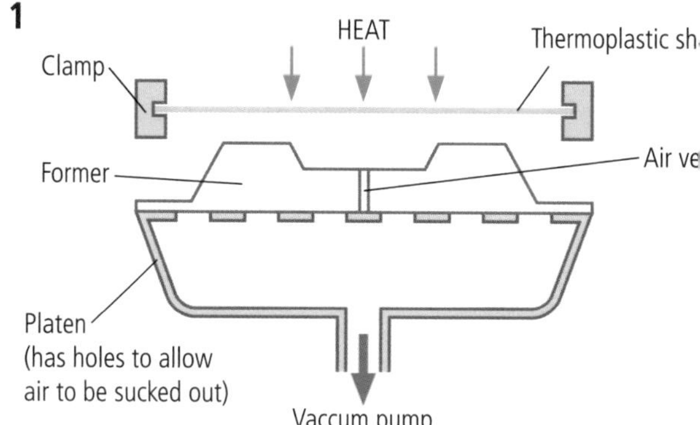

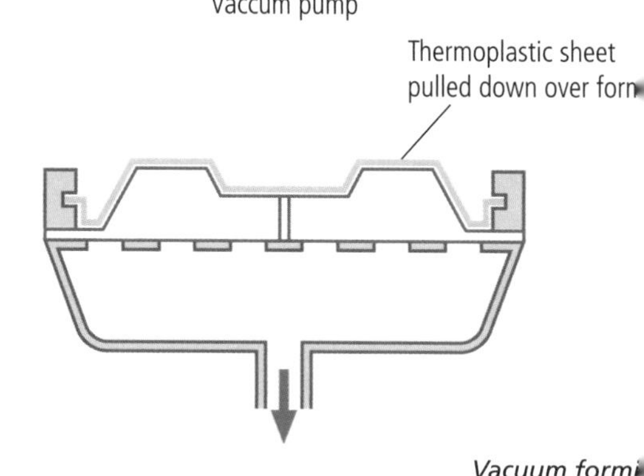

Vacuum formi

Plastic extrusion

Extrusion forces molten plastic through a shaped hole or d rather like squeezing toothpaste from a tube. Warm extrud plastic can be fed into a mould and then blown into shape This can be used to produce hollow plastic containers such as squeezy polypropylene tomato sauce bottles.

...jection moulding

...injection-moulding process uses pressure to inject ...id plastic into moulds, reforming granules into ...ducts. See 7.5 *Case study: Eurotech Mouldings Ltd* for ...rmation on this technique.

...ie casting

...s is a low-cost method of producing small plastic items ...h as chess pieces, toy soldiers and sporting trophies. ...hermosetting plastic like polyester resin is mixed with ...atalyst and a colour pigment before being poured into ...open mould. The catalyst causes the plastic to set. One ...ilable form of this process is known as cold enamelling ...d can be used to produce buttons, badges and costume ...ellery. With care, it can be used to fill engraved areas ...t could have been milled or laser cut by CAM machinery.

...ee-blow moulding

...heet of heated thermoplastic is clamped to the bed ...the former. Air is blown under it, which forces the ...rmoplastic up through the ring to form a bubble or ...me. This technique is used to make dome-shaped ...ducts such as clear acrylic clock faces, incubator covers ...d skylights. This process is often available in the school ...rkshop and can be used as part of your coursework.

Coursework

When developing your design you should consider how your product might be manufactured in quantity.

Activities

1. What type of process can be used to manufacture fizzy drinks bottles?
2. When vacuum forming, why is important to have sloping sides to a former?
3. What type of low-cost process is often used for producing chess pieces?
4. Why do thermosetting plastics have to be compression moulded?

Summary

★ There are many different ways of producing plastic components in large quantities.

★ Compression moulding uses pressure, vacuum forming uses a vacuum to pull the plastic into shape, extrusion is like squeezing a tube of toothpaste, free-blow moulding is like blowing up a balloon, die casting is like making a jelly in a mould, injection moulding is like an injection.

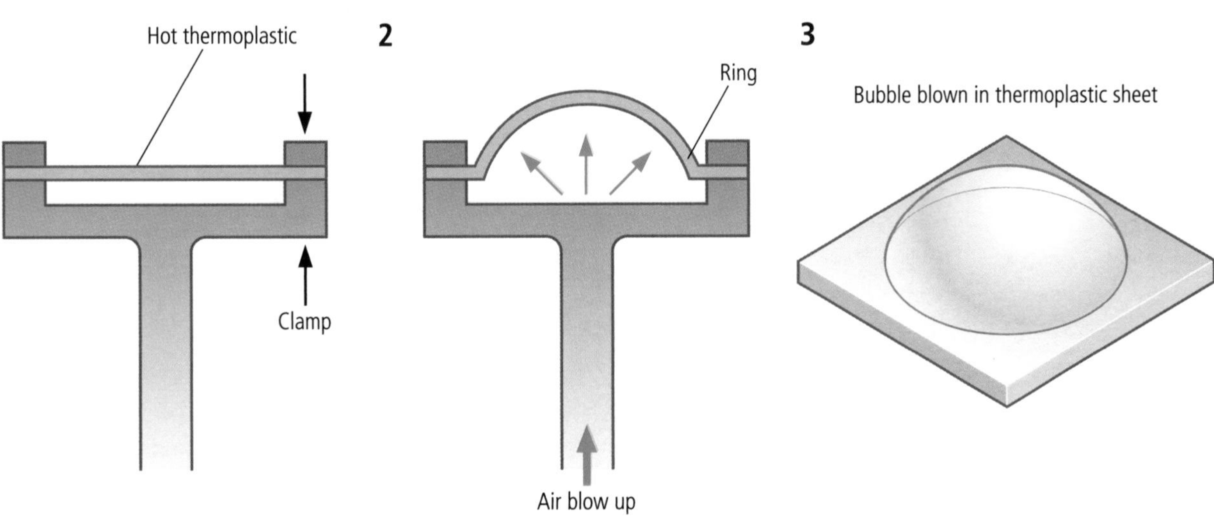

Free-blow moulding

Forming wood 1

In this chapter you will learn about:

- ★ how to bend wood
- ★ how wood can be laminated to create curves.

Making curves in wood can present a number of problems. Simply cutting curved pieces from straight-grained boards causes weakness. Traditionally, curved pieces were cut from trees that were naturally curved. For example, ribs for ships and roof timbers for buildings were often produced this way. There are a number of ways of creating curves in wood without having to wait for it to grow that way.

Kerfing

This traditional technique is used to make curved-sided musical instruments such as guitars. To allow the wood to be bent, a number of close, parallel saw cuts are made on the concave side of the bend. The saw cuts allow the inside surface of the board to be compressed and give a smooth and unbroken curve on the outside surface. The curves need a lot of support and are fairly weak.

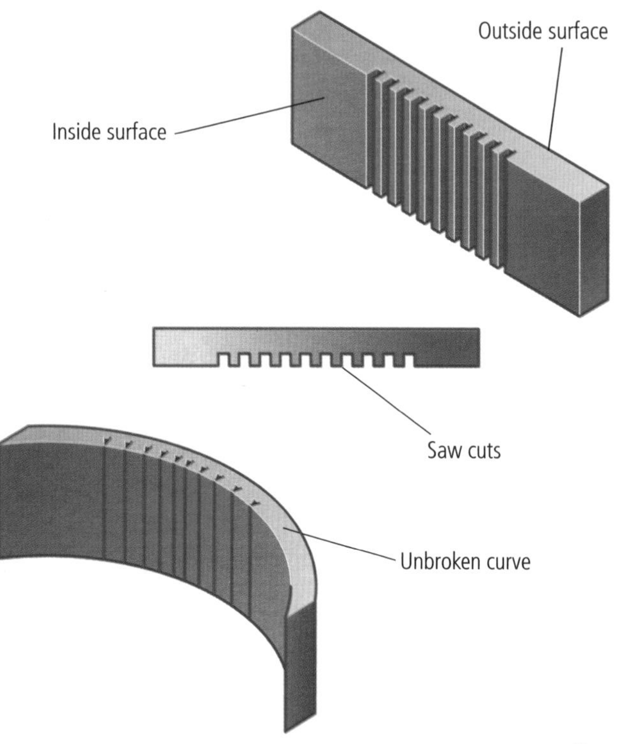

Kerfing

Bendy MDF and ply

These new forms of material enable curves to be readily formed. Bendy MDF is simply a ready-kerfed form of MDF that can be bent in one direction. Bendy ply is flexible because the grain of the core of the ply is layered across the sheet with thin decorative veneer surfaces. This ply is fairly weak but ideal for decorative work and low-strengt uses. It is often used to add decorative trimming to interi in shops and home makeovers.

Steam bending

In this process, steam provides a combination of heat anc moisture, which makes the wood become semi-plastic an formable. The wood is placed inside a steam chest, steam passed into the box to heat the wood to 100°C, saturatin it with moisture. About an hour is needed per 25 mm of thickness for the wood to become semi-plastic. The wood is then formed quickly while it is still warm. It must be hel clamped in a forming jig until it cools and dries. Quality furniture often makes effective use of steam bending. The chair shown on page 10 features steam bent component

Laminating

Formers and cramps

Laminating is a straightforward and accurate way of creating curves. In this process, layers of veneer are glued and clamped between wooden formers using G cramps. The completed laminate holds its shape as soon as the glue sets. A strong adhesive such as a cross-linking PVA is essential for this process. Both large and small products can be made this way, such as long, curved roof beams for buildings like sports halls. Lamination creates strong components for many uses.

The bag presses

This is an effective way of creating laminated forms, both large and small. The technique uses a heavy polyethylene bag and a vacuum pump. The glued laminates are taped onto the former, which is then placed in the bag. The bag is sealed with a simple plastic clip. A vacuum pump is the connected and the air extracted.

A GCSE project guitar stand made by laminating

e atmospheric pressure acts on the bag and presses the ninates together. The formers for this process can be ıde quickly and cheaply using polystyrene foam.

Smaller products are laminated using veneers and larger products can be made using laminates of 4 mm birch plywood. Typically, three layers of 4 mm plywood can be formed at one time using this process. If strong laminates are required, a second set of laminates can be formed on top of the first set to create a 24 mm thick product.

Activity

Use an Internet search engine like Google to explore images of laminated wood furniture.

- **a** What other examples of laminated wood products you can find?
- **b** What is the largest laminated wooden beam product you can find?

Summary

- ★ There are a number of ways of creating curved forms in wood.
- ★ Some methods are weak so are used for decoration, while others are strong and can create architectural structures.

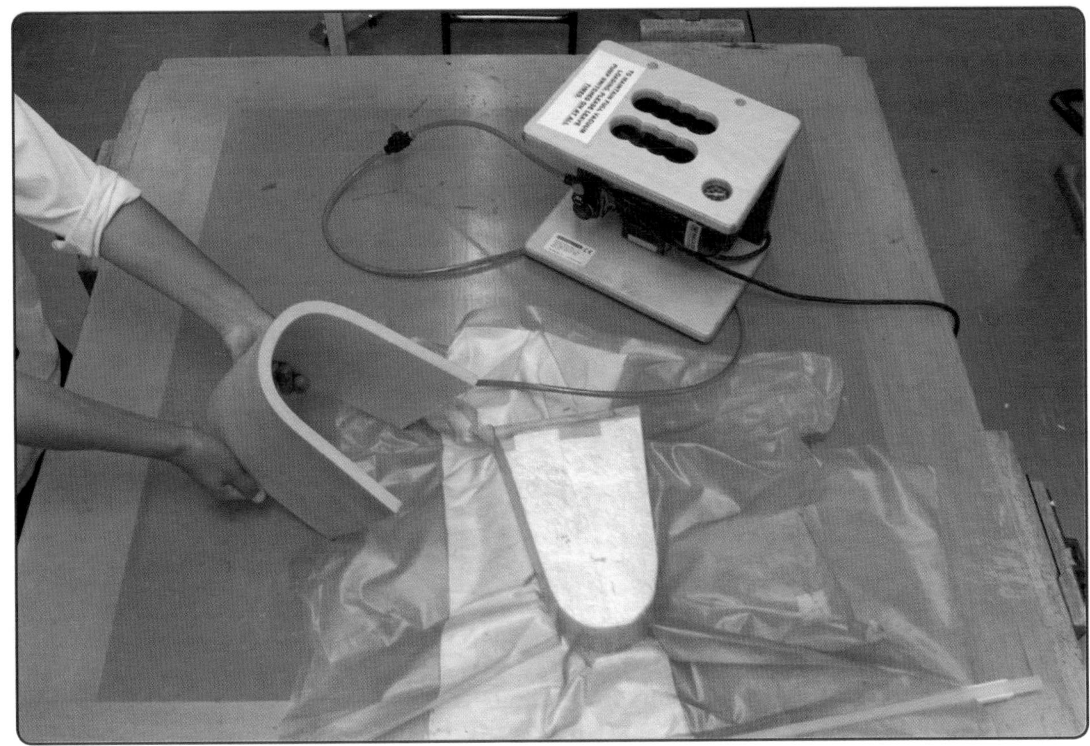

A bag press in use

Forming wood 2

In this chapter you will learn about:

★ **how to form wood using a wood-turning lathe**

★ **wood forming using carving techniques.**

Complex free forms, like these chair spindles, can be produc[ed] using a wood-turning lat[he]

Wood turning

Wood turning is an effective and creative way of forming wood. A wooden blank is rotated at speed in a wood-turning lathe. The wood is freely shaped by holding different chisels against it as it turns. A wide variety of forms can be created quickly. The work can even be sanded and finished while still in the lathe, giving a high-quality result.

Wood can be turned in two ways.

- Faceplate turning is done on the outboard spindle of the machine. The wooden blank is mounted on a faceplate using woodscrews. Gouges and scraper chisels are held against the blank to shape it. Flat work like bowls, plates, formers and bases are made this way.
- Between centres turning is used for longer pieces of work that are supported at both ends. A three-pronged driving centre is used at the headstock end to ensure the work is driven around positively, and a dead centre is used at the tailstock end to support the work and allow it to rotate. Stair spindles, table and chair legs can be made like this.

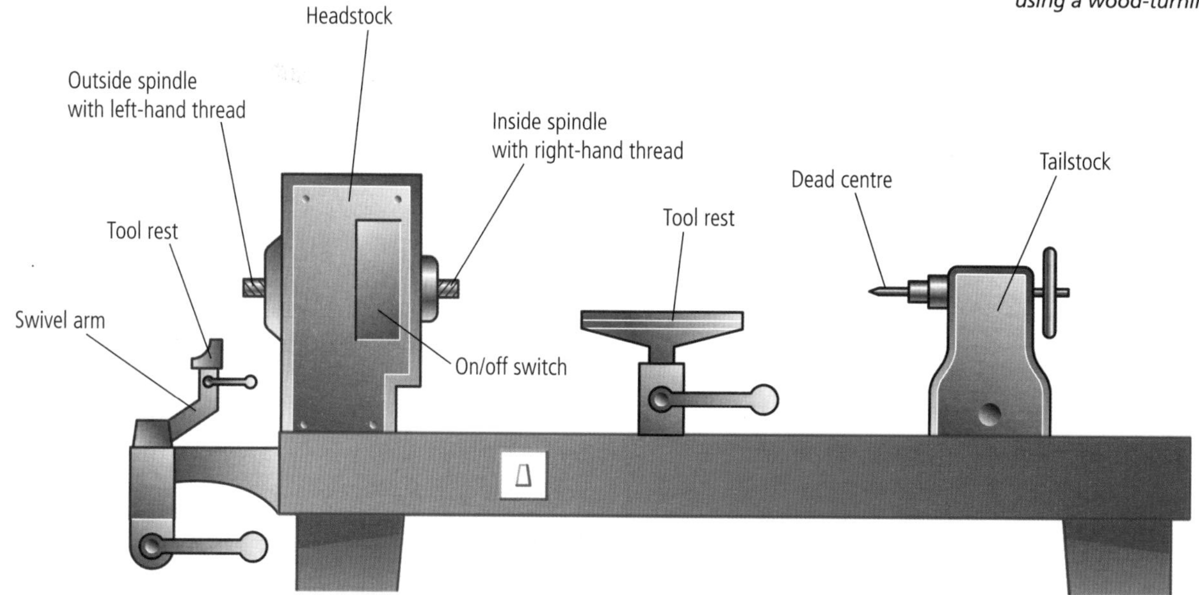

A wood-turning lat[he]

'ood turning tips

/lake sure the tool rest is as close as possible to the 'vork and remember to adjust as the work reduces.

3efore switching on and after any adjustment, always otate the work by hand to ensure it runs freely. Check ıdjustments often.

Select the correct speed and tool for each operation: ,low for roughing work and larger diameters; medium or further shaping and sanding; high for small work and ,ome finishing operations.

Always wear protective clothing and safety glasses. Use dust extraction – an extra dust mask may be needed for ;ome operations.

nishing

vays finish turned items on the lathe. Sanding down ough the grades of abrasive paper can be done at dium speed to achieve a near-perfect surface. A sealer h as a shellac-based polish should be applied with the ıe turned by hand. Wax polishing can be completed at dium speed to achieve a high-quality surface finish.

/ood carving

Waste wood is best removed by sawing to remove as much as possible.

Wood-carving chisels and gouges are used with a wooden mallet and remove waste material quickly. They can be used with great accuracy to produce complex items.

Surforms are like heavy duty cheese graters. They remove waste material quickly but leave a rough finish.

Rasps and rough files are less coarse than surforms and can be used before abrasive papers to achieve a smooth surface.

Wood is an excellent material for carving using a variety of tools

Activities

1. Make a sketch of the wood-turning lathe with a wooden blank held between centres.
2. Make sketches of the main wood-turning tools and use reference books to describe their uses.
3. How many different kinds of turned wooden products can you find in your home? Draw one and describe how it might have been made.

Summary

- ★ Wood turning can be an effective and creative process. It is the only way that wood can be formed freely by hand into complex forms.
- ★ High-quality components can be made using this process.
- ★ Wood carving allows complex decorative work to be produced using simple tools.

5.17 Using jigs and templates

In this chapter you will learn about:

- ★ **increasing the quality of making by using jigs and templates**
- ★ **repeating making processes again and again.**

Jigs and fixtures

When a number of identical components are to be made as a batch, it is time consuming to measure and mark out each component individually. Jigs and fixtures are guides and holding devices that are used to speed up the production process while maintaining quality and accuracy. Using a jig or fixture that is specifically designed to repeat a task like drilling can save time and money.

Jigs

A jig is a work-holding device specifically designed to suit a single component. Components are held in exactly the same position every time, ensuring dimensions are maintained accurately and consistently. The jig is not fixed to a machine or work piece but is free to be held by hand and moved about the workshop. Bending jigs are used with woods, metals and plastics. The diagram below shows a bending jig that holds an acrylic strip in place until it cools and sets.

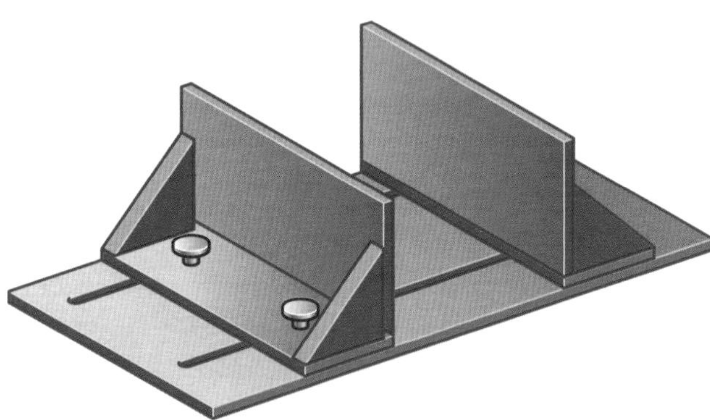

An adjustable right-angle bending jig for L, U and tent-style products

Fixtures

A fixture is a work-holding device that is clamped or fixed to the machine table. Fixtures can be designed and used for operations such as milling, drilling, turning and welding.

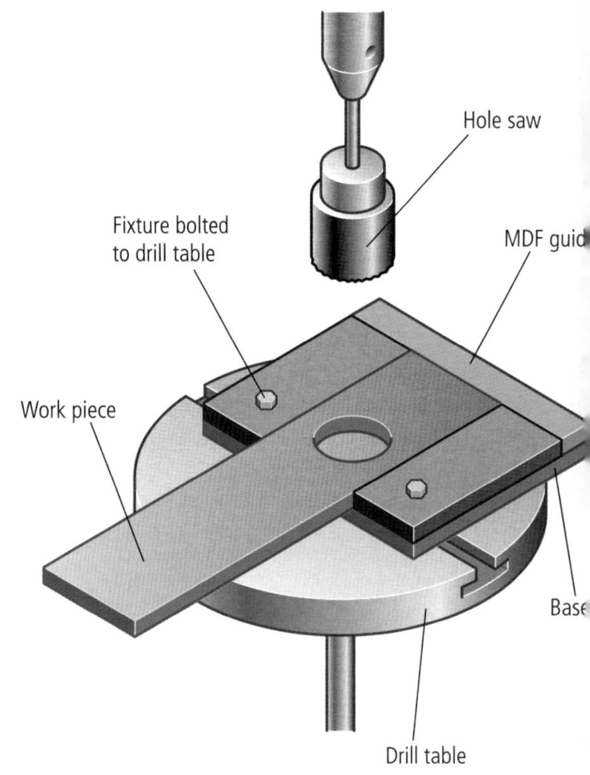

A simple drilling fix

Jigs and fixtures should have:

- a method of quickly locating the component
- a design that allows the component to sit properly
- a foolproof design so that the component can be locat only the correct way around
- a clean, smooth finish that will not mark the compone
- a method of positioning the cutting tool accurately, within tolerance
- space for the machine guards to be used correctly
- access to remove swarf, wood and plastic waste quick after each operation
- access to remove the component easily.

Usually jigs and fixtures are so specific to the component that they have to be made especially for it, but general-purpose jigs are available in most workshops. A mitre sa held in an adjustable jig is useful for a variety of angles. router dovetail jig is designed to speed up the manufactu of dovetail joints. The wood is clamped onto the device a a router is used to cut the joint accurately and with minir preparation. Stops and guides are used to allow work to marked out or cut without measuring.

A router dovetail jig

A small tube jig

emplates

nplates are used when a number of identical nponents need to be marked out. A template is often de from metal for accuracy, and it is used by marking und the edges. Templates are particularly useful for sellating complex shapes, transferring irregular shapes l making maximum use of materials. They can also used as a paper method of transferring detail from a wing to the work piece. CAD programs can be used to w accurate patterns and profiles. These can be printed o paper or card and glued to the materials to be cut.

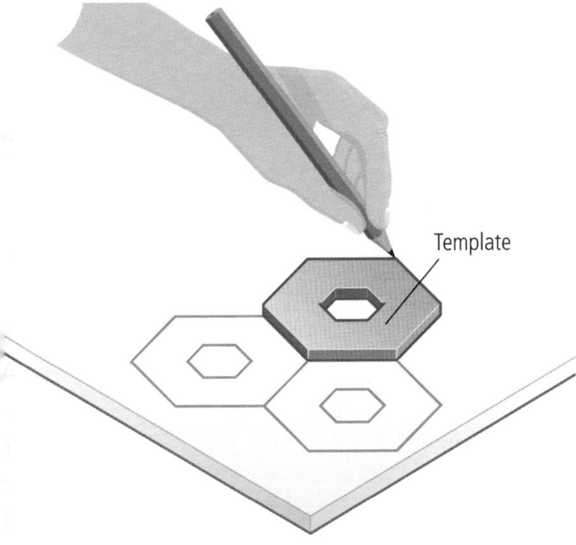

CAD can be used to produce accurate templates

Coursework

In your design project you should think about ways to improve the accuracy and efficient making of multiple components, e.g. CD dividers, cabinet feet, shelf-supports and dowel joints. You will gain additional marks if you have designed and made a jig, fixture or template, so make sure the examiner sees it.

Activities

1 Give three reasons for using a jig.
2 List the differences between a jig and a fixture.
3 Why might you use a template when making jewellery?
4 Imagine a fixture is to be used to mill a slot in 20 aluminium blocks. List six specifications for the fixture's design.

Summary

★ Most designers work on products that have the potential for mass production, so they need to think about how their designs can be produced in a consistent way.

★ Jigs, fixtures and templates are designed to speed up production without reducing quality.

5.18 Finishing

In this chapter you will learn about:

★ **abrasives**
★ **selecting an applied finish**
★ **creating a suitable finish on your project.**

Finishing your work does not just mean meeting the deadline. It also means making all the surfaces suitable for their purpose. Your choice of finish is an important aspect of the aesthetics of your work. A really good finish on your project is important for its function and maintenance. It is also essential for good coursework marks.

Abrasives

Selecting and using the correct abrasive saves time and produces a good result. An abrasive is a grit that scours the surface of the material. Some are supplied as powders, e.g. pumice, but most are bonded to a paper or fabric sheet. Abrasive sheets come in a variety of grits and grades. Each sheet is numbered to show the grade: the smaller the number, the coarser the grade.

Typical grades are:

- course: 60 and 80
- medium: 120 and 180
- fine: 320 and 400
- very fine: 1000 and 1200.

Wet and dry paper (silicon carbide) is used on plastics ar non-ferrous metals for fine finishing. Using this abrasive wet, usually with water, helps prevent clogging. It can be stuck to board for use.

Glass paper or aluminium oxide paper (used dry) is used wood, with emery cloth (lubricated with light oil) for ferr metals. A supported abrasive sheet cuts the surface even producing a fine finish. Glass paper can be wrapped arou a cork block, whereas emery is wrapped around a file.

Applied finishes

Applied finishes provide protection and decoration to correctly prepared material.

- Anodising is a corrosion-resistant process used to thicken and colour the natural oxide film on aluminiun components. It is often used in industry to improve the look of sports equipment, including bicycles.

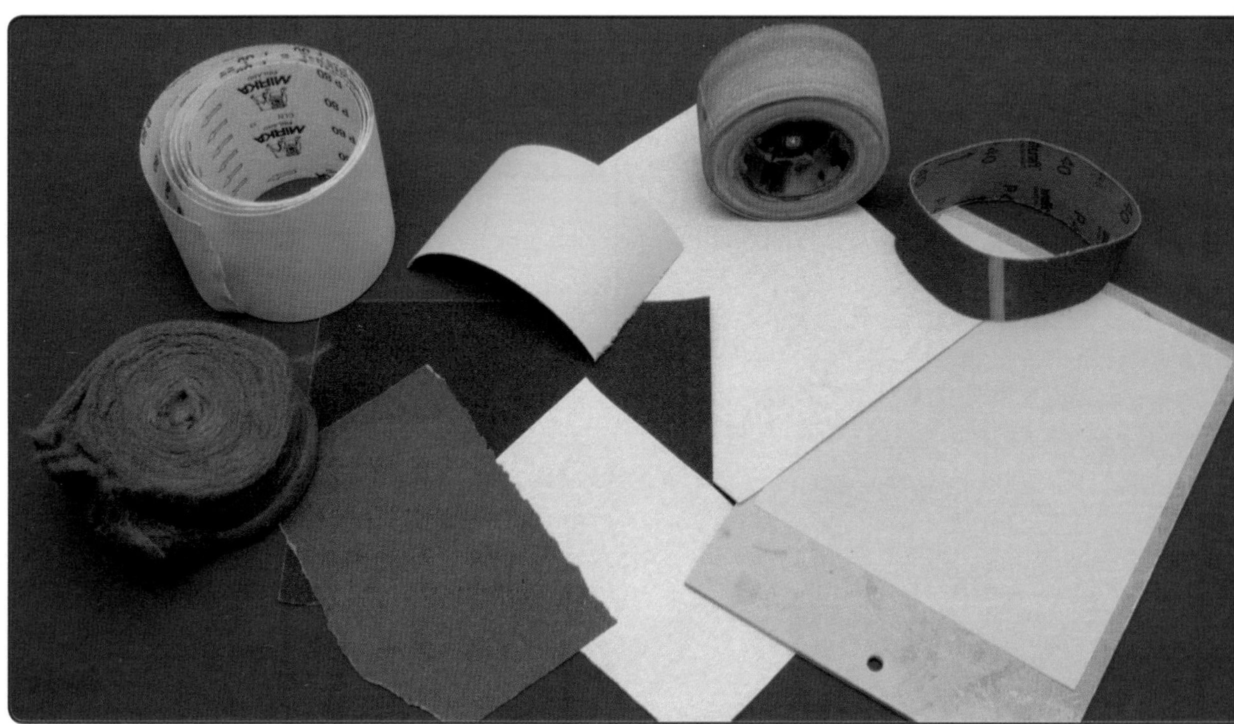

Common abras

Etching is a decorative process for metals. Painting on an etch-resistant product protects some areas while the acid dissolves the exposed parts. Nitric acid is used to make patterns and textures on silver jewellery.

Spirit varnish, lacquers and paints consist of a man-made resin, e.g. acrylic, and a carrier (e.g. water). They can be sprayed or applied with a brush. Each product needs a suitable brush cleaner.

Enamelling is an applied finish used on some metals. Powdered glass is melted, flowing over the metal surface to give a hard, colourful, protective finish. Vitreous or stove enamel is used on steel cookers. It is heat- and chemical-resistant, providing good wear protection.

Dip coating is suitable for most metals. It is used for coating metal baskets, tool handles and fittings with a plastic layer. The metal product is thoroughly degreased, heated to 180°C and lowered into a fluidising tank. The tank contains fine particles of a thermoplastic that is made to act like a liquid by blowing air through it. The fluidised plastic – often polythene – melts and sticks to the hot metal, producing a thin skin that provides good protection when cool.

Electroplating is used to give metals like brass a coating of another more decorative metal such as chrome, e.g. bathroom taps. The initials EPNS mean Electro-Plated Nickel Silver and can be found on many pieces of cutlery. They indicate that the base metal (nickel silver) has been given a plating of silver.

Galvanising involves dipping mild steel into a bath of molten zinc. The zinc provides a corrosion-resistant finish, although it is not attractive. This process is widely used to protect railings, fencing and other mild steel outdoor products from rusting.

elf-finished products

any plastics, such as injection-moulded components, ve excellent resistance to corrosion and decay, making unnecessary to apply a finish. The die or mould is highly lished or textured and this surface is transferred onto the oduct.

Galvanised, polished, painted or self-finished plastic. Look at these watering cans. What are the advantages of each type of finish?

Coursework

Every surface, corner and edge of your project needs the correct finish so that it functions and looks according to your specifications. Select the correct finish, read the manufacturer's instructions and try it out on a sample.

Activity

Imagine a 12 mm diameter copper tube, 300 mm long, forms part of a DVD rack. Suggest a suitable finish and draw a flow chart to explain the finishing process from stock material to completed item.

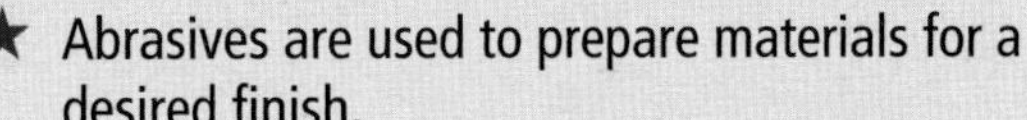

Summary

★ Abrasives are used to prepare materials for a desired finish.

★ The finish may be applied or self-finished.

Exam questions

1 Study the drawing of the acrylic toothbrush holder shown below.

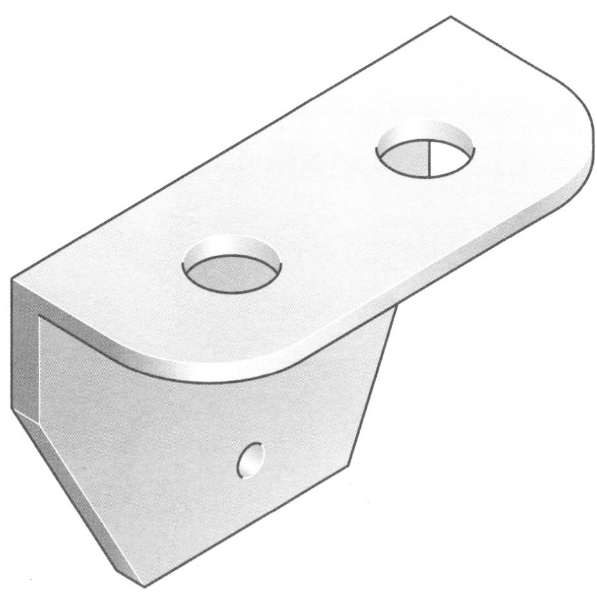

Using notes and sketches clearly show, stage by stage, how you would make the toothbrush holder in the school workshop. Remember to name all the tools and equipment you would use.

Stage one:	Marking out or CAD	*(4 marks)*
Stage two:	Cutting, Shaping and drilling or CAM	*(4 marks)*
Stage three:	Bending	*(4 marks)*
Stage four:	Finishing	*(4 marks)*
Quality of notes and sketches		*(4 marks)*

2 Study the exploded drawing of the frame and tabletop shown below.

The frame is made from tubular mild steel. The tabletop is made from melamine covered MDF.

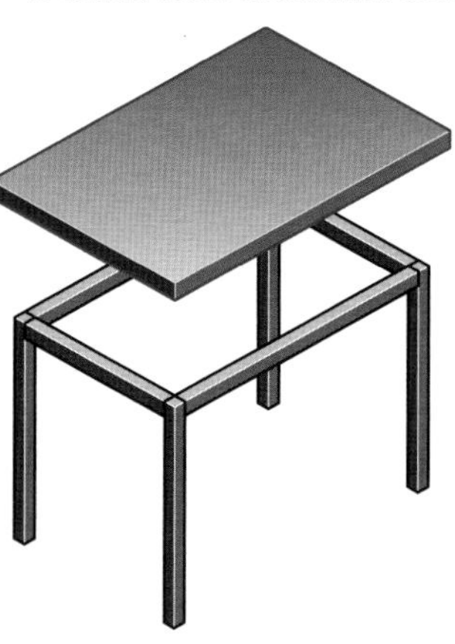

a Use notes and sketches to show the method you would use to attach the tabletop to the frame.

(5 marks)

b Copy and complete the chart below to show the stages in the process of joining the tabletop to the frame. Name **one** tool used in each process.

Process	Tool
Marking out …	
Preparation …	
Fixing …	

(9 marks)

(AQA 200

ICT: CAD/CAM

this section you will learn about how mputers enable designers to work in w and exciting ways to develop designs. mputers have also brought about a major ange in how products are manufactured at levels of production. This section looks at w the process works at a simple level for a e-off product for a school project, through complex computer-integrated manufacture mass production.

What's in this section?

Computer controlled machines are powerful production tools for the manufacturing industry. Exciting developments in CAD CAM technology are a feature of many courses in schools

6.1 Using CAD

In this chapter you will learn about:

- ★ **how computer-aided design (CAD) has changed the ways in which designs can be developed and communicated**
- ★ **the advantages and disadvantages of using CAD.**

CAD can be used to model design ideas in 3D and then to use these to create 2D working drawings in one operation. The software available in many schools, such as Pro/DESKTOP®, CorelDRAW® and Techsoft 2D Design, allows you to work in a new way. Using CAD, designers can create 'virtual' products that can be viewed and rotated on screen to enable the design ideas to be explored fully. Today's designers are often expected to have high-level CAD skills to enable them to develop and communicate ideas.

Modelling design ideas

The following steps show how models can be built up using CAD.

1 The wire frame model is like a skeleton of the drawing. The object is drawn as a series of lines.

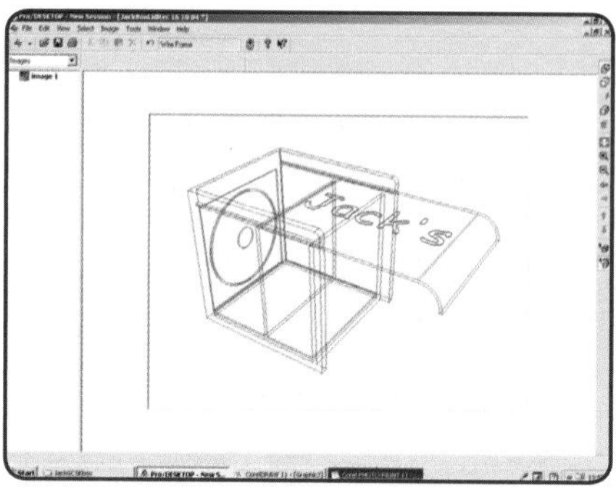

2 In the solid model stage the skin is added to the skeleton and the model begins to take on a solid form.

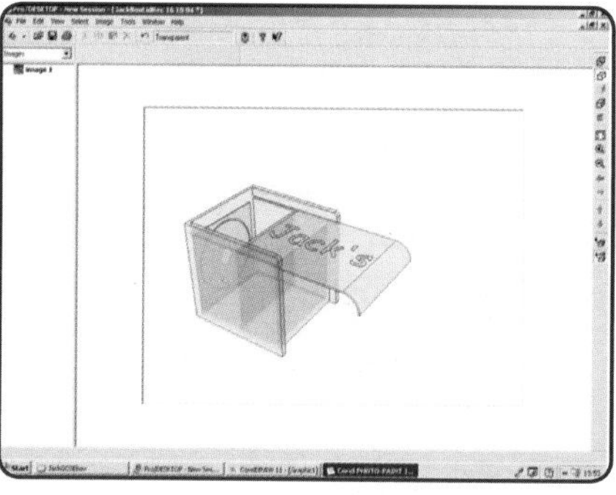

3 The rendered model stage is when the surface skin of model is given coloured textures to represent the materials from which it will be made.

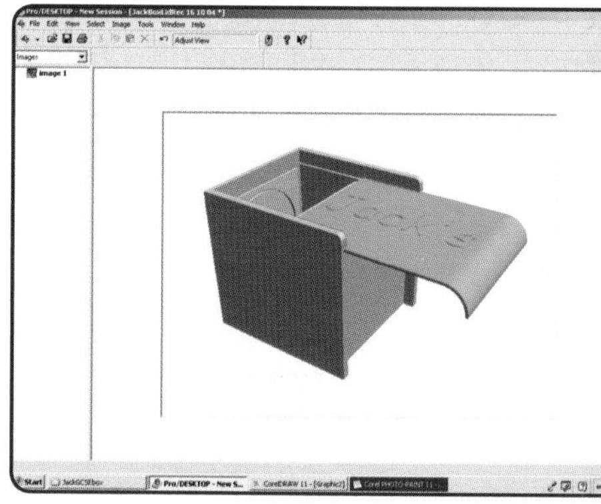

4 The final output from the CAD system can be a photo-realistic view of the object placed on a background an lit to create a lifelike view.

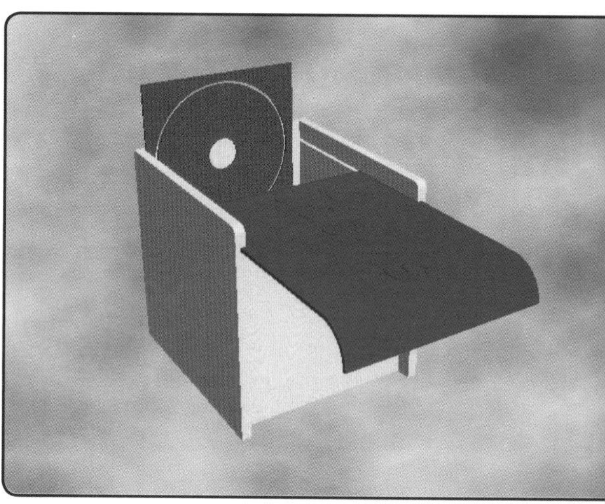

5 Animation can be added to enable parts of the object t be moved, demonstrating their function.

Creating working drawings

The full set of working drawings needed to prepare for final manufacture can be created using CAD. Once the 3D model is complete, the software can automatically produc a full set of orthographic views complete with dimensions and details. It is even possible to modify the working drawings and the software will correct the 3D model. Wh you amend one drawing, all the other forms of the drawir are modified automatically.

ırning virtual designs into ɘality

ɕe a design has been modelled using CAD, it can turned into a real model of the product using rapid prototyping (RPT). 7.8 *Prototyping* explains the most commonly used methods to produce RPT models.

CAD has changed many aspects of design, as shown in the table below.

dvantages	Disadvantages
Complex products can be designed with ease using 3D modelling software	• Expensive hardware and software are required to work at an effective level
Work can be electronically shared with other designers, enabling more than one person to be involved	• Designers need training in the use of the software
Work can be developed 24 hours a day and passed around the world	• CAD modelling can be time consuming compared to real quick sketch modelling
Designs can be modified and updated at any time in the process	• Designers need high levels of experience and skills to enable them to use CAD
Highly detailed designs can be created with less need for expensive models and prototypes	• Experienced designers are costly to employ
Photo-realistic models can be created and animated to display as virtual prototypes	• Software and hardware need regular and costly updates to keep pace with developments
Real 3D models can be created using data from the CAD package	

Some advantages and disadvantages of CAD

Coursework

CAD can be an exciting and powerful way to generate, develop, model and communicate your design proposals. Creating a storyboard of screenshots is an effective way of recording the process of making the drawing to include in your project folder.

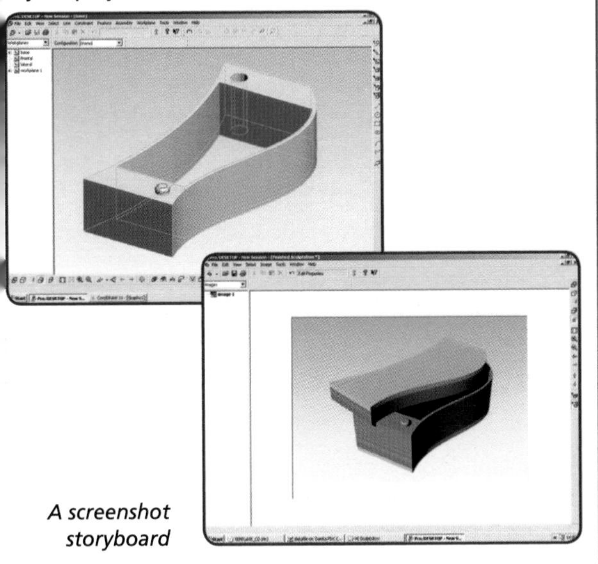

A screenshot storyboard

Activities

1 Explain how designers use CAD to help them to:

   a Design better products.

   b Share ideas with other designers.

   c Work faster.

   d Communicate with their clients.

2 If you have access to CAD, you could use it to model your ideas and produce working drawings. Pro/DESKTOP® can do this job very effectively but it takes time to learn how to use it.

Summary

★ CAD can speed up the whole design process and enable designers to work in new and exciting ways.

★ There are advantages and disadvantages to using CAD.

6.2 Using CAM

In this chapter you will learn about:

- ★ **how computer-aided manufacture (CAM) enables designers to move from designing to making prototypes**
- ★ **the different types of CAM machines and what types of work they can produce**
- ★ **the advantages and disadvantages of using CAM.**

Using CAM

CAM is the way in which CAD designs can be turned into real components and products using computer-controlled machines. The drawing files can be used to create cutting files, which can be used by **computer numerical control (CNC)** machines. These machines are controlled using numbers or digital information through a computer. In your school you may have a range of CAM equipment. Typical machines to be found in schools and colleges are as follows.

- **Sign cutters**: these machines are easy to set up and use. They trace designs using a special knife directly on a sheet of self-adhesive vinyl plastic to create signs. The cutter can also be used to score and cut card for packaging and model making.
- **Milling machines and routers**: these machines can be used to cut a variety of materials, including woods, metals and plastics. Many different types of these machines can be found in schools. Some operate in two axes and produce 2D products such as signs and jewellery. Other machines have 3 axes and can cut complex 3D forms such as moulds for vacuum forming. Large machines can cut wooden components for furniture projects.
- **Lathes**: these can be used for a variety of tasks and cu cylindrical components in woods, metals and plastics. Complex curves can be produced easily, as well as sma engineering components.
- **Laser cutters**: these are the most recent pieces of CNC equipment to arrive in schools. They cut woods and plastics quickly and leave a ready-polished edge on acrylic sheet. The work does not even need to be clamped as it is touched only by a beam of intense lase light during cutting. The cut is so fine (0.02 mm) that jigsaws and inlays can be cut perfectly. Although laser cutters can only cut in two axes, their speed and ease c use make them useful.

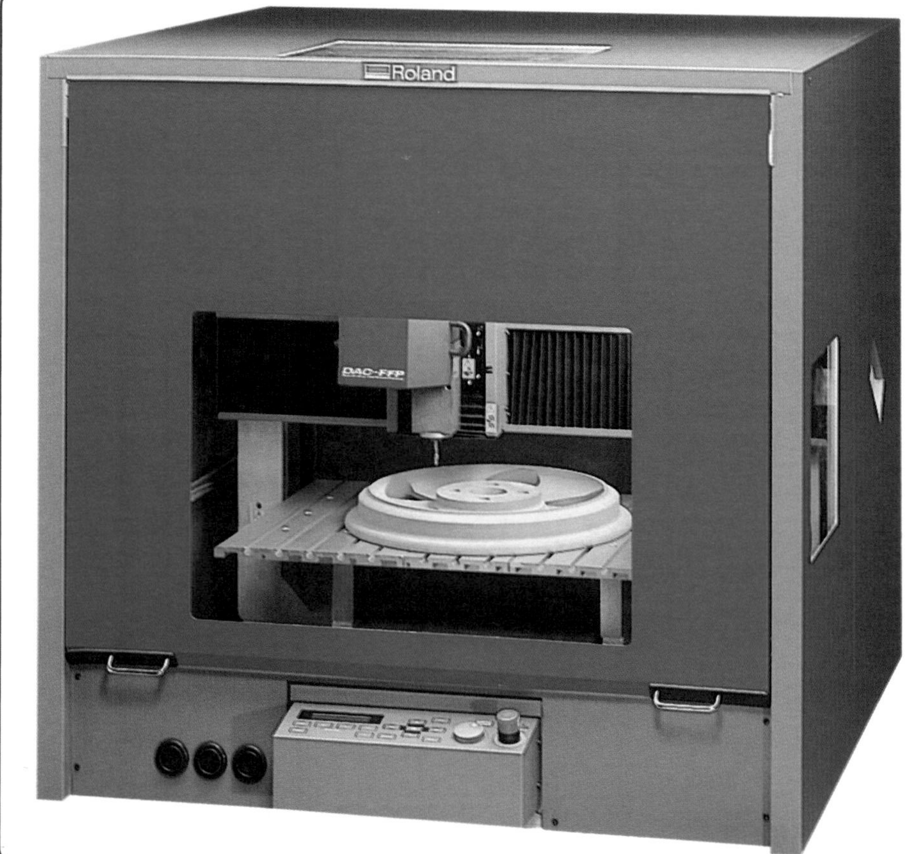

A 3D milling machi

A laser cutter

AM for quantity and omplexity

IC machines can be used to manufacture single mponents as well as items in quantity as small oduction runs. The complex shapes that can be produced er a new and exciting set of possibilities for designers.

AM has created many new opportunities for making oducts, as shown in the table below.

Advantages	Disadvantages
Accurate, high-quality components can be produced quickly	• A knowledge of CAD is required to prepare the drawings to use as the basis for making
Any number of components can be produced easily time after time	• The machinery costs are high
Complex forms can be cut easily	• The range of equipment available and the cutting capacity may be limited
• Modifications can be made and tested quickly	• Setting up the machine can be complex and time consuming
• Small, complex components can be made easily	
• Quality of finish is so high that no further finishing may be needed	

Some advantages and disadvantages of CAM

Coursework

Using CAM can help you to turn design ideas into reality and offers the opportunity to include new and complex components into design projects. It gives you the scope to produce items both as one-offs and in quantity.

Activity

Explore the CAM machines available in your school workshop.

a What can be produced and in which materials?

b How do designs need to be created so that they can be cut using CAM?

Summary

★ Using CAM allows complex forms to be produced in quantity with high levels of accuracy and finish, but it requires high-level CAD skills to create the designs in the first place.

★ There are various types of CAM machines, each with its own use.

★ There are advantages and disadvantages to using CAM.

6.3 CAD/CAM systems in industry

In this chapter you will learn about:

- ★ how CAD/CAM systems can speed up manufacturing by integrating all the computer-controlled elements
- ★ how computer-integrated manufacture (CIM) can make manufacturing more flexible, productive and efficient.

Computers in manufacturing

ICT is a vital aspect of the manufacturing industry

One of the biggest impacts that computers and ICT has had on society is in the manufacturing industry. The pace of change in the world today requires companies to be ever-more productive. If companies are to get their products developed and produced to high-quality standards and delivered to the **market place** faster than their competitors, ICT holds the key.

Computerised manufacturing is expensive to set up and requires a smaller, more highly skilled and flexible workforce than traditional manufacturing. The work is interesting, challenging, safer and cleaner. Modern manufacturing companies are very different from the factories of the past.

Computer-integrated manufacture

Computer-integrated manufacture (CIM) uses computer technology to join together the various computer-assisted parts of a manufacturing company. This creates a highly productive and flexible manufacturing capability.

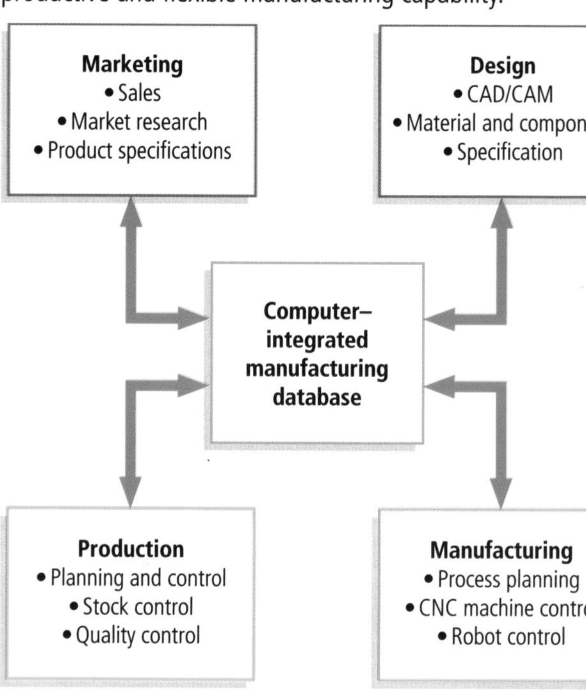

A CIM mo

The illustration on page 113 shows how the various parts of a company are linked together into a whole manufacturing system.

- The marketing team prepares data about current and projected sales, undertakes market research and works out target costs and specifications of new products.
- The design team prepares new designs, uses CAD/CAM to prepare data for CNC manufacturing and prepares material and component specifications.
- The production team plans details of how the manufacturing will be managed and quality maintained and how the stock will be ordered and distributed.
- The manufacturing team manages the production, sets up CNC machines and handling robots, ensures quality control checks are made and any changes made.
- The CIM database coordinates the whole activity with a the computers linked together on a network. Each one used on its own but they are all linked together.

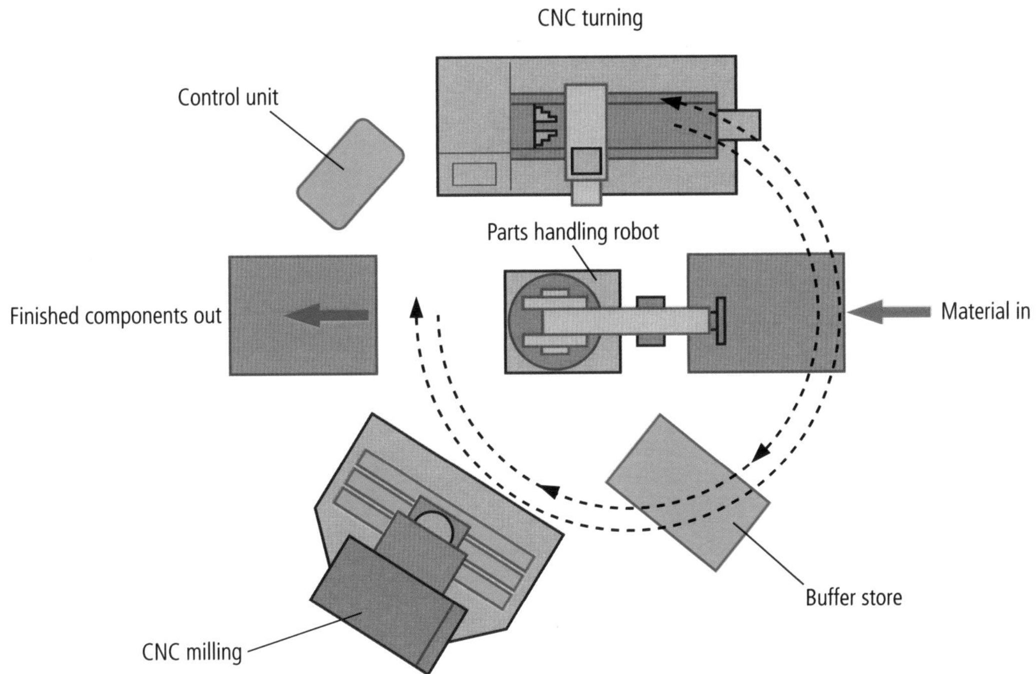

A manufacturing cell is a highly efficient unit that needs little human intervention

r example, if a design is modified using CAD, any changes the CAM program are made automatically by the M database. If a new order is placed by the marketing am, the production and manufacturing data is updated tomatically to ensure more products can be made on time.

M brings together more than just the manufacturing: it cludes all aspects of production. Quality assurance plays y role in planning that standards and tolerances are met.

Ianufacturing cells

; a part of the CIM approach, parts of the production e grouped together to create manufacturing cells. These lls link together the different CAM machines with robots move work through the system. A cell performs the erations needed to produce a complete component.

Coursework

Plan the stages in the production of your coursework project and work out where and how you might use CAD and CAM.

Activity

Imagine the IKEA marketing team has decided that the brightly-coloured plastic watering can (see page 8) needs to be updated by making the design in a new shape and in new colours.

a Work out the main steps involved for the company in moving from this decision to achieving a modified finished product.

b List and plot the steps from marketing plan to new product using the CIM model to help you.

Summary

★ Computers have had a major impact on all aspects of manufacturing industry.

★ CAD and CAM systems can speed up manufacturing.

★ CIM can make manufacturing more flexible, productive and efficient.

Exam questions

1 State **three** ways in which a designer can make use of the Internet. In each case, explain how this improves the quality of the designer's work.

(6 marks)

2 Discuss the **advantages** and **disadvantages** to the **manufacturer** of making products by computer-aided manufacturing techniques (CAM).

(8 marks)

3 Explain the benefits to the designer of using computer aided design (CAD) rather than traditional methods of drawing.

(6 marks)

4 State **three** ways in which the use of computer aided manufacture (CAM) has made the working environment a safer place. In each case explain your answer.

(6 marks)

Industrial practices

this section you will find information lating to the production of products a large scale. Successful designers derstand how a company takes an idea d makes it into a commercial success. ood designers and manufacturers are ghly respected across the world, with many pportunities to work at the cutting edge of chnology on a wide range of projects from rcraft to architecture and vacuum cleaners radios.

Vhat's in this section?

The 'Dyson Ball'

7.1 The role of the industrial designer

> **In this chapter you will learn about:**
> - ★ **the role of the industrial designer**
> - ★ **the people who influence the work of designers.**

The industrial designer

The role of the industrial designer is rather like that of a juggler. There are many different parts to consider and unless they are all in place and in balance, the design for a new product is unlikely to be successful. The ideal product design can only exist if the designer balances the functional, aesthetic, financial and manufacturing aspects of the design and ensures they are in a form that matches the expectations of the consumer.

Teamwork

The industrial designer is part of a team of people who together develop designs for new products for a company. This team approach helps to give a range of expertise, creating a powerful group that can quickly and efficiently produce new designs. The production departments within the company work with the designer to ensure that the components for a design can be made efficiently and reliably and assembled to create the new product.

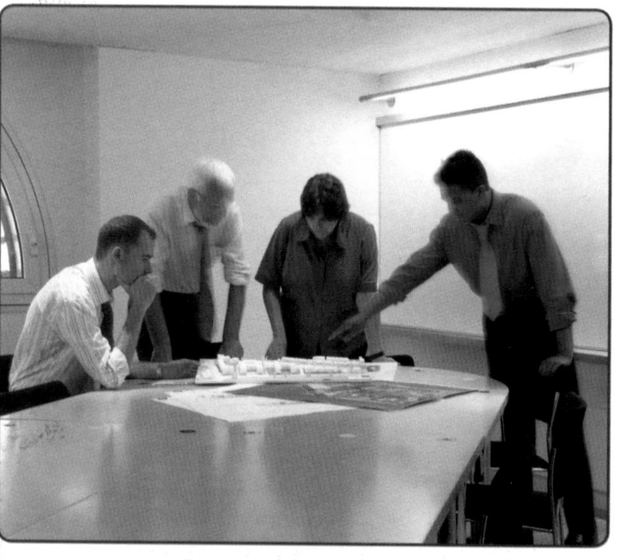

Team work has a vital role to play in industry

Influences on the designer

Marketing

The marketing team is responsible for finding out exactly what consumers want, need and will pay for new product It does this by surveys, questionnaires, product testing and looking at the products of its competitors. The marketing team is an important part of the company as it targets areas for development and establishes new markets. It anticipates the kind of reaction target consumers will have to the product and its advertising.

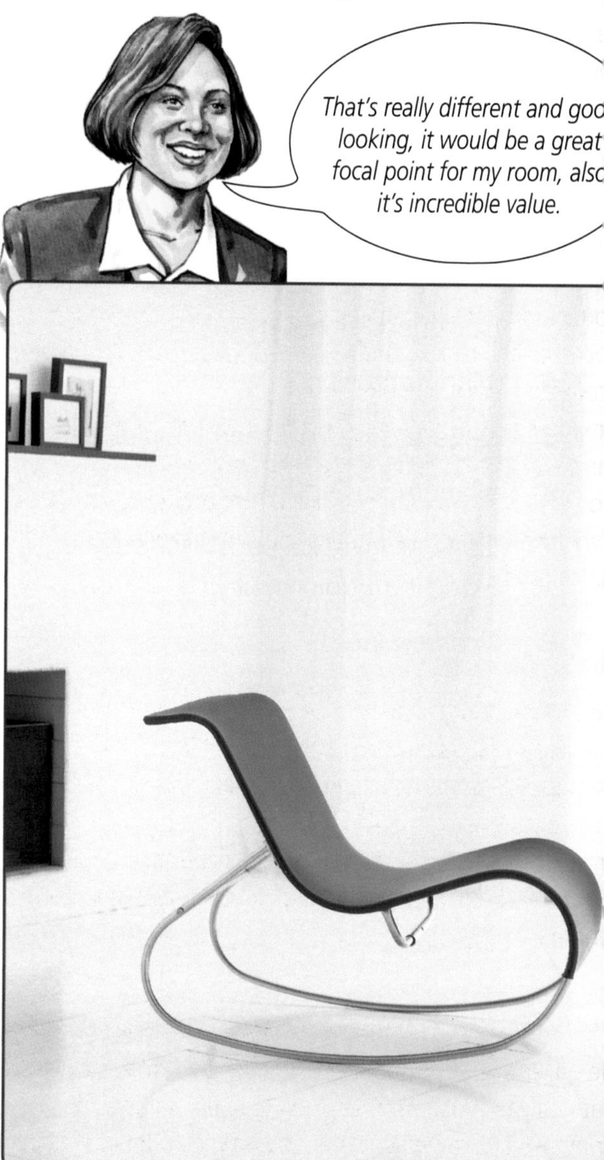

That's really different and goo looking, it would be a great focal point for my room, also it's incredible value.

Finding out exactly what consumers want is a cruci part of the proce

dvertising

e advertising team is ponsible for promoting both e products and the image of the mpany. Targeting the advertising kes sure the right group of ople are informed in a way at will attract their attention. r example, look at the different oducts advertised throughout e day on television to see how ey are matched to different es of programme and viewers.

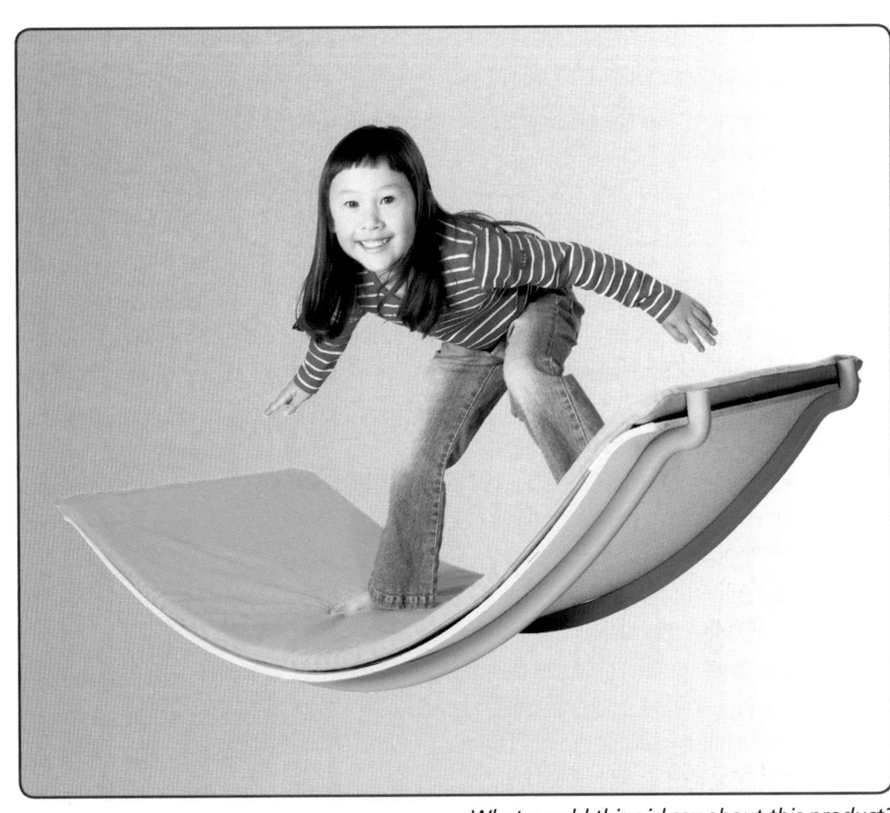

What would this girl say about this product?

roduction

e job of the production partment is tailoring the sign and manufacture of a new oduct to match the equipment, ocesses and expertise of company. Using standard mponents such as screws, hinges, gears and other andard parts is important to keep costs down. This task is own as standardisation. Making sure production workers ve the skills, materials and equipment needed to produce ality products is important.

inance

e economic well-being of the company and the profits generates for its directors and shareholders is the sponsibility of the company's financiers and bankers. All ajor decisions involve this group. The development budget r a new project is set by the finance department and termines how much design and development time can be forded.

overnment

e government is responsible for new laws and standards at apply to products. These ensure public safety, value r money and fair play. There are many legal requirements r products and if they fail to meet them, fines and legal tion from consumers can be damaging to the company.

Coursework

Planning consumer response to a product is important. Who is the target consumer for your coursework product? What is special about it? How does it stand out from other similar products on the market?

Activity

Visit the IKEA website at www.heinemann.co.uk/hotlinks and find three products that you would like to include in a makeover for your ideal bedroom. What reaction line might the advertising team have written for your chosen products?

Summary

★ Industrial designers have to ensure all the different parts and people involved in designing a new product come together effectively.

7.2 Product development and costs

> **In this chapter you will learn about:**
> ★ **the roles of the client, designer, manufacturer, and consumer**
> ★ **the costs involved in making products.**

The market place is the term used to describe all those who might use your product. The environment is all the situations, places, circumstances, conditions and times that the product will be used. Developing a product ready for the market place involves four groups of people.

- The client is the motivation behind any new product. The client can see the needs and wants of the customer and recognises an opportunity. They can spot a gap in the market and employ designers and manufacturers to come up with the product to meet the need. They supply the money, investing in research, design, manufacture, advertising, marketing and distribution, and usually take on the financial risk of the project failing.
- The designer agrees the brief with the client and starts to develop the solution. Getting the specification right and recognising influences and market forces are important. The designer researches existing products; looks at new technology and production methods; considers social, moral, environmental and safety issues; and develops t style and aesthetics of the project.
- The manufacturer needs to work closely with the designer, checking proposals and offering technical advice so that the new design can actually be made. They consider the cost and **scale of production** and assemble the workers, equipment and materials. They ensure that the production of the product will be safe.
- The consumer expects the product to solve the need identified by the client. They demand a safe product th is value for money, with a price that reflects the quality and complexity of the product. They choose to buy the product for environmental, aesthetic and functional reasons.

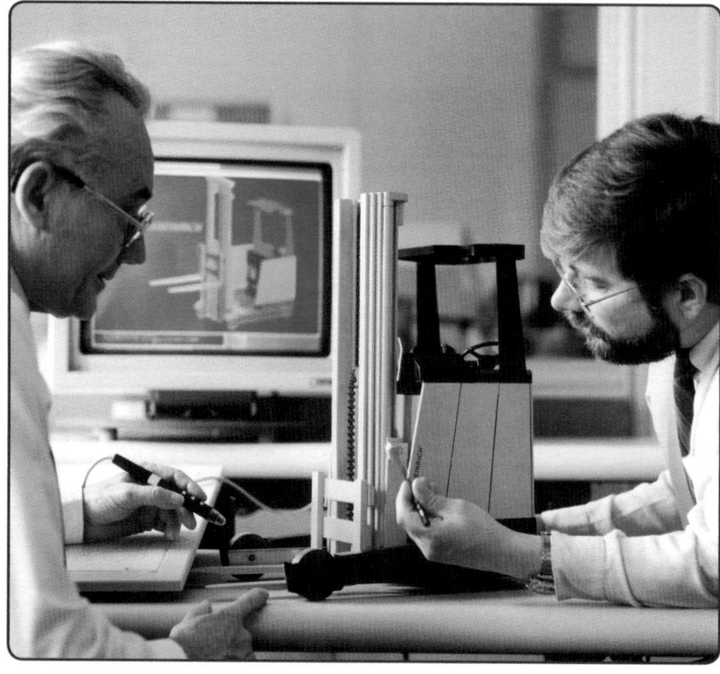
The product needs to fit the market place

Cost

The cost of a product is important for the client, designer, manufacturer and consumer. Investment (the amount of money) into a new project can be great. For mass-produc items, high initial costs can be spread over many products For one-off products it is often necessary for all the costs to be tied to the same product, which can make them expensive. Some of the things that will affect the cost of a product are:

- research (consumers, materials, new technology)
- development (prototyping, modelling, testing, trialling)
- materials (including waste and waste disposa
- fastenings and fitting (e.g. screws, nails, hinge
- sundries (e.g. glasspaper, paints, adhesives, brushes and thinners)
- equipment (any special equipment or machinery, repairs and replacements)
- labour costs (wages)
- overheads (e.g. heating, lighting, rent, water rates, toilet facilities)
- packaging and distribution (e.g. transport, postage)
- advertising (e.g. websites, magazines, catalogue
- retailer costs (the shop mark-up is often three times the price at the factory gate)
- profit margins (for future investment).

osting your project

u can cost your project in a similar way to a nufactured product.

Add up the costs of material. Don't forget to include the waste and the parts you had to remake. A computer program like the Focus on Resistant Materials 2 database can create a costing sheet for you.

£

Add a small amount to cover sundries (miscellaneous items). Don't forget that you will have to include the price of the whole tin of paint – not just the amount you used.

£

Did you have to buy any specialist tools or equipment, such as a particular drill size or a varnish brush? Did you have to have a jig made to help production?

£

How many hours did it take you to make your project? Don't forget to include the designing time.

Hours

How much are your skills worth per hour – £5, £25? Multiply your hourly rate by the number of hours to give the labour costs.

£

Add everything together to get a total price for your one-off project.

£

this a realistic price for your project? Don't forget that u still have to add things like:

overheads for the use of the workshop (and your teacher's advice!)
advertising and marketing
distribution, postage and packaging
retailer costs.

u have probably found that for you to make a profit your oduct needs to sell at a high price. In your design folder, plain how you could reduce costs. Think about the choice materials, investment in equipment, design time and the mplexity of the product. Try to predict your costs if you ere to make a batch of ten.

Coursework

Complete the costing exercise above for your project and include it in your folder.

Activity

Select a simple product such as a CD case, an A4 ring binder or a metal pencil case. Make a detailed list of the costs you would need to consider if you were going to mass produce this item.

Summary

★ Developing a product ready for the market place involves the client, designer, manufacturer and consumer.

★ The cost of the product needs to be calculated realistically.

7.3 Commercial issues

In this chapter you will learn about:
- ★ the role of marketing
- ★ changing fashions and product life.

A consumer-driven society

Our consumer society is driven by a demand for new products that clever marketing makes us believe we must have. At the same time, new technologies are pushing the market along with new and exciting features and possibilities. Designers are sometimes pulled along by the market's demand for new products. At other times, they are pushed along by technological developments that enable new and exciting products.

Marketing

Marketing is one of the most important parts of design as it helps to ensure that the products a company makes are a commercial success. Marketing is the science of discovering people's behaviour and using this to sell products time and time again. Advertising and market research are important parts of the marketing process.

Market research helps to inform designers exactly what people will want from a product. Market research also informs manufacturers exactly what people are prepared to pay for a product and what their competitors are doing. Designs people want will sell well and will ensure the commercial success of the company.

What people want

Marketing depends upon finding out what people want. You may have:

- seen people in the street conducting surveys
- filled in a questionnaire that is distributed with a new product's guarantee
- given your personal details in a store when buying something.

These processes are part of market research and are used to collect information so that new products can be targeted at specific consumers.

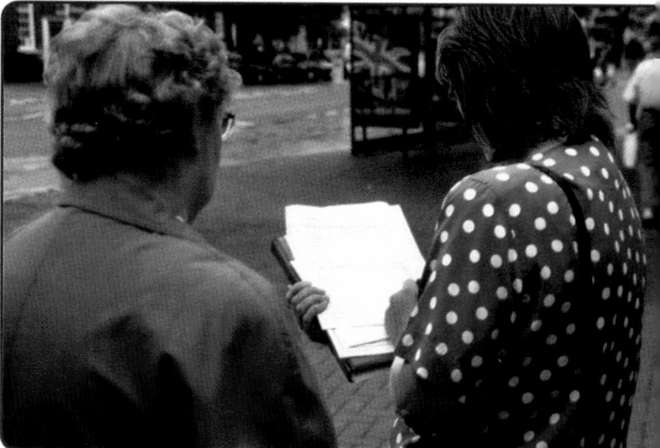

Market resea

Product life

In the past, many products were built to last a long time. Today, most products have an expected useful life and ar priced accordingly. They will not last forever. This change approach helps to ensure that consumers are able to buy fashionable products at a reasonable price.

Mobile phones have an expected useful l

signers are responsible for ensuring that products rform safely and reliably during their intended lifespan. any products have become unfashionable by the end their useful life, so designers are also responsible for signing them to be recyclable.

Mobile phones are designed to be recycled

ie life of larger products is prolonged by regular servicing. iey are designed to be serviced to keep them operating ficiently and safely. For example, cars, aircraft and ashing machines are designed to be serviced easily. They in be linked to a computer to help diagnose faults and any components are designed to be changed easily as hole modules.

)isposable products

lany products, such as single-use cameras, razors and allpoint pens, have a short lifespan or may only be used nce. They are made in high volume and thrown away after se. This is called planned obsolescence. Products like these re wasteful and damaging to the environment but help ompanies to increase turnover and profits.

Throw-away philosophy

In today's society we tend to have a throw-away philosophy. When something does not work or breaks, we throw it away. A service engineer sent to repair a large item like a dishwasher often removes and replaces a whole electronic circuit board. The circuit boards are designed as whole modules, produced by robotic production machines and impossible to repair.

Coursework

Research to find out exactly what is required in a design and how it relates to other products in the market place is essential to ensure success. It is important to carry out market ressearch as early on into the design process as possible.

Activity

a Compare two top-selling personal products on the market such as mobile phones or MP3 players. Draw up a table of performance criteria and analyse the two products.

b How have the products improved since the last model?

c How is the market-leading product different from its competitors?

Summary

★ Successful marketing results in getting the right product to the consumer at the right time and for the right price.

★ Marketing is essential if companies are to be successful.

7.4 Manufacturing in quantity

In this chapter you will learn about:
- ★ **different scales of production**
- ★ **designing to manufacture products as one-offs and in quantity.**

Designers need to think about where their new product will be sold and who will want it: the market. Identifying the market helps them generate designs that are matched to the right scale of production. The scale of production means the quantity of products that are going to be produced. All scales of production can use computer-aided design (CAD) and computer-aided manufacture (CAM). When a large quantity of products is to be produced, the production method may also involve computer-integrated manufacture (CIM). There are four main scales of production: **one-off (bespoke) manufacture**, **batch production**, **mass production** and **flow-line production**.

One-off (bespoke) manufacture

When making a single product, each item will differ from any others and can be specifically designed and made to match the customer's requirements. A one-off item is often expensive because it takes time to produce and requires the specialised work of a skilled maker. Examples of this work include custom-made jewellery, made-to-measure furniture, prototypes and larger, never to be repeated, items like the Millennium Dome, public buildings and bridges.

The Millenium Dome! One-off manufacture

Batch production

Batch production means the designer has decided to make a specific quantity of products. The materials and equipment costs are spread across the batch of products, making them cheaper than making bespoke items one af the other. It is often useful to make jigs and templates as well as using CAD and CAM so that production technique can be repeated. For this to work well, the machinery and labour need to be flexible so that they can change quickly from one product to the next. The time between batches is known as down time, an unproductive period because i still costs the company money even though nothing is bei made. Many companies produce several different product at the same time, overlapping the down time to ensure the workforce always has something to do. Examples of products produced in this way are seasonal items such as Christmas cards and Hallowe'en masks, and items where the final volume is not known so batches are made, like CDs, toasters, kettles and vacuum cleaners.

Batch productic

Mass production

Mass production

ass production means making things on a large scale ch as Lego bricks, ballpoint pens, cars and electrical ods. A company often invests in expensive, specialised uipment including computer numerical controlled (CNC) achinery like robot welders because this equipment can ep making the same quality of product time and again. e company workforce may be large but they do not need to be highly skilled. Some workers are trained carry out one particular operation while other, more illed, workers oversee several machines and their use. The anufacturing process is broken down into repetitive tasks. eparing the machinery ready for manufacture is called the t-up time.

nskilled labour can be used to assemble and move mponents along the production line. This is known as -line assembly. It is usually not flexible and takes place here most of the production system is automated.

low production

ow-line (continuous) production means 24 hours a day, ven days a week, and often for most of the year. This non-stop, uninterrupted manufacture with specialist uipment. This method of production often means the sts of turning off the machines would be high. Examples this process include oil, steel and chemical manufacture.

Coursework

- In school you will normally be working on a one-off project you have designed specifically. However, if your design is modular (e.g. stacking DVD units) or you wish to make it several times (e.g. cutlery), you should explain any changes, developments or improvements in your folder.
- You will also need to consider how your product could be manufactured in quantity.

Activity

Ask your teacher to show you an example of a bespoke item. If you were to repeat the production, how would you simplify its construction and make it more suitable for batch production? Record your ideas.

Summary

★ Identifying the market place helps generate designs that match the right scale of production.

★ There are four main scales of production: one-off (bespoke) manufacture, batch production, mass production and flow-line production.

Eurotech Mouldings Ltd

In this chapter you will learn about:

★ **the injection-moulding process**

★ **batch producing injection-moulded plastic products.**

This chapter is linked with many others in this book, including 5.14 *Manufacturing plastics in quantity*, 5.17 *Using jigs and templates*, 7.4 *Manufacturing in quantity* and 7.6 *Manufacturing systems*.

Background

Eurotech Mouldings is a small batch-production company in the city of Wells in Somerset. The company operates a number of specialist injection-moulding machines that produce a range of products from castor tyres used on shopping trolleys to polycarbonate washers. This successful company employs three people to operate up to ten semi-automatic injection-moulding machines. Batches of between 200 and 200,000 products are manufactured specifically to order and few finished products are held in stock. Eurotech prides itself in delivering the right product at the right time: the **Just in Time (JIT)** system.

A number of thermoplastics are injection moulded: nylon (with glass strands for stiffness) for electrical switches, polycarbonate for washers and double-glazing fittings, ABS shopping trolley components such as child seats and handl

Low-density polyethylene (LDPE) castor tyres used on shopp troll

The process

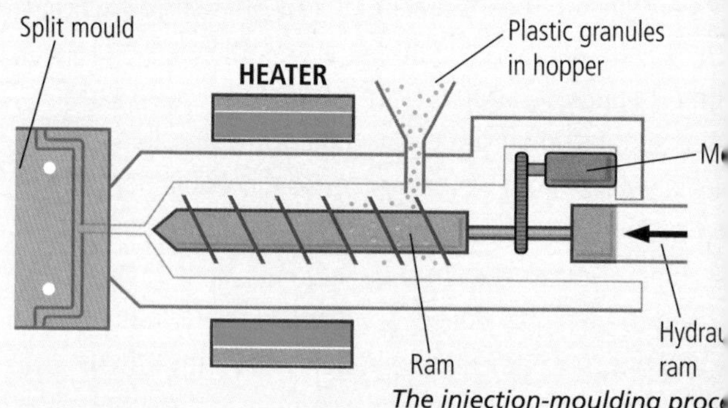

The injection-moulding proc

The injection-moulding process uses pressure to reform plastic granules into components. Injection-moulding machines and moulds are expensive, but once the machine is running many thousands of products can be made for little extra cost. This is a horizontal injection-moulding machine. The hopper is filled with plastic granules that are fed into a heated cylinder or barrel.

This is a mould ready to be fitted to the machine. The liquid plastic is pushed along the machine barrel by a screw thread and ram. It is forced through a small nozzle into a closed mould where it is allowed to cool. Because of the pressures involved, the moulds are made from hardened steel.

strial injection-moulding machines and moulds are ensive, but a simple version is available in many school kshops. Here is a picture of a school injection mould le from aluminium to produce draughts pieces.

A school mould and draughts pieces

Coursework

Producing your own injection mouldings as part of a project is not usually possible. However, selecting and purchasing injection moulded components from other suppliers can often add that special touch to a project. The Internet is a great resource for finding the things you need. Make sure you record the cost and the reasons for choosing bought-in components.

Activities

1 List three advantages of injection moulding.

2 Find six plastic products in your home. For each one:

   a How do you think it has been made?

   b Can you find any spru or ejector pin marks?

   c What type of plastic has been used?

   d Could it have been injection moulded?

Summary

★ Injection-moulding machines often run continuously to produce the batch quantity required.

★ Moulds can be stored and reused when the customer orders a further quantity.

Vater is fed through the pipes to cool the ould and help speed up production. The nished components are ejected and fall own the shoot into the collecting basket.

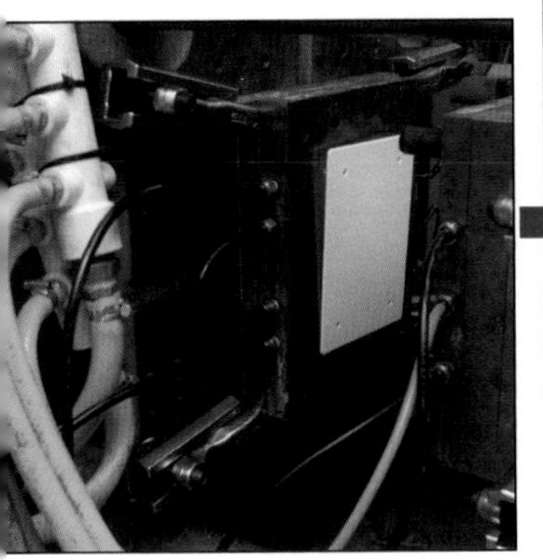

Each component is connected to a piece of waste plastic called the spru, which needs to be removed. This is usually done by hand.

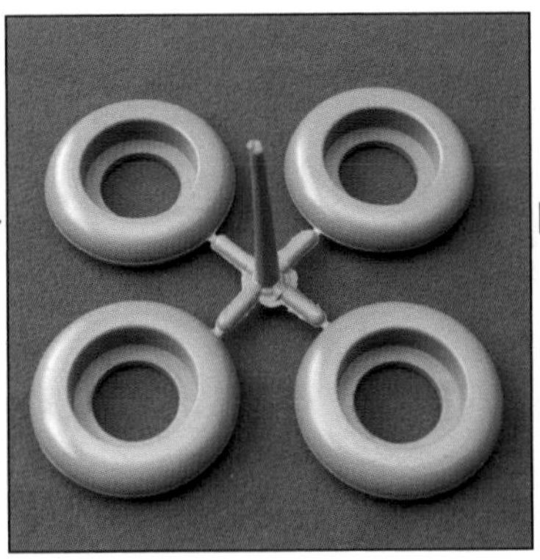

Sometimes a machine can be used to tumble and separate the component from the spru.

7.6 Manufacturing systems

In this chapter you will learn about:

- ★ systems, sub-systems and feedback
- ★ how to plan using flow and Gantt charts
- ★ the Just in Time (JIT) system.

A system is a series of steps used to make production more efficient and individual tasks easier to carry out and check. A system is usually divided into three parts: input, process and output.

- Input: this is the start and the information and materials you need to carry out the task. (For example, a piece of silver jewellery that has been prepared and is ready to be polished.)
- Process: this is what is done and how the input is changed. It could include heating, moulding and joining. (For example, select the polishing mops, polish and holding device; carry out a safety check; polish the jewellery.)
- Output: this is the result of the process acting on the input. It is the final result of the system. (For example, polished silver.)

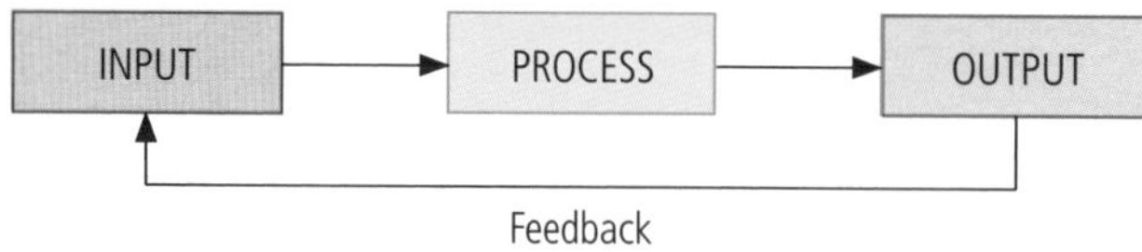

A closed loop system

Feedback is used to check or monitor the output and then make any necessary changes to the input. For example, is the silver polished beautifully? If No, go back to the process. If Yes, stop the system. This is part of quality control.

Closed loop systems

A closed loop system includes feedback. A modern electric jug kettle is a simple closed loop system. It 'knows' when the water has boiled and so turns itself off. The thermostat measures the rise in temperature and provides the feedback. Other examples of closed loop systems include central heating systems, toilet cisterns and pop-up toasters. There are many closed loop systems working together in a modern washing machine.

Open loop systems

A pan of water on a gas hob is an open loop system as t provides no feedback. The gas will keep heating the pan even if all the water has boiled away.

Manufacturing systems

In industry, a manufacturing system can be seen as a seri of sub-systems or cells. Each sub-system has to be trainec work and communicate effectively with other sub-system specially designed environment (the factory) is created wi areas for storage, finishing, quality control and packaging that allow the right equipment and materials to be arranged, managed and maintained. Planning for product is important: tasks need to be designed and put in the rig order and one sub-system depends on another to supply, or manufacture components ready for the next stage.

Flow and Gantt charts

Planning helps to predict problems, control resources anc avoid mistakes and delays. Time plans such as flow chart and **Gantt charts** are used to plan the stages involved i making a product.

Flow charts help to organise a planned sequence of step for a task and should include feedback to check quality before proceeding to the next task. One advantage of flo charts is that they help you to communicate visually the plan of work and sequence of operations. Flow charts us special symbols for each stage of the process.

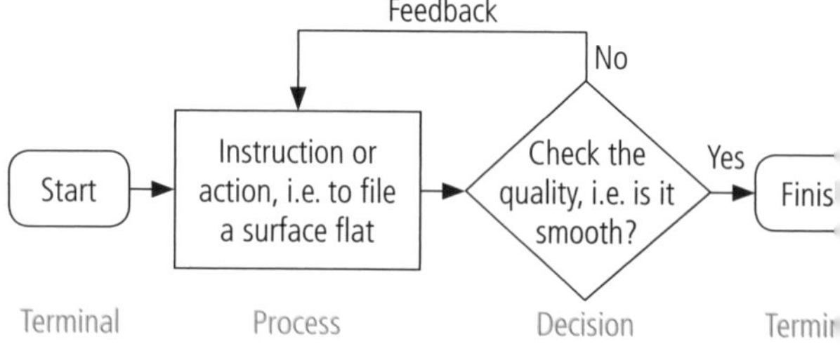

A flow chart for a closed loop syst

Gantt charts help to plan the length of tasks within the production process and indicate the earliest point at whic a task might start and the absolute time within which it must be completed.

Activity	Lesson									
Time plan for the construction of a jewellery box **All lessons 2 hours** **Total time 20 hours**	1	2	3	4	5	6	7	8	9	10
Mark out sides, lap joints and rebates Cut out and check for fit	■	■								
Glue sides together Measure and mark lid/bottom Cut out and check for fit			■							
Set up CAD/CAM for lid Cut out detailing on lid Glue lid and bottom into rebates				■						
Clean up/sand box Mark where lid is to be cut Cut lid					■					
Mark out rebates for hinges Chisel out rebates					■	■				
Test fit hinges Mark out lock for box Cut/drill to fit lock							■			
Test fit lock Clean/sand inside of lid							■			
Cut out velvet for the inside Test fit velvet								■		
Final clean up/sand inside and outside box Varnish box								■		
Sand box down lightly Apply second coat of varnish									■	
Glue in velvet Fit hinges and lock										■

A Gantt chart

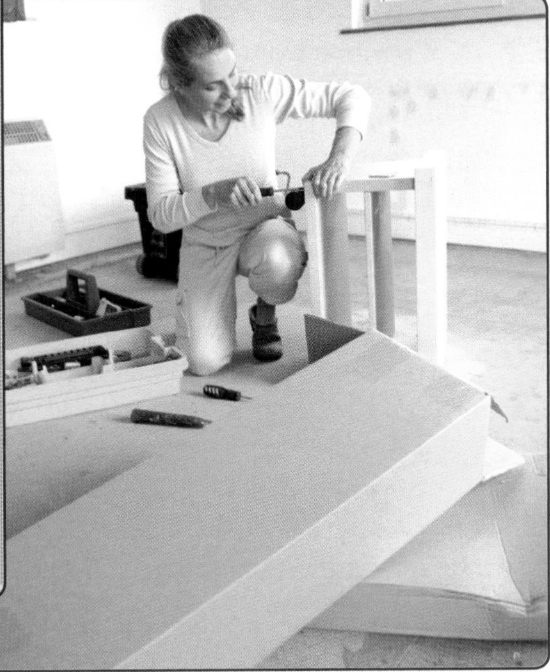

Some products are sold as kits

ıst in Time

: Just in Time manufacturing system needs detailed ward planning. The components and parts arrive at the duction line 'just in time' (i.e. when they are needed). s saves stockpiling resources and finished items, saving ney and space. However, the system can go wrong if any the components are not delivered on time.

lanning ahead

nufacturing in quantity is a risky business; organising d planning a good environment, buying specialist chinery, costing overheads (e.g. rent, heating, lighting), ting up and training cells of workers, and preparing roduction plan all take time and money. Large-scale nufacturing systems are inflexible. A company that ooses to manufacture a new product must plan ahead d choose the right scale of production. Some companies luce their costs by getting the customer to finish making : product for them!

Coursework

Planning the making of your project is essential and will help you organise your time and avoid problems. Always think ahead and use feedback to check the quality of your work.

Activity

Draw a flow chart to show how a piece of brass is brought to a high polish using a buffing machine. Include at least one feedback loop.

Summary

★ A system includes an input, process and output.

★ Some systems are open loop and have no feedback. Closed loop systems have feedback.

★ Planning tasks can be shown as flow charts and Gantt charts.

7.7 Clares Merchandise Handling Equipment Ltd

In this chapter you will learn about:

★ **how the different parts of production work together in a large company**

★ **how computer-controlled machines can be used to make metal components during volume batch production.**

Clares, a large British manufacturing company, occupies a 12-acre site in Somerset. First formed in 1966, it supplies metal trolleys and storage carts to most of south-west England. These products include shopping and airport trolleys. Clares holds contracts with most major supermarkets such as Tesco, Sainsbury's and Marks & Spencer, as well as other organisations like the NHS. It produces over 6000 trolleys and storage carts per week through volume batch production.

A CAD presentation drawing

Departmental responsibilities

- The design engineering department uses AutoCAD® as its main design program. This program allows engineers to produce technical designs before sending this manufacturing information directly to a variety of CNC robot machines. See section 6 *ICT: CAD/CAM* for information on CNC machines.
- The purchasing department uses a computer system to monitor the buying of components and materials such as castors and steel tube. This system tells Clares when the order was placed, when it is expected for delivery, and the cost and transport arrangements.

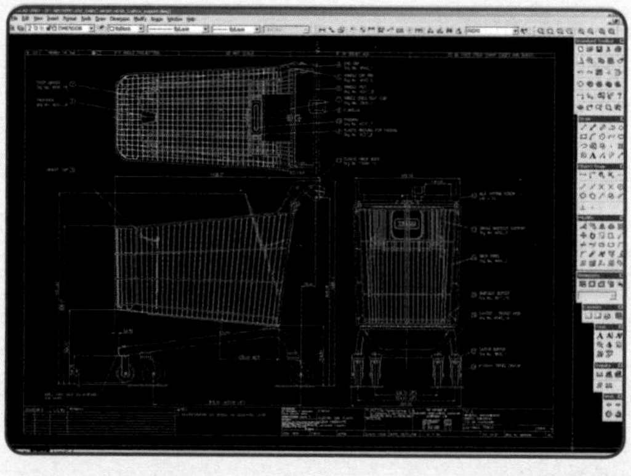

AutoCA work draw

- The quality assurance department makes regular check on products and components, ensuring that nothing leaves the shop floor below standard. This process includes testing products and dealing with customer complaints. A weekly quality meeting is held to discuss any major quality faults from the previous week's production. Products and components are tested on a series of machines, where the durability of component and the suitability of sub-components like castors are examined. The department tests the design of the finished product to make sure it passes stringent safety standards. See 2.6 *Legislation in design* and 4.1 *Safety the workshop* for information on safety standards.

Making the trolleys

- Cutting the metal: a large coil of wire is unwound and straightened ready to cut into lengths. These lengths a eventually made into the wire baskets. Box section tub is bought in as straight lengths that are then sawn into pieces to be made into the trolley frame.
- Bending the metal: computer-controlled bending machines are used to accurately shape the metal sectio

Bending the metal tu

Using jigs and fixtures: special jigs and fixtures are made to hold the separate wires and tubes in position before the robot spot welding can start.

Special jigs hold the parts before welding

Welding: within British manufacturing there is a demand for skilled manual welders. It is a specialised trade and most manual welders are self-employed. Clares employ five or six manual welders at a time. They support and oversee 12 CNC robot-operated welding machines called robot cells. The robot cells are reliable, fast and accurate, producing the complex welds required.

The robot cell has a cage to protect the workers

Finishing: the final stage of production is to add a finish to the trolley. This is usually metal plating such as zinc or a coloured plastic coating.

Rows of trolleys ready for finishing

Health and safety

All workers and visitors to the Clares site are expected to follow the company's health and safety rules and so create a safe working workplace for themselves and others. Safety equipment to be worn on site includes a high-visibility jacket, safety goggles, earplugs, overalls and suitable boots. Around the site there are safety notices informing visitors and employees of the regulations.

Coursework

Your coursework should show that you have considered or understand terms such as quality assurance, testing, CNC manufacture, and health and safety. You should also be able to explain in your folder how your project might be changed if it were to be mass or batch produced.

Activity

A product analysis is a good way to start to understand industrial construction processes. The next time you visit your local supermarket, examine a shopping trolley and take a photo of it.

- **a** Is it still working as it should?
- **b** What parts are beginning to wear out? Explain why.
- **c** How many parts has it been made from?
- **d** Can you identify the welds?
- **e** What finish has been applied?
- **f** What other joining methods have been used?
- **g** Are sections recyclable?

Summary

★ Looking at the way a large manufacturing company makes products is a good way of learning about design and technology in the real world.

7.8 Prototyping

In this chapter you will learn about:

- ★ **why a prototype is needed**
- ★ **rapid prototyping processes used in industry**

Models and prototypes

During the designing process, several models are produced to learn about different aspects of the project, such as shape and style, function, and construction. These help the development of the product but eventually a more realistic model needs to be made to bring the development together. A model that works or functions in the same way as the final product is called a prototype. The prototype should work but it may be made from slightly different materials and by more handcrafted techniques.

In the development of the Dyson vacuum cleaner, James Dyson took 15 years and 5127 prototypes before he launched the DC01. He used foam and card to model the shape, MDF to model the catches and parts that move, and parts of old

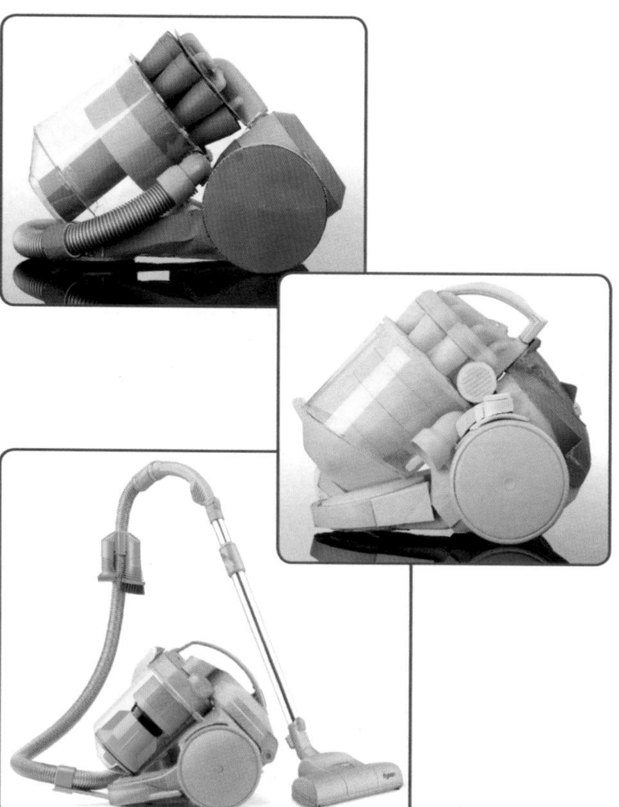

Models and prototypes of the Dyson vacuum cleaner

upright cleaners to test function. Eventually, rapid prototypi techniques such as stereolithography and selective laser sintering (SLS) were used to produce working prototypes.

In the case of car design and development, the prototype is a fully functioning vehicle that can be driven and road tested. Engineers check everything from how well the windscreen wipers work to the comfort of the seats.

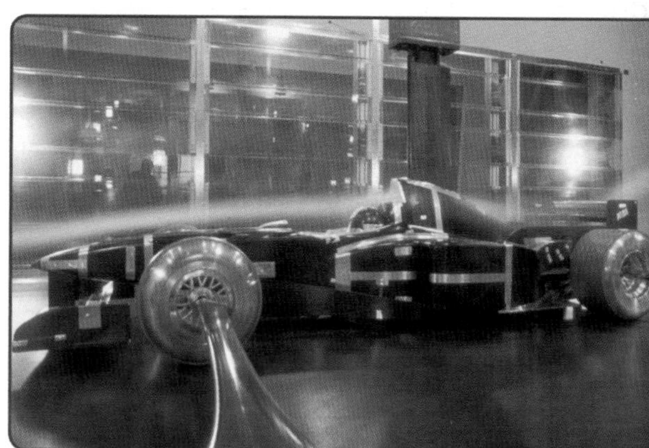

Wind tunnel tests on a prototype racing

Prototypes are used to give feedback to the designer and the manufacturer that can lead to improvements and modifications. They help to check the quality of the manufacturing and assembling processes. They are used to help anticipate how the product might not work, and so improve the design for product maintenance and the replacement of parts; for example, making the car wing pan too low might not allow the tyres to be changed. Prototypes are used to check that the design fits the specifications.

Stereolithography and selective laser sintering (SLS) are advanced modern rapid prototyping processes. They allow quick (up to 24 hours), accurate production of a prototype component in a suitable material. Both these processes start with computer-generated design work.

Stereolithography

Stereolithography, also known as 3D layering or 3D printin is used in industry to create solid plastic objects. It works by using a liquid plastic (a photopolymer) that is sensitive to ultraviolet light. A special laser traces the designed shape into the liquid plastic – the plastic hardens where the laser touches it. By tracing lots of layers one on top of the other, a 3D shape is created. The system is computer ntrolled and can be left to get on with the task, often ernight. Once the run is complete, the object is rinsed h a solvent and placed in an ultraviolet oven that cures plastic. Stereolithography is an expensive process: the chines themselves usually cost over £500,000. They need extraction because of fumes created by the polymer. e polymer itself is also expensive, so stereolithography chines are found only in large companies.

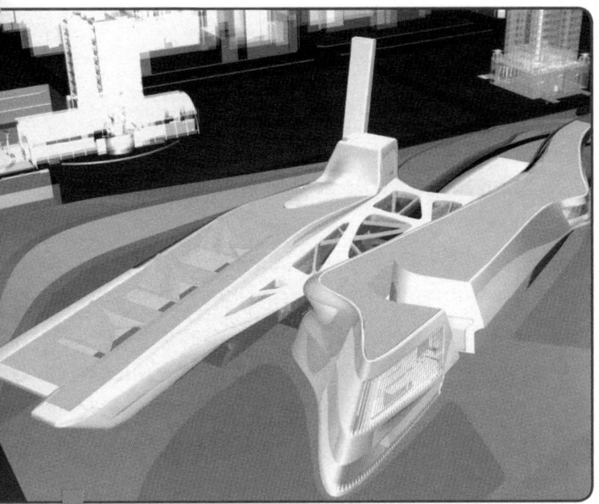

CAD images can be produced as 3D models

Stereolithography is used to produce scale models such as this of the Guggenheim Museum in Taiwan

Coursework

Your final project is really a very good working prototype. Use your evaluation to explain how your product has been tested and the improvements and modifications you would make if you were going to produce another one.

Selective laser sintering

SLS is a heat process that uses a laser to sinter (fuse) layers of powdered thermoplastic materials together to form solid 3D objects. The process is similar to stereolithography but a wider range of materials can be formed.

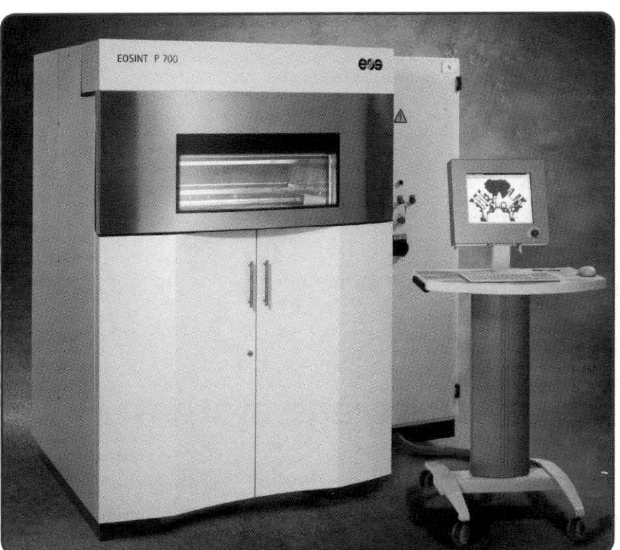

Selective laser sintering

Activity

Write a list of ten specifications for a microwave oven. Consider each specification, and suggest a model or prototype that would develop an improvement, i.e. the 'ping' should be louder. Make a note against each specification to explain your choice of model material and what you are hoping to achieve.

Summary

- ★ Prototyping is essential in the development of a product.
- ★ Prototyping provides feedback, which leads to improvements and modifications.
- ★ Prototyping helps to make changes that can improve aesthetics, performance and maintenance.

7.9 IKEA

In this chapter you will learn about:

★ **the complex issues related to designing a mass-produced product.**

This case study links with 7.4 *Manufacturing in quantity*.

The Swedish company IKEA is a major international organisation that specialises in flat-pack furniture and accessories. The IKEA principle is 'good design for everyone – without the need to save hard first'.

Ingvar Kamprad founded IKEA in 1943. His vision was to make good design accessible to all. This vision is the inspiration behind one of the most successful companies in the world.

The IVAR storage system

The IVAR storage system is one of IKEA's products. The design is modular, which simply means it is based on standard-size units that can be assembled in various ways.

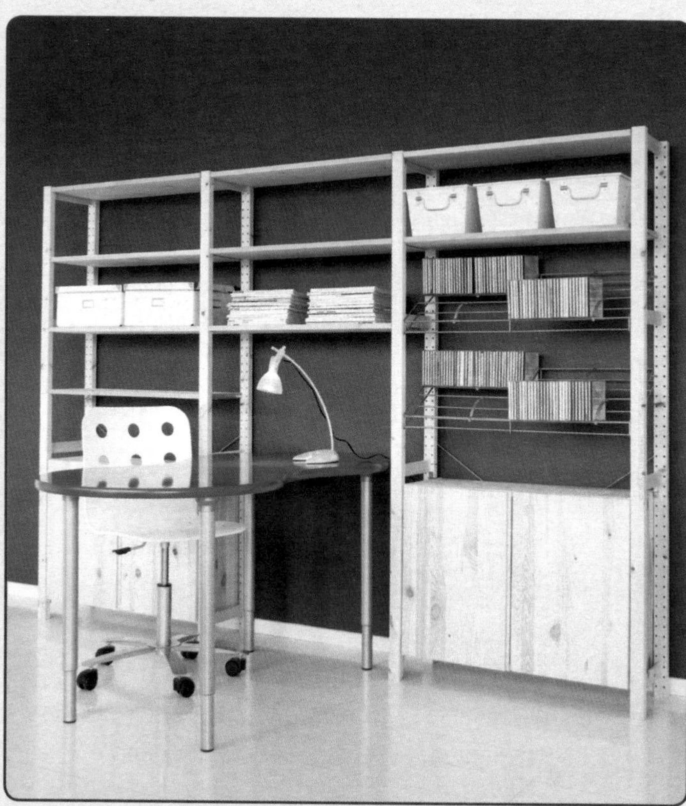

The IVAR storage system

The description of the IVAR storage system in the IKEA catalogue gives a valuable insight into the design approach

> ***IVAR: do your own thing***
>
> *Long lasting and low cost, solid pine. IVAR is a versatile storage system with the potential to match up to your life and your ideas. As your situation changes, so can IVAR thanks to its incredible diversity.*

The key design principles for this product are based on IKEA's vision and have been targeted by the marketing team to meet the needs of people setting up home for th first time.

Most IKEA products are sold as flat-packs. This has many advantages, both for the company and for the consumer:

- prices are low because the user assembles the product
- the products can be transported and stored cheaply by the company
- the product is packed into small boxes that can be fitte into the consumer's car to take home.

See 3.7 *Fixtures and fittings* and 5.8 *Joining wooc frame joints* for information on knock-down (KD) fittings used in flat-pack furniture.

Adaptable design has a number of advantages for consumers:

- the units can be arranged in different ways to su different homes and to match various needs anc budgets
- the units can be customised by adding colour an with optional extras such as handles and lightin
- the units enable consumers to design their own unique arrangement
- the units can be rearranged in different ways to suit new homes as young consumers are likely tc be on the move.

Modular design storage units have a number of good design features:

- the shelving can be adapted to a wide range of heights, widths and layouts
- the standard sizes of the modules give total flexibility

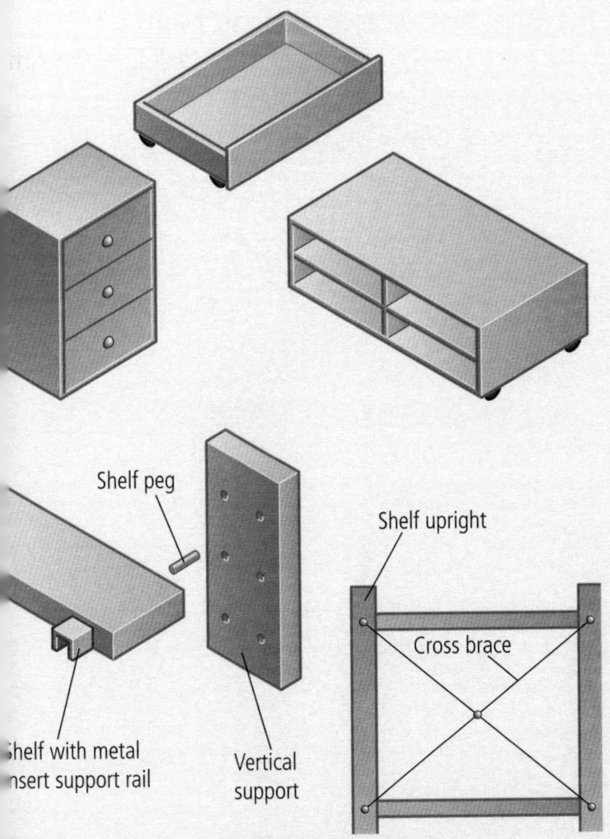

Storage system components and details

- the storage cabinets can be mixed and matched with the shelves to meet many different needs and budgets
- the modern minimalist design appeals to a wide section of the market.

Environmentally conscious design is at the core of IKEA's approach:

- the company does not accept solid wood from intact natural forests
- untreated natural wood can be finished by the consumer with non-toxic finishes, reducing pollution
- bulk transportation reduces emissions and energy usage.

See 2.4 *Environmental issues in design* for information on environmental issues.

Quality-assured products feature:

- well-designed, strong, safe structures
- accurately made parts with easy-to-use assembly components and instructions
- well-seasoned, good quality wood to suit centrally heated homes
- good packaging to protect the product during storage and transport
- strict quality control measures to ensure standards are maintained.

Advertising and Marketing

One of the main reasons for the success of IKEA has been the approach that the company has to marketing. IKEA grew out of a mail order furniture company set up in Sweden. The idea of selling furniture in self assembly form by mail order meant that prices to customers were lower because:

- labour costs are reduced as customers assemble their own products
- Storage and distribution costs are less because self-assembly kits are compact and more easily protected from damage
- The company was able to sell goods all over the country which meant that the sales quickly grew enabling costs to be reduced because of the large quantities sold.

Many other companies operate in this way, particularly with the growth in internet shopping. Furniture shops and stores offer a more personal service and products are ready assembled, but are more expensive.

Coursework

Write a description of your coursework piece that could be used to describe it in an IKEA catalogue. Describe the key features of your design: what environmental considerations have you included? How could you make your product more environmentally friendly? What have you done to ensure that a quality product can be produced?

Activity

Explain the advantages of a modular storage system compared with an item of fixed furniture designed for the same purpose.

Summary

★ Getting good design into stores at a price people can afford is a complex business.

Exam questions

1 Injection moulding is a widely used industrial method of producing plastic components in quantity.

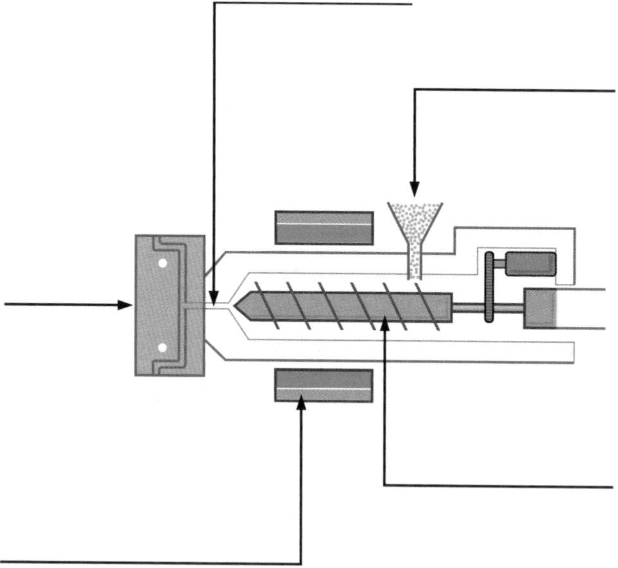

a Label the key parts of the injection moulding machine. *(5 marks)*

b Describe in detail the injection moulding process. *(7 marks)*

Doing your coursework project

is section takes you through each stage your coursework project and helps you to derstand exactly what needs to be done to cceed.

ur coursework project should be the most eresting and exciting piece of work you ve done in design and technology. The ursework is also the key to achieving a good ade as is worth 60% of the GCSE marks.

ɔst chapters in this section include an sessment criteria box for grades A and C · either designing or making, similar to the ample below.

In this part of your coursework you must:

Designing

A GRADE

1 Use a wide variety of appropriate sources to gather relevant research information.
2 Analyse the task and the research material logically, thoroughly and effectively.

C GRADE

1 Use a variety of appropriate sources to gather and order relevant research information.
2 Analyse the task and the research material.

What's in this section?

Creative and thorough design work in the folder, together with high-level making skills, ensures a top-quality finished product and a rewarding and enjoyable experience

What you have to do

In this chapter you will learn about:

- ★ **what the coursework project entails**
- ★ **how to approach the project and ensure success.**

The best way to approach your major project is to imagine you are employed by a company to work as a professional designer. Working from this point of view will help you to consider the best aspects of designing and making to gain marks. Work with your teacher and discuss things regularly to ensure the project goes well.

The following chapters will guide you through the coursework section of your GCSE in Resistant Materials Technology. You have to design and manufacture a product prototype. The product should be capable of commercial production and may well be in the form of a final marketable product.

The main aim of the project is to produce a prototype or range of products to meet the needs of clients and consumers. The product may be produced as a full-size prototype or it could be a scale model of a large product There is considerable potential to incorporate CAD/CAM part of your project. The potential for products to be furtl developed for production may also be a consideration.

As there are time limits for completing the work, it is important to choose a project that can be completed successfully on time: 40 hours for full course or 20 hours for short course. A typical design folder should contain approximately 15–20 sheets of paper at the most. Alway aim for quality rather than quantity.

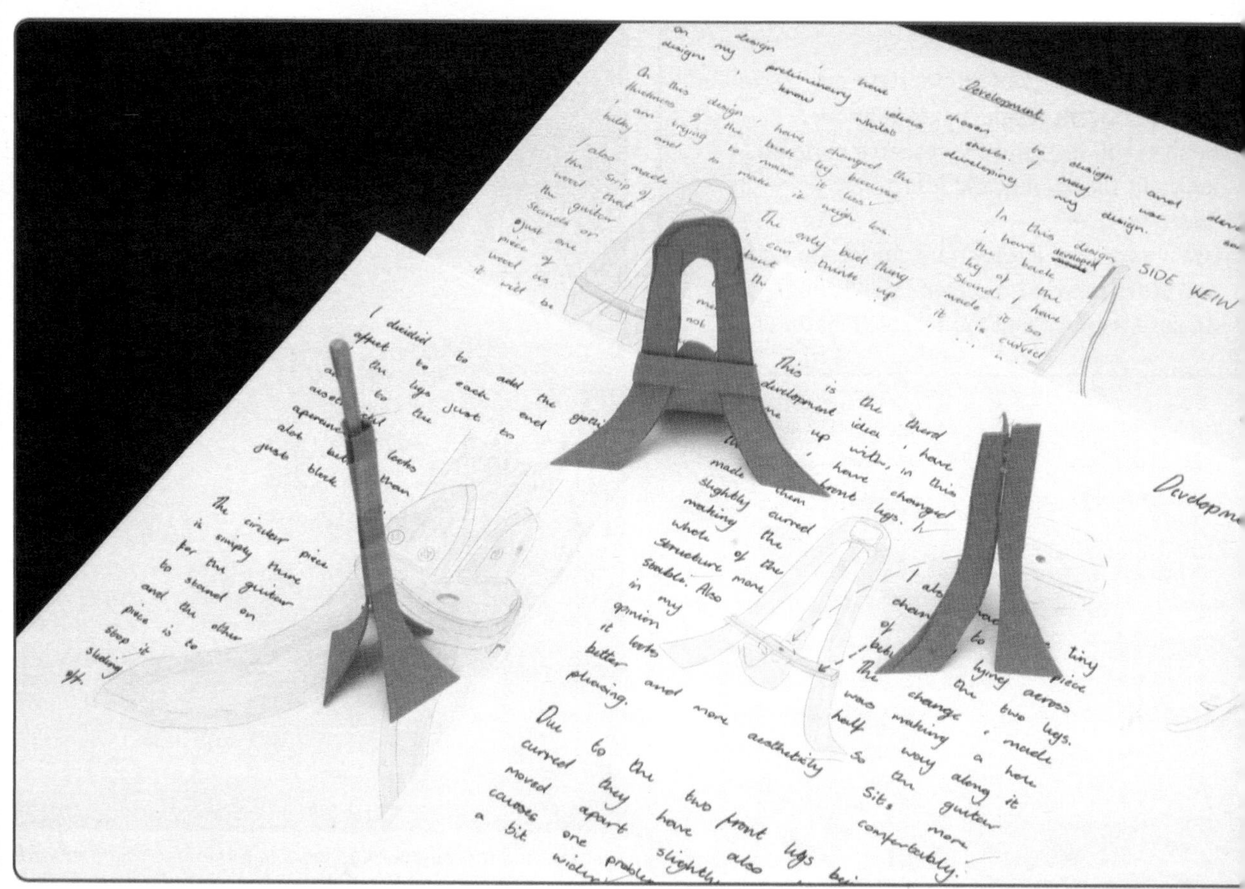

Exploring design ideas using models and sketc

checklist

es the project give you enough scope to really show the lowing:

- Is there enough opportunity for original design work?
- Does the designing take you beyond a personal project and into a more industrial product for the market place?
- Will the making enable you to show a wide range of skills and techniques with a range of materials?
- Does your school have all the resources you need for the making process?
- Is there the opportunity for you to show what you can do using ICT, including CAD/CAM?
- Will you be able to achieve a quality product without taking too many risks?
- Is the project challenging enough without being daunting?

ur coursework project is worth 60% of your GCSE arks. It is broken down into two main sections for sessment:

- designing (worth 20% of your GCSE marks): a project folder that is a record of your designing and planning skills
- making (worth 40% of your GCSE marks): a product or range of products that may include production proposals.

Summary

★ The coursework project is a major piece of work so make sure that you choose what you are going to do carefully. Make sure the project gives you enough scope to gain the grade you are capable of achieving.

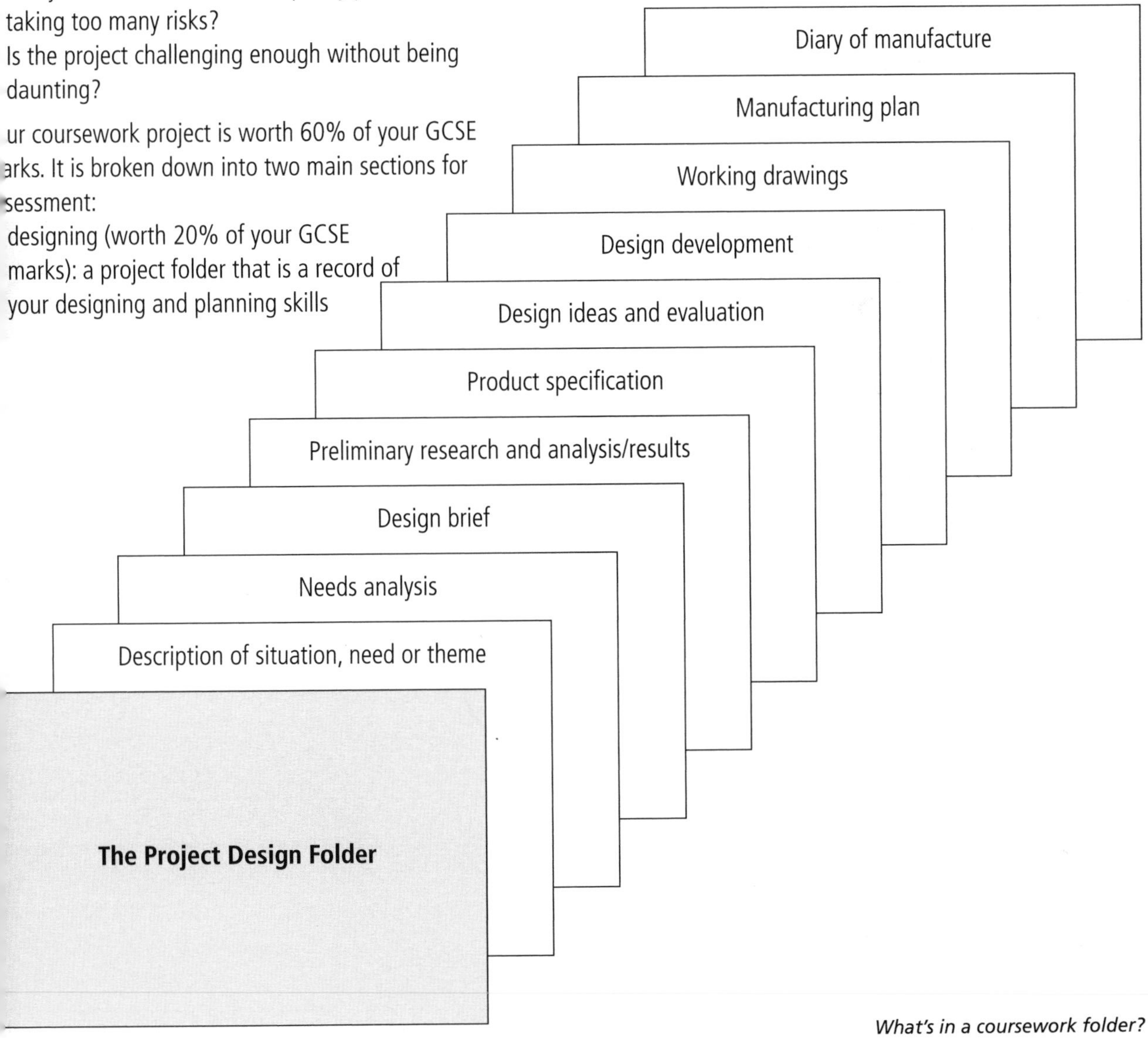

Diary of manufacture
Manufacturing plan
Working drawings
Design development
Design ideas and evaluation
Product specification
Preliminary research and analysis/results
Design brief
Needs analysis
Description of situation, need or theme
The Project Design Folder

What's in a coursework folder?

8.2 Unpacking the design brief

In this chapter you will learn about:

- ★ analysing the need and preparing your design brief
- ★ analysing the task as a whole to decide what to do.

In this part of your coursework you must:

Designing

A GRADE

1. Use a wide variety of appropriate sources to gather relevant research information.
2. Analyse the task and the research material logically, thoroughly and effectively.

C GRADE

1. Use a variety of appropriate sources to gather and order relevant research information.
2. Analyse the task and the research material.

Situation/need

The client comes to the designer with a specific need, for example a company wishing to produce and market a new product like a toy for young children with moving parts. Th company will have some specific thoughts but will also be looking to the designer to bring some fresh ideas and nev approaches. The company may need to sell more products and wish to extend their range to bring something new to their customers. Often companies identify a gap in the market that they wish to fill with a new product.

Imagine you are working as a designer for a real compan adopting the role of a professional designer is helpful wit many aspects of your project.

Deciding what to do

You may be given a variety of project outlines to choose from or asked to investigate a situation where you can find a practical problem to solve yourself. You need to finc a project that can keep you interested for the whole time. Here is an example of a project outline provided by AQA:

'Toys or learning activity centres are always popula with young children. Those that are most effective usually have some type of action or moving parts built in. A manufacturer of this type of product has asked you to design and make a small range of toys one of which has an action feature and a storage system in which to store these toys.'

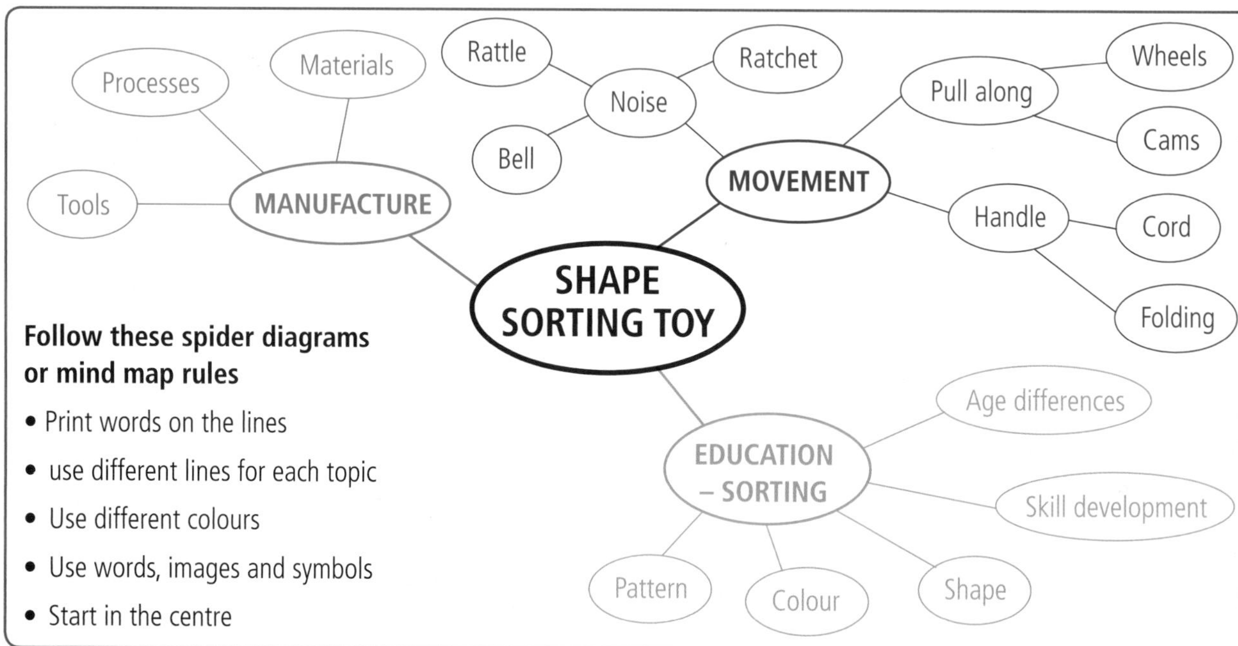

Part of a mind m

help define more clearly what you could do, it is often ful to analyse the area of study using a mind map or der diagram. Write down as many related things as you think of about the situation you are studying. You may n find that you can focus on a more specific area where esign problem can be found.

analysis should direct you to the most suitable forms research, which will provide the basis for your product cification.

esign brief

ce you have analysed the need, it should be possible write a short statement that clearly gives your design entions. This is called a design brief. The brief should give a ar outline of what you intend to do without being vague.

example, the AQA project outline above could give rise the following design brief:

design and make a prototype range of ucational wooden toys for young children that tures movement and shape sorting for a toy nufacturer that wishes to batch produce the al design.'

tice that the brief states what is to be designed (in this se an educational toy) without actually stating what the duct might be. It also states who the target market is. A ef like this allows a good range of ideas to be explored. ges 44–47 of the AQA specification give a list of project tlines for both the full course and the short course GCSE.

sk analysis

e next stage is to analyse the task. This analysis needs to much more focused. A good way of breaking down the k into manageable chunks is to use the 5WH approach:

- **Who** is the intended user (target market)? What age group are they? What is their gender? What images would you associate them with? What else are they likely to be interested in?
- **What** has the product got to do? This is to do with its function. What shape does it need to be? Do you need to use certain materials? What features should it have? What processes and technologies could be used? What does your client expect? What are their requirements and limitations? What is the budget for the project?
- **Where** will the product be used/displayed? This is to do with its working environment. Will its position affect its design, weight and properties? Does it need to be weatherproof?
- **When** must the product be finished? What is the deadline? Try to finish your work before the deadline as this allows time for you to get some feedback.
- **Why** is the product needed? Is there a similar alternative? Must it be a particular size, shape or colour?
- **How** could the product be made? How much will it cost? How will the cost affect how it could be made? How will the product affect the environment? Will it be recyclable? How will you ensure a quality product?

A clear brief is vital to ensure a successful product

Some of the answers to the above questions will be easy to answer, but others may be more difficult. To ensure you obtain the correct answers so that you can design the product you need to carry out some research.

Summary

★ Analysing the need will help you to prepare your design brief.

★ Analysing the task using the 5WH approach will help you to decide what to do.

8.3 Researching

In this chapter you will learn about:

★ how to undertake effective research

★ using product analysis as a research tool.

In this part of your coursework you must:

Designing

A GRADE

1 Use a wide variety of appropriate sources to gather relevant research information.
2 Analyse the task and the research material logically, thoroughly and effectively.

C GRADE

1 Use a variety of appropriate sources to gather and order relevant research information.
2 Analyse the task and the research material.

Carrying out research means finding out information, analysing it and then drawing conclusions about it that will help you with designing. Research is not just an exercise done at the start of a project; it takes place throughout the entire process as problems and questions arise. For example, investigating materials would be done during the design ideas stage. Every time you ask someone a question, browse on the Internet or look up details in a book, you are carrying out research.

Research needs to be focused and relevant. Pages of printouts from the Internet or photocopies from magazines have little value and gain few marks unless the information is relevant.

There are two main types of research: primary and secondary. The type of research you do depends on what information you need to find out. You should include no more than two or three pages of A3 in this section of your folder.

Primary research

Primary research is sometimes called first-hand research and is where you find out information that is not already available in a book or on the Internet. It helps you find out information first-hand. You can carry out primary research

- visits and interviews
- conducting surveys to produce questionnaires
- conducting consumer trials
- undertaking product analysis of existing products
- taking photos of situations or environments relevant t[o] your project theme.

In your project you need to show evidence of compiling research from a number of sources. Two or three exampl[es] from the above list is fine. However, it is recommended th[at] you carry out research into existing products and conduc[t a] survey as a minimum.

Questionnaires

Questionnaires can be a good source of information but they need to be designed and targeted carefully.

You should choose a sample of people to reflect the likel[y] users of the product. Questionnaires are useful for findin[g] out user preferences (what people like or dislike).

Care should be taken when writing questionnaires so tha[t] you get exactly what information you need:

- use tick boxes where possible and keep questions brief
- ask questions that will give you useful information
- use closed questions (with a choice of answers to cho[ose] from) rather than asking what people like in general
- visuals are useful for finding out what style or colours people like
- finishing with an open question can help to gain some interesting opinions
- think about how you can use and analyse the answers before you ask them.

Analysing questionnaires

The information collected from questionnaires should be analysed so that you can draw conclusions about your ow[n] design work. Use the following questions to analyse your results:

- What are the main things the users prefer?
- How will the results affect your design specification?
- Does the question help you to make decisions about things like colour, shape, cost, size, weight and function of the product you will make?

nalysing existing products

ot can be learned by analysing existing products similar the one you intend to make, such as use of materials, nstruction methods and manufacturing methods. Look the product below to see how the designer has made it peal to young children. The textile flag and canopy add a ry creative twist to the design.

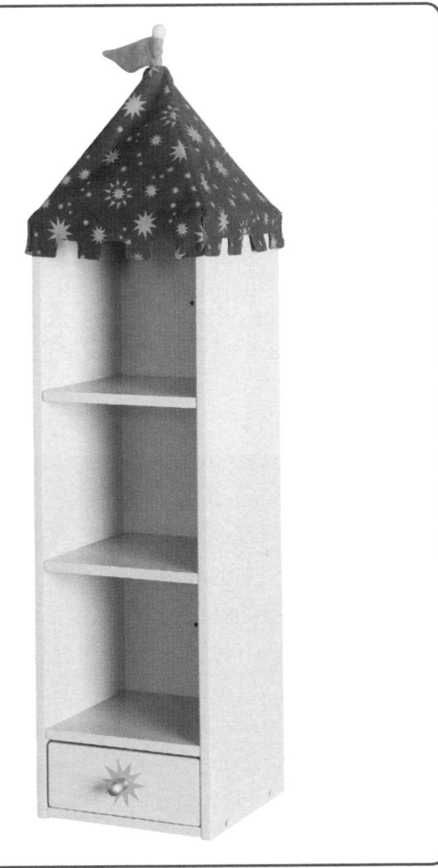

A great deal can be learnt by looking at existing products

) be successful at product analysis:

analyse the products against a set of criteria

ensure the analysis results lead you towards writing a specification of your own

make sure the analysis is well presented and easy to understand.

roduct analysis is covered in depth in 2.1 *Product analysis*.

Secondary research

Secondary research involves looking at work produced by other people, such as books or websites on the Internet. Secondary sources include:

- magazines
- newspaper articles
- CD-ROMs
- websites
- books
- experts in their field.

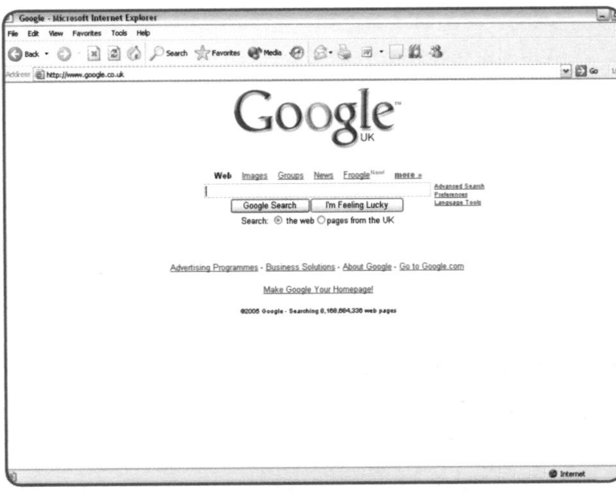

The Internet is a valuable secondary research tool

Once you have completed some research and analysed it, you are ready to move on to writing a product specification.

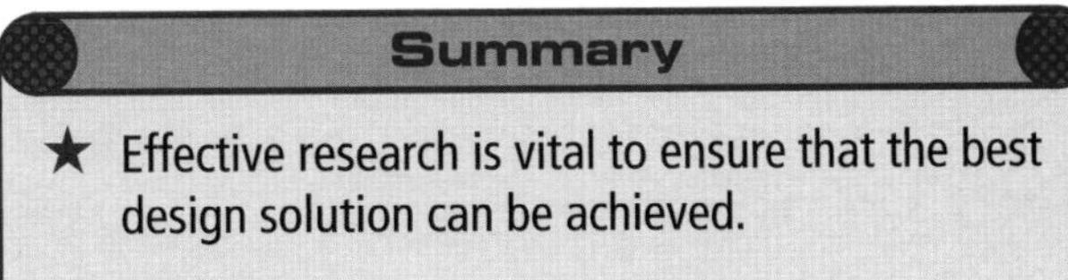

Summary

★ Effective research is vital to ensure that the best design solution can be achieved.

Producing a specification

In this chapter you will learn about:

- ★ **producing a detailed design specification**
- ★ **using ongoing (formative) evaluation to work out the best ways forward.**

In this part of your coursework you must:

Designing

A GRADE

2 Analyse the task and the research material logically,thoroughly and effectively.

3 Produce a detailed specification which focuses closely on the analysis.

C GRADE

2 Analyse the task and the research material.

3 Produce a specification which reflects the analysis.

The product specification is the most important part of yo folder as it sets out exactly what the product must do. The specifications are the criteria your project must meet.

You need to analyse your research and use it to produce a specification. The criteria may change as you develop the project. The specification should be no more than 1 or 2 pages of A3 paper. Word processing your specification is a good idea as you can number the points it contains and edit it as you go. Keep the file safe as it will also be part c your evaluation.

The best specifications use headings for key features and bullets points for specific criteria. Use the following headings as the basis for your own specification. Answer the questions as they apply to your own project. Rememb that some aspects will be more relevant than others – it depends on what you are making. Remember to concentrate on the product *not* the process.

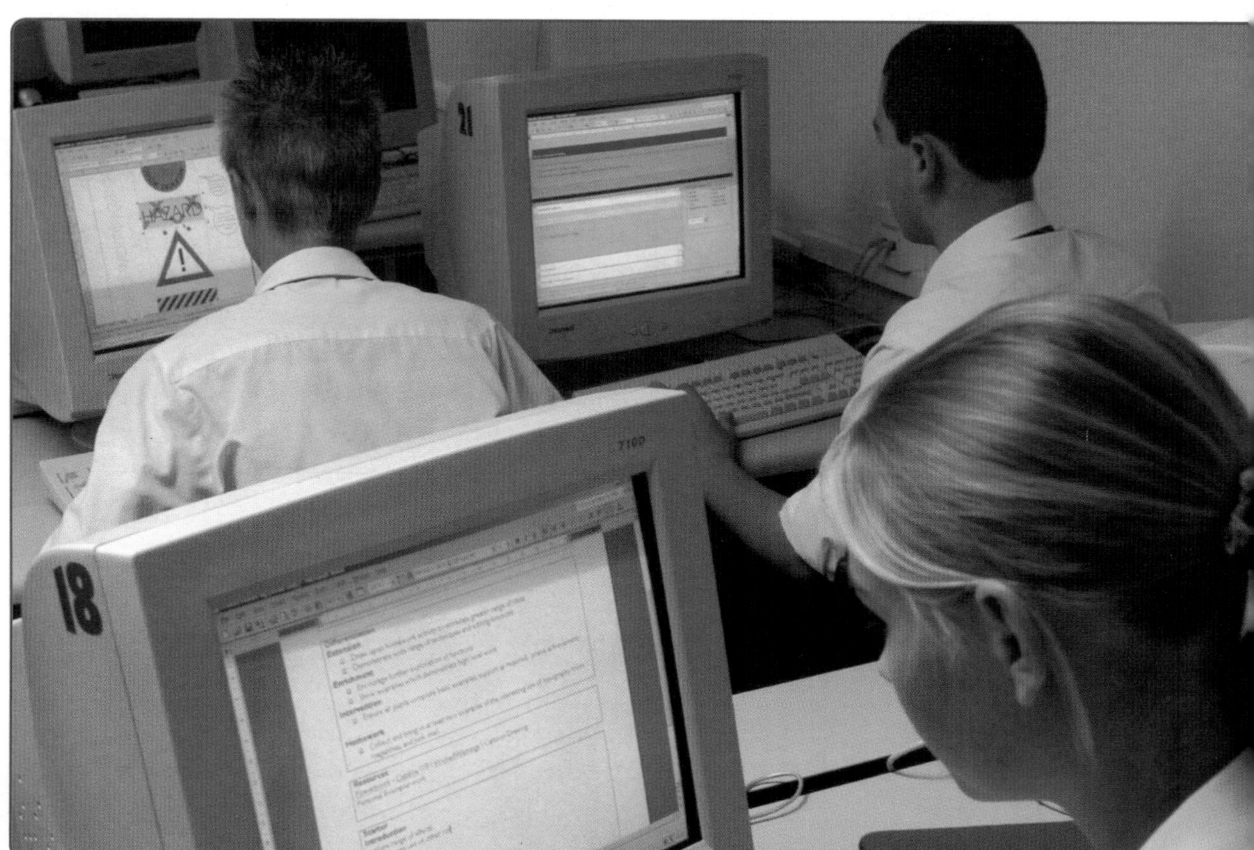

Producing the product specificati

Timescale for production
- What is the project deadline?

Function
- What is the design meant to do – what is its purpose?

Performance
- How will the product satisfy the function?
- Where will it be used?

Target market
- What age group are you aiming at?
- What is their social type, e.g. students, young professionals?
- Who will use your product?

Aesthetics
- How will colour, line, shape, form, texture, pattern, layout and tone contribute to the visual appeal of your design?
- What style or fashion will the final product be?

Ergonomics
- What effect should your design have on its user?
- What anthropometric data will you need to use in your design?
- How will the size of the product be determined?

Materials
- Which materials will be suitable to use and why?
- What material properties are you looking for, e.g. weatherproof, easy to clean, lightweight, cheap, recyclable, easy to print on, reflective, matt, scratch-resistant?

Quantity of manufacture
- How will your design be produced and in what quantity?
- Will it use CNC machinery or manually-operated equipment?

Quality of manufacture
- What level of accuracy, precision and finish do you expect to achieve?
- How will you plan for this (quality assurance)?
- How will you check this is being achieved (quality control)?

Reliability
- How can you ensure the product will work each time it is used?
- How long do you intend the product to last?

Cost
- Is there a budget?
- What will be the selling price?
- What will be the product cost to manufacture in large quantities?
- How many items need to be sold to break even?

Weight
- Will the product be light or heavy? Does it matter?

Safety
- What safety factors do you need to consider?
- What standards are there, e.g. BSI, CE, ISO.

Environmental and social issues
- How will you ensure your product minimises any potential damage to the environment?
- Think about the 3Rs: reduce, recycle and reuse.
- How will you ensure your design takes into account any moral, social and cultural issues? These often produce conflicts which can be difficult to resolve.

Ongoing (formative) evaluation

It can be valuable at this stage to stop and look back at the work you have done and decide:
- What have you learned so far?
- What is important and what is not?
- Is there anything you have not covered yet, which you know you need?

Summary

★ The specification is an important aspect of your project.

8.5 Generating ideas

In this chapter you will learn about:

- ★ beginning to formulate your design ideas
- ★ using simple visualisation techniques.

In this part of your coursework you must:

Designing

A GRADE

4 Produce a wide range of distinct proposals which satisfy the specification.

5 Use one or more of your proposals and relevant knowledge of techniques, manufacturing and working characteristics to develop a detailed and coherent design solution.

7 Test, objectively evaluate and effectively modify your work throughout the process as appropriate.

C GRADE

4 Produce a range of proposals which satisfy the specification.

5 Use your proposals and relevant knowledge to develop a detailed design solution which satisfies the specification.

7 Test, evaluate and modify your work throughout the process as appropriate.

Initial ideas

For your coursework you must produce a wide range (at least 6–8 different ideas) of possible solutions. It is important to make sure that each idea is different, not jus the same basic idea drawn to slightly different sizes.

Designers often call these first ideas rough visuals and they do not need to be a work of art in terms of quality. What you will be graded on is how many ideas you can come up with and how accurately they match your design specification.

See 1.3 *Visualising by quick sketching* to help you with th

Visualising your ideas

Turning these first ideas into real sketches and models is a vital skill for designers as it enables them to:

- think more clearly about form and function
- develop and clarify ideas further
- share ideas with others
- evaluate ideas to decide which ones it is best to develo

This is an important design skill and known as visualising. See 1.3 *Visualising by quick sketching* and 1.8 *Presenting design ideas* for some effective ways of doing this well.

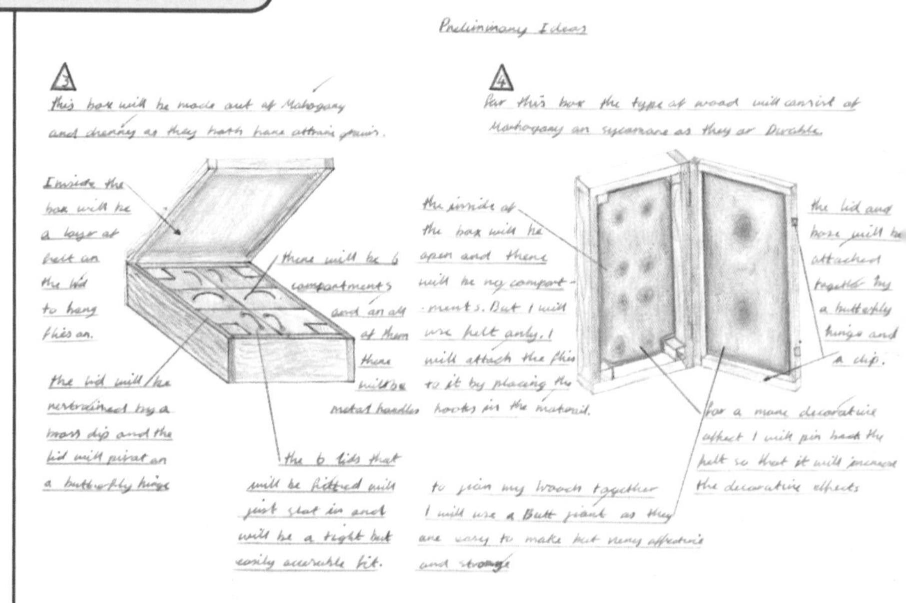

Initial ideas

Ideas drawing with model photograph

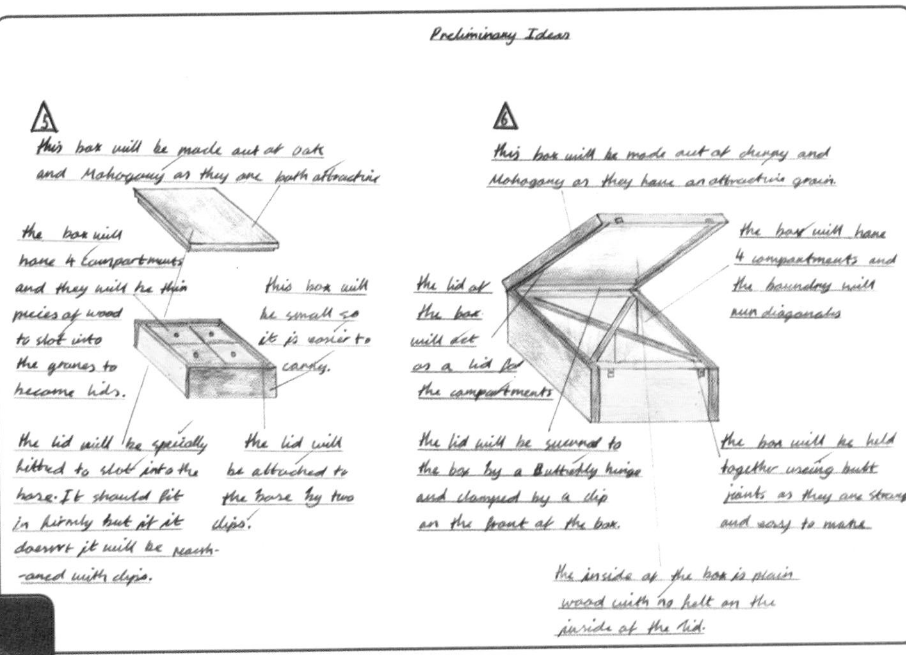
Preliminary Ideas
5
this box will be made out of oak and Mahogany as they are both attractive
the box will have 4 compartments and they will be thin pieces of wood to slot into the graves to become lids.
this box will be small so it is easier to carry.
the lid will be specially fitted to slot into the base. It should fit in firmly but if it doesn't it will be reattached with clips.
the lid will be attached to the base by two clips.
6
this box will be made out of cherry and Mahogany as they have an attractive grain.
the box will have 4 compartments and the boundary will run diagonals
the lid of the box will act as a lid for the compartments
the lid will be secured to the box by a Butterfly hinge and clamped by a clip on the front of the box.
the box will be held together using butt joints as they are strong and easy to make
the inside of the box is plain wood with no felt on the inside of the lid.

this early stage you should:

concentrate on quick drawings to explore your ideas – 2D is faster than 3D and two simple views of the same idea may help to clarify things better

keep things simple then add details later

try making a model in two minutes and then draw it – do not feel you have to draw first because for many people modelling is more productive

take digital photos of models to be added to your folder

spend time creating a wide range of ideas

draw ideas larger and with more detail as they become clearer

make your pages look compact and lively.

sing a little colour can help to clarify ideas and can make ore important ideas stand out. Working in ink or fine-oint marker will help you to work in an appropriate style. you draw an idea you do not like, simply ignore it and aw one that you do. The aim is to explore possibilities not produce nonsense.

Evaluating your ideas

When you have created a range of ideas, you need to decide which designs to use and which to reject. Your decisions should be shown on your design page by annotating them with evaluative comments. You should evaluate your ideas against your design specification by asking the following questions.

- What are the best features?
- What are the worst features?
- How could it be made?
- What materials could be used and why would you choose them?
- How well do the ideas match the whole specification?

These notes will be a part of your ongoing (formative) evaluation.

Summary

★ Concentrate on generating creative ideas, either by drawing or modelling.

★ Remember that it is ideas that count, not producing perfect models or sketches

8.6 Developing ideas

In this chapter you will learn about:

★ developing a detailed design proposal

★ producing a set of detailed working drawings.

In this part of your coursework you must:

Designing

A GRADE

4 Produce a wide range of distinct proposals which satisfy the specification.

5 Use one or more of your proposals and relevant knowledge of techniques, manufacturing and working characteristics to develop a detailed and coherent design solution.

9 Provide evidence that you have considered and taken account of relevant issues, industrial practices and systems and control.

C GRADE

4 Produce a range of proposals which satisfy the specification.

5 Use your proposals and relevant knowledge to develop a detailed design solution which satisfies the specification.

9 Provide evidence of having considered relevant issues, industrial practices and systems and control.

The development stage is an important part of your coursework. It is the part of the design process where you add more details to your chosen idea or ideas to improve them or to develop a better solution. This is where you can combine ideas, using drawings and models to develop the final design.

Modelling will help you to work out the design in 3D and to begin to sort out how it can be made. Starting with rapid modelling and moving to more detailed scale models, link your ideas to detailed drawings. Digital photography is a great way of capturing early models and adding them to your folder. Modelling can also be by computer modelling using a CAD program like Pro/DESKTOP®.

Development checklist

Use the checklist below to make sure that you have not forgotten anything. You should have produced a sequenc of drawings and models (freehand and/or CAD-generatec to show the development of your design from initial idea to fully detailed plans. These should include:

- Concept sketches and models: first ideas and modifications, attempts at combining ideas, changing materials, exploring different shapes, forms and texture This is the place to show how creative and imaginative you are.
- Development drawings: the development of your final design is an important stage in the process so ensure you include as much detail as possible. A good way to approach this is to imagine that you need to explain to someone else how to make the design for you. You can add small drawings to explain how things fit together (add sectional views to show construction.
- Manufacturing details: decide on the workshop process and equipment, materials and components, joining methods, assembly and applied finishes that you intenc to use to make your product.
- Quality assurance: how can you best use the workshop facilities to make a quality product? Which jigs, fixtures and templates could you use to help make a quality product? What quality control checks will be necessary
- Manufacturing details: sizes and tolerances for each pa of the design; materials and finishes; scientific principle and technologies being used, e.g. smart materials, mechanisms to create movement.
- Additional research: finding extra information about materials and construction techniques; consulting with experts both in and out of school.
- Ongoing (formative) evaluation: check your ideas again your specification. Does it do what you said it would?

Look at the examples below of some students' GCSE work to see how development has occurred in both 2D and 3D designs and through modelling.

Working drawings

The final stage of your development is the production of a set of working drawings. Working drawings enable you to

Development

Development of Joints

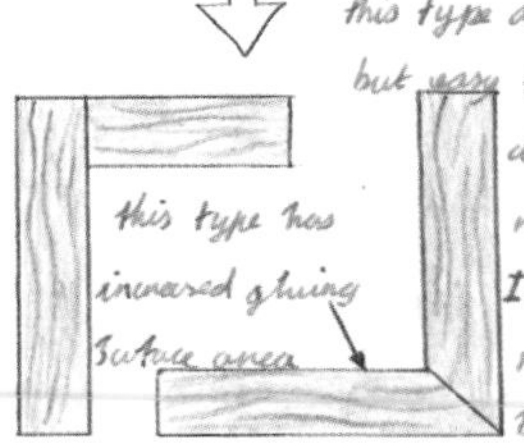

this type of joint called a comb joint is strong and was a major possibility but there was to much work involved and many places to go wrong.

It looks very decorative and skillfull as the diferent woods contrast on either side.

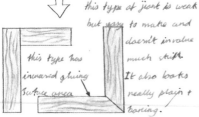

this type of joint is weak but easy to make and doesn't involve much skill. It also looks really plain + boring.

this type has increased gluing suface area

this is going to be the final joint I will use on my box as it is stronger than a normal butt joint and it can also looks very attractive if modifacations are made.

all this side of the box will be grinded of so that the coloured veneer is revealed and the block contrasts are shown.

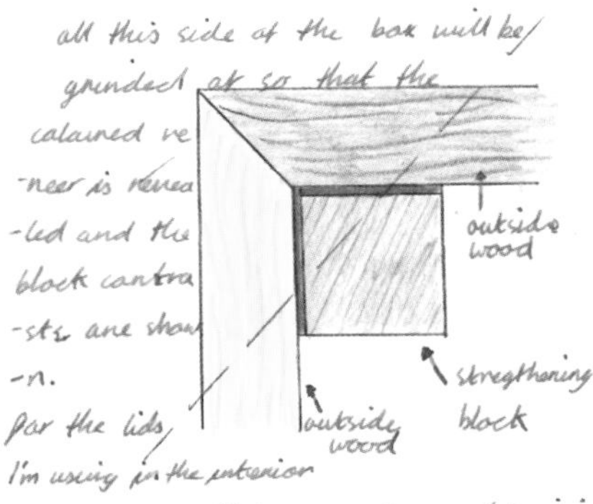

For the lids, I'm using in the interior I will have to shape around the block.

If I didn't choose this joint I wouldn't be able to use the coloured veneer development in between the woods

there are some problems with this joint as the added block takes up vital storage space and you would be unable to use a plug lid as the added stregthening blocks are there. So I will have to use a standard lid witha butterfly hinge.

velopment work

mmunicate accurately and clearly all the information for e making of your project. See 1.9 *Working drawings* for ore information. Your final set of drawings should include:

- orthographic drawings (third angle)
- a parts list with dimensions, quantity and outline costing.

e Focus on Resistant Materials 2 database can be used to oduce a costed list with minimal effort.

successful set of working drawings should be able to be ed by a manufacturer other than yourself to make the oduct to the standard you require.

Summary

★ Attention to detail at this stage saves time and costly mistakes later.

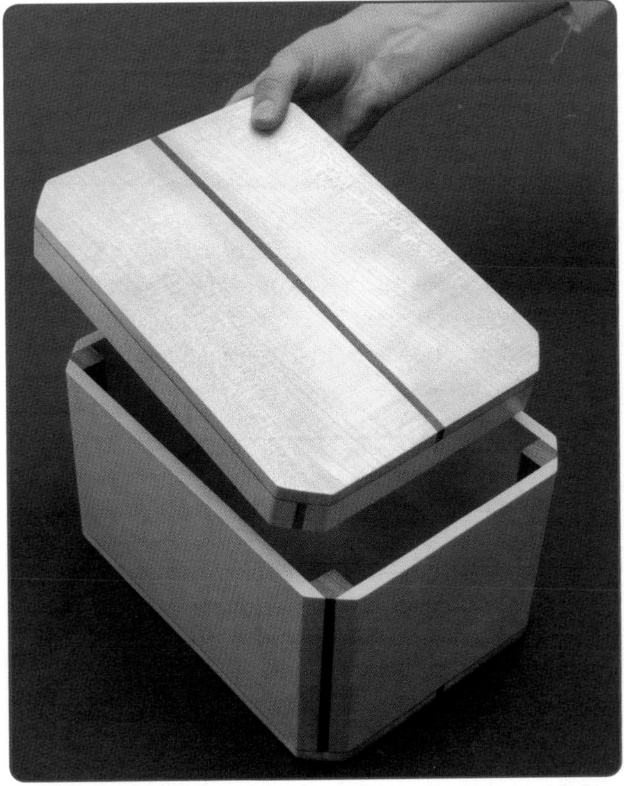

Decorative corner joints and a coloured inlay show interesting development

8.7 Manufacturing your product

In this chapter you will learn about:

★ planning to ensure quality and to make efficient use of time and resources.

In this part of your coursework you must:

Making

A GRADE

1. Record and justify the need for any changes or adaptations.
2. Use appropriate materials, components, equipment and processes (including CAM) consistently correctly, skilfully and safely.
3. Make a complete product of high quality.
4. Demonstrate an ability to satisfy accurately and completely all the demands of the design solution.
5. Thoroughly consider QA and QC and apply them consistently and successfully.

C GRADE

1. Recognise the need for and justify any changes or adaptations.
2. Use appropriate materials, components, tools, equipment and processes (including CAM) correctly and safely.
3. Produce a complete, effective and well-assembled outcome.
4. Demonstrate a level of accuracy and finish in the product which satisfies most of the demands of the design solution.
5. Clearly used QA and QC to control quality in most activities.

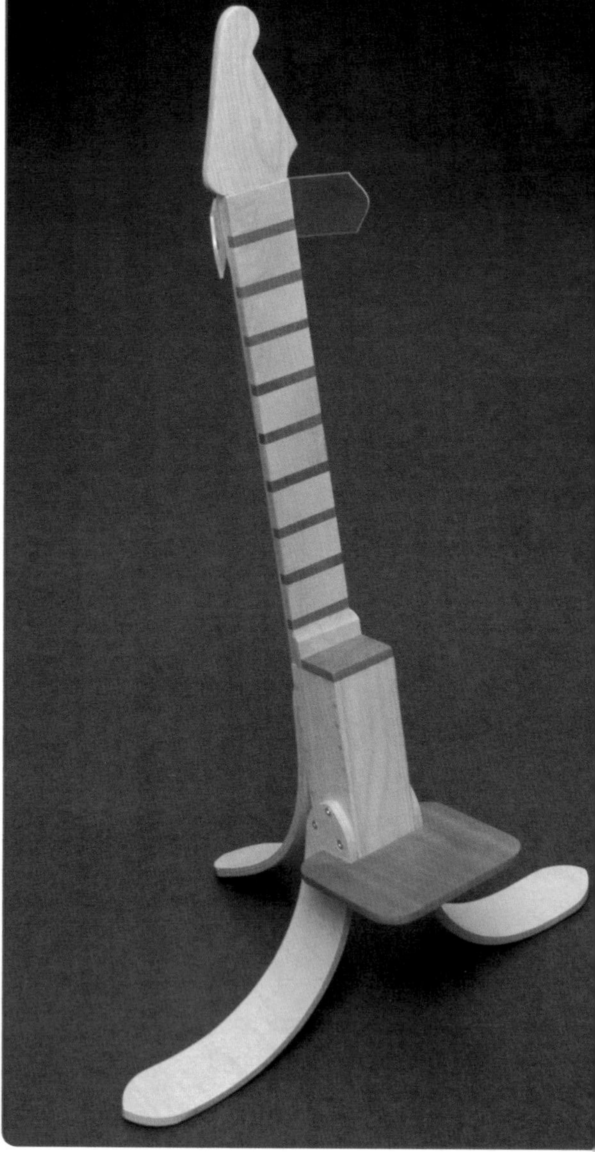

Making can involve many processes and materi

Turning ideas into reality

Once you have decided on your final design, you need to plan how it will be made. If you have planned and prepared thoroughly, the making should be straightforward. You are likely to find some parts of the design that you will choose to improve as you make; this is a normal part of the process. You may have to change the design for many reasons but keep a record of any changes you make as you go along. These modifications will be part of your evaluation.

The making may involve working with new processes and skills, so make sure you experiment and practise on scrap material first. These experiments are also part of the process, so make sure you record them.

Health and safety are important and you must work safely at all times. You should include simple risk assessments in your planning notes and folder.

lanning

e making section is the most important part of your ursework. It is the area where you can gain 40% of your SE marks. It is essential that you plan the work properly make best use of workshop time. Planning your making achieve the highest quality you can is also important. s is called quality assurance (QA). See 2.2 *Quality* to p you to do this well. You also need to plan the quality ntrol (QC) checks that you will make along the way to ke sure that everything works out.

antt charts

ntt charts are a simple and effective way to plan the ne available for the making of your project. See 7.6 *anufacturing systems* for more information on Gantt arts.

Brainstorm all the making tasks for each of your products. Think about these tasks as steps: some will be short; some long. Some you can do at any time; others can only happen in the correct order.

- For each product, write down how much time in lessons each task is likely to take.
- Fill in a Gantt chart to show clearly when tasks start and finish. You will have some tasks that can happen at the same time, e.g. while adhesive is drying you can cut other pieces.
- Use colour to present your time estimates.

Add annotations to show if your plans change. Include notes about how you have improved the quality and accuracy of your work. Add quality control checks in the same way.

Summary

★ **Making is the most important part of your project. It is worth 40% of your GCSE marks.**

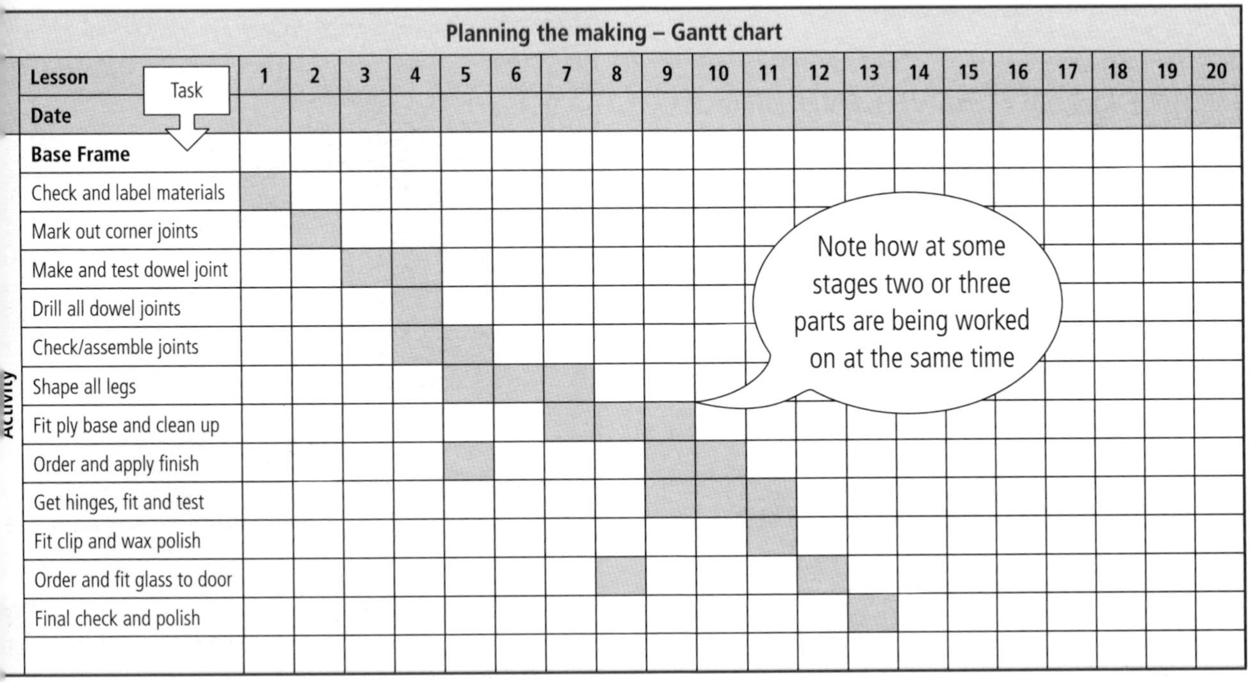

Planning the making – Gantt chart

	Lesson	1	2	3	4	5	6	7	8	9	10	11	12	13	14	15	16	17	18	19	20
	Date																				
	Base Frame																				
	Check and label materials																				
	Mark out corner joints																				
	Make and test dowel joint																				
	Drill all dowel joints																				
	Check/assemble joints																				
Activity	Shape all legs																				
	Fit ply base and clean up																				
	Order and apply finish																				
	Get hinges, fit and test																				
	Fit clip and wax polish																				
	Order and fit glass to door																				
	Final check and polish																				

Task

Note how at some stages two or three parts are being worked on at the same time

Complete a Gantt chart for each product

8.8 Testing and evaluating your product

AQA Resistant Materials Technology 9.1 and 10.4

In this chapter you will learn about:

★ testing and evaluating your product

★ ensuring you show a good range of communication skills.

In this part of your coursework you must:

Designing

A GRADE

7 Test, objectively evaluate and effectively modify your work throughout the process as appropriate.

C GRADE

7 Test, evaluate and modify your work throughout the process as appropriate.

An evaluation is a series of questions about how well your design has met the requirements of your specification. There are two main types of evaluative methods you need to use: ongoing and final evaluation.

Ongoing (formative) evaluation

Evaluation does not just take place at the end of a project; it is an ongoing process throughout the whole project. **Formative evaluation** occurs every time you make a decision or judgement about your work. A good example of this is when you were annotating your design ideas. It can also be useful to make some notes at the end of designing sections to cover what you have learned and how it will be used.

Final (summative) evaluation

At the end of your project you must complete a detailed analysis of your final outcome. This is called a **summative evaluation** and it must relate directly to your specification. It judges your final product against each criteria in your specification. A detailed specification is the key to doing this well. If the original specification was word processed and the file saved, you can use this as the basis of your evaluation. If the specification is not detailed, it may be difficult to do a meaningful evaluation.

How to evaluate

- Check each point on your specification. Have you done what you said you would do? Use the same headings t make it easy to follow your logic.
- Include sketches or photos to show how you could improve the product.
- Write in the 'third person' (do not say 'I think that...')
- Say what could be improved and what effect any improvements will have on the function and performan of the product.
- Get other people's views, e.g. your client or someone in the product's target market.
- Test your product in action. Does it function and perfor as required? Observe and record people's reactions to i Do they like it? Did they find it easy to use?

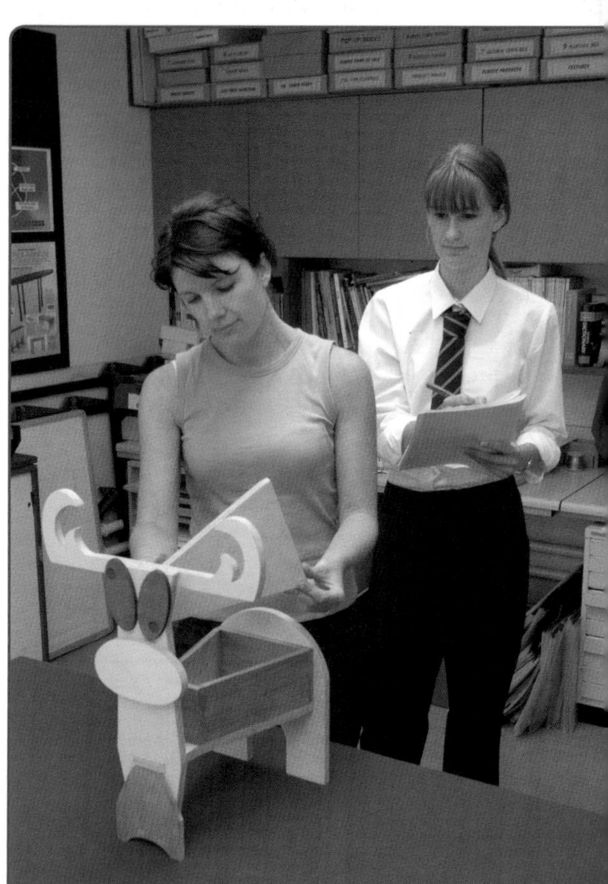

Finding out what other people thi

Preparing for the exam

e coursework project and folder are
gether worth 60% of your final mark. It is
sential that you focus on the coursework
it is the key to success. The working
owledge of materials, components and
chnologies you will gain through completing
ur project is the first step towards exam
ccess.

e exam is worth 40% of your final mark.
e two-hour exam for the full course is
orth 125 marks overall. The short course
am is $1\frac{1}{2}$ hours and is worth 100 marks
erall. This makes approximately one mark
r minute in either exam.

e questions in the exam test your
plication of knowledge and understanding of:

- three materials: metal, plastics and wood (plastics and wood for the short course)
- components, processes, techniques and technologies
- the evaluation of commercial practices and products
- ICT including CAD/CAM.

e exam questions are compulsory and test
e understanding, knowledge and skills you
ve gained during Key Stage 3 and your
CSE course.

ur teacher will have entered you into
her the higher-tier examination paper or
e foundation paper – make sure you know
ich one you are taking. The higher-tier
per is targeted at GCSE grades A–D. The
undation paper is targeted at grades C–G.

The exam theme

At the beginning of March you will be given a double-sided exam preparation sheet, which sets out the design context (or theme) for the exam questions and outlines areas of study to prepare for the exam. Studying the theme and doing some research is an important part of your exam preparation. Make use of this preparation material to gain the highest marks you can.

You will have up to ten weeks to prepare for the exam. If you use this time well, you will have time to:

- ★ make a study of the context and similar products
- ★ practise producing design ideas of these products
- ★ revise other topics mentioned on the preparation sheet.

You also need to revise thoroughly all the topics covered throughout your two-year course.

What's in this section?

9.1 Using exam preparation sheets and tackling the design questio

In this chapter you will learn about:
- ★ how to use the preparation sheet to guide you in your revision
- ★ how to tackle the design question.

Using the preparation sheet

General Certificate of Secondary Education
Summer 2003
Foundation and Higher Examination

AQA ASSESSMENT and QUALIFICATIONS ALLIANCE

PREPARATION SHEET FOR THE 2003 EXAMINATION 3545/55PM

Design and Technology: Resistant Materials Technology
(For the Foundation and Higher Tiers of the Short and Full Courses)

Instructions
- This Preparation Sheet will be given to you on or after 1 March 2003.
- The context for **some** of the examination questions is given below and further information is given overleaf.
- Between March and the examination date you will have the opportunity to research the context with the guidance of your teacher.
- **No Preparation Sheets or any associated material may be taken into the examination room.**
- You **must** take some colouring pencils into the examination.

RESEARCH CONTEXT: COMPUTER WORKSTATIONS
The personal computer can now be found in many homes and is used by members of the family. A computer workstation is a convenient way to store and work at the computer.

Make a study of computer workstations.

Use the information overleaf to guide you in your research.

Higher tier candidates should also consider the needs of a wheelchair user who will require a work height 100 mm higher than the other members of the family will need.

Short course candidates will not be asked questions relating to metal processes.

Permission to reproduce all copyright material has been applied for. Efforts to contact copyright owners have been unsuccessful and AQA will be happy to rectify any omissions of acknowledgements in future papers if notified.

 Turn over ▶

TP/0203/3545/55PM

The exam preparation sheet

You need to read the front of the preparation sheet carefully. This should help you to find out what you already know and what you need to revise in more detail.

Step 1

Analyse the words of the research context given by the exam board. Make sure you understand exactly what is required. Think about what they mean. You probably did this with your coursework so you will have practised it before. Analyse each word carefully, for example:

RESEARCH CONTEXT: Activity toys for young children

Activity toys – toys which are designed to encourage children to perform or practise an activity such as shape or colour sorting

Action or moving parts – parts of the toy which move as the toy is pulled along or which are designed to be moved or hit

Built-in – features which are designed as a part of the whole toy

A manufacturer – a commercial manufacturing compar

An action feature – part which moves or can be removed

A storage system – a planned method of storage

Step 2

The back page of the sheet gives illustrations of products you should be researching, together with a mind map. Study the pictures and the mind map. This is a product analysis exercise and 2.1 *Product analysis* will help you to do this effectively. There are two things you can do with t information:
- Extend the mind map or list of products given.
- Many teachers research the preparation sheet and shar their work on the Internet. Use a search engine to find out information.

Preparing for the design question

The design question is based on the preparation sheet context. You should be good at designing as you have already had a lot of practice, but for the design question you will be working in a focused way with limited time so practise working in this way.

The design question can be broken down into four parts:
- the design specification
- design ideas
- the construction of your chosen design idea
- using ICT when designing and making.

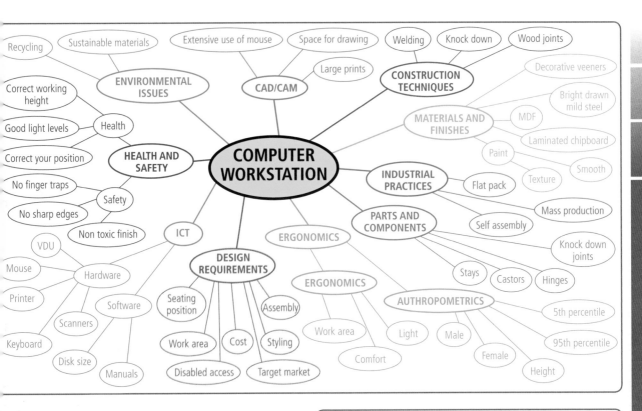

- **COMPUTER WORKSTATION**
  - ENVIRONMENTAL ISSUES
    - Recycling
    - Sustainable materials
  - CAD/CAM
    - Extensive use of mouse
    - Space for drawing
    - Large prints
  - CONSTRUCTION TECHNIQUES
    - Welding
    - Knock down
    - Wood joints
  - MATERIALS AND FINISHES
    - Decorative veneers
    - Bright drawn mild steel
    - MDF
    - Laminated chipboard
    - Paint
      - Texture
      - Smooth
  - INDUSTRIAL PRACTICES
    - Flat pack
    - Mass production
    - Self assembly
  - PARTS AND COMPONENTS
    - Knock down joints
    - Stays
    - Castors
    - Hinges
  - ERGONOMICS
    - ERGONOMICS
      - Work area
      - Comfort
      - Light
    - AUTHROPOMETRICS
      - Male
      - Female
      - Height
      - 5th percentile
      - 95th percentile
  - DESIGN REQUIREMENTS
    - Seating position
    - Work area
    - Cost
    - Disabled access
    - Target market
    - Styling
    - Assembly
  - ICT
    - Hardware
      - VDU
      - Mouse
      - Printer
      - Keyboard
      - Scanners
    - Software
      - Disk size
      - Manuals
  - HEALTH AND SAFETY
    - Health
      - Correct working height
      - Good light levels
      - Correct your position
    - Safety
      - No finger traps
      - No sharp edges
      - Non toxic finish

actise:

writing specifications with explanations

writing specifications for one of the products illustrated

drawing:

- six-minute design ideas
- two-minute notes on designs (use your specifications to help)
- two-minute evaluations – again, base these on your specification.

me yourself and get used to working quickly.

Summary

★ Practical experience of the products identified in the preparation sheet is essential.

★ The design question is the key to success.

The disabled access sign suggests that there will be a question about how access can be improved for wheelchair users. How might the needs of a wheelchair user be different? How could the work height be adjusted for different users?

The printer, computer and disks are typical of the things a desk would need to accommodate. What weight and size is a computer? How much space is needed around a computer to allow it to be used?

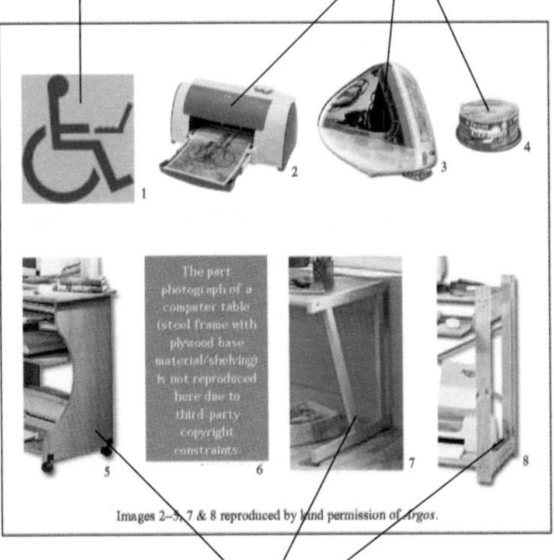

Images 2–5, 7 & 8 reproduced by kind permission of Argos.

The three different kinds of desk shown are made of different materials. How is each one constructed? What has the designer done to make them strong and stable? Which one do you think is the most expensive?

Getting ready for the exam

In this chapter you will learn about:
- ★ **preparing and revising for the exam**
- ★ **exam technique.**

Preparing a revision plan

Write the plan on paper, noting all critical dates and times. Be reasonable and build in some free time. Make sure the following are identified:
- All exam dates.
- Coursework deadlines.
- Study leave.
- Family occasions, birthdays, holidays and trips.
- Allow some time for relaxation and exercise – you will need to be fit for your exams.

Divide the remaining time between all your subjects. When allocating time to each subject, take into account the following factors.
- How well did you do in the mock exam? This will help you identify areas you are strong or weak at.
- When is the date of each exam?
- What is your preferred method of learning? Do not allocate yourself time that you will not use effectively. Variety created by 'little and often' or 'topic by topic' may be more effective.
- Use colour-coded blocks for each subject to give you a clearer indication of how much time you have allocated time to each subject.
- Buy some Post-it® Notes and write things on them that you find difficult to remember. Stick them in prominent places around your bedroom such as on your mirror, so you are constantly reminded of them.
- Do not be afraid to alter your plans as circumstances change, but try to stick to it as closely as possible.

Revising

We all have our preferred ways to revise – you must do what works for you. As a part of your revision program, try the following:
- work to half an hour time periods and take regular short breaks. Stand up and walk around to refresh yourself
- use quick drawings and notes when you revise topics
- use mind maps with drawings to help you to visualise processes and sequences
- practice rapid drawing techniques to use in your design questions
- practise sketching 2D and 3D views
- go through practice papers as much as possible to get used to the language, layout and vocabulary
- learn specific types of woods, metals and plastics, together with their properties and uses.

Making effective use of the exam preparation sheet

The exam preparation sheet will tell you what the context of the exam questions is to be and will show you a sample of the kind of products you should study to prepare for the exam. An outline spider diagram will show you the areas you should study. The context will be different each year.

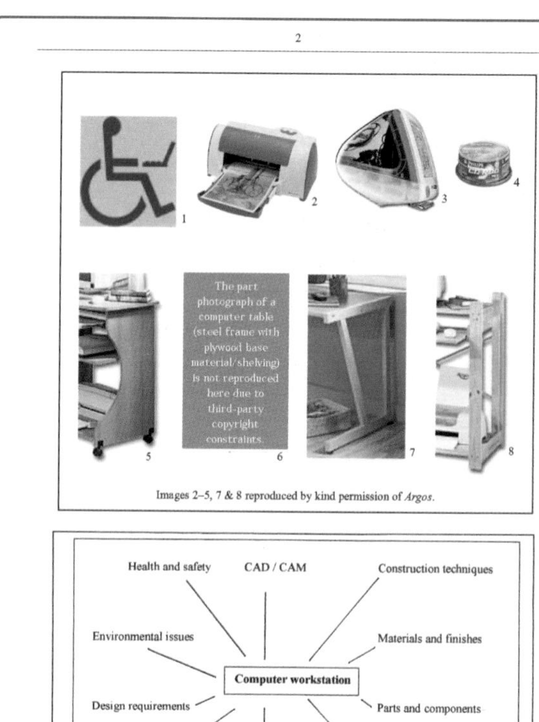

Example exam preparation shee

ıe right equipment

ing the exam you need to show your designing and phic skills, so you need to have the right equipment to this. Make sure you bring a good HB pencil, a pencil rpener, a good pen, a selection of colouring pencils, a r and a rubber. You must be able to produce pictorial vs that are well drawn, colour rendered and well otated.

ıe right approach

list below contains some important tips for success.

Always read and reread each question before you answer t. Underline key words in the question.

)o not be put off by the first few sentences of a question. Read it all as there are often clues later in the question that will help you to understand it better.

.ook at the marks for each question – as a rough guide, allow no more than one minute for each mark.

Before sketching, think carefully about what you want to draw and check the space you have to use to ensure you ise it wisely.

Try to show your knowledge of materials and making processes by giving specific answers.

Never leave an answer blank – always write something and have a go at every part.

Never doodle on your exam paper.

f you have any time left at the end, go through the questions and check your answers.

Exam vocabulary

Understanding the vocabulary used in the exam is essential.

Compare You are expected to analyse the similarities and differences between two or more objects.

Describe This means to give an idea of something by specifying its nature or properties.

Develop This means to improve a basic idea. You will need to make changes and come up with a workable solution.

Evaluate This involves making judgements about something, often giving advantages and disadvantages.

Explain This usually requires reasons and depth about the subject.

Explain (or describe) in detail This requires a longer answer with more facts.

List This requires single words or phrases.

Name This is asking for the specific name of something. The examiner will want to see exact words, for example the name of a material.

Use notes and sketches The answer must include diagrams. Full marks will only be awarded if notes or sketches are used.

Exam Hint

The top of each page identifies what the questions are about.

Exam Hint

Learn and use the specific names for materials, e.g. oak (not wood), high-impact polystyrene (not plastic).

Summary

★ Good exam technique and thorough revision will ensure success.

9.3 Getting maximum marks

In this chapter you will learn about:

★ how to answer the design question

★ how to answer the making question

★ how to answer open ended questions.

The design question

Question

Design a computer workstation that can be adjusted to accommodate a wheelchair. The work surface will need to rise by 100 mm.

Answer

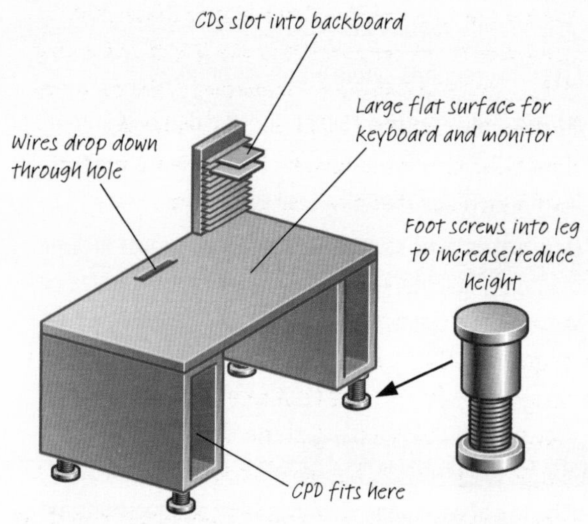

Evaluation *"Screw in leg" gives height adjustment but it is slow and difficult to use. Simple traditional style. Wire are well hidden.*

This is one of the three designs the candidate produced.

This is how the candidate achieved high marks.

- The design fulfils the design brief.
- This is one of three original and different ideas.
- It is a 3D pictorial sketch which is in proportion and shows material thickness.
- Additional views have been used to aid understanding.
- There is good use of colour.
- There are detailed notes explaining the idea.
- The idea is fully evaluated.

The making question

Question

Study the drawing of the acrylic notepad holder shown below.

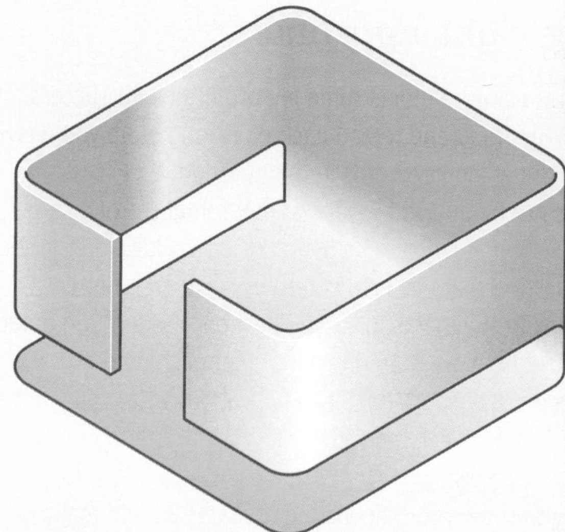

Using notes and sketches clearly show, stage by stage, how you would make the notepad holder in the school workshop. Remember to name all the tools and equipment you would use.

Stage one:	Marking out or CAD	*(4 marks)*
Stage two:	Cutting, Shaping and drilling or CAM	*(4 marks)*
Stage three:	Bending	*(4 marks)*
Stage four:	Finishing	*(4 marks)*
Quality of notes and sketches		*(4 marks)*

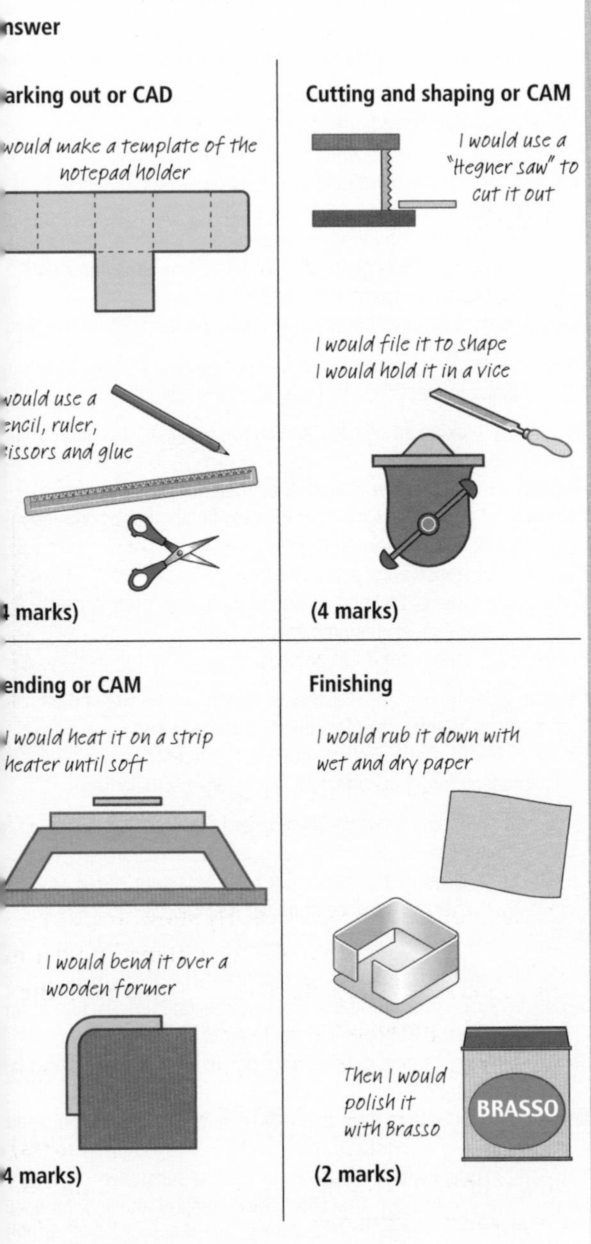
nswer
arking out or CAD
would make a template of the notepad holder
would use a encil, ruler, issors and glue
 marks)
Cutting and shaping or CAM
I would use a "Hegner saw" to cut it out
I would file it to shape
I would hold it in a vice
(4 marks)
ending or CAM
I would heat it on a strip heater until soft
I would bend it over a wooden former
4 marks)
Finishing
I would rub it down with wet and dry paper
Then I would polish it with Brasso
BRASSO
(2 marks)

s is how the candidate gained marks.

- The correct tools and equipment have been sketched and abelled for each stage.
- Each stage of the process has been clearly described in sufficient detail for someone else to carry it out.
- The quality of the notes and sketching make the whole process easy to follow.

The open ended question

When answering this type of open ended question it is important to look at the marks allocated to the question and the number of lines you are expected to fill. This will give you an idea of the amount of detail that will be required in your answer.

Question

Describe the work of the BSI (British Standards Institute) and explain its importance to the consumer. *(6 marks)*

Answer

The BSI checks everything that might be considered dangerous to the consumer. They will give it a Kitemark if it passes their tests. This is important to the consumer because they now know that the product is safe. Consumers can rest assured that if they buy a product with a Kitemark that it will not hurt them.

The candidate gained marks by:

- suggesting that the BSI checks products
- suggesting that it carries out safety checks
- having an understanding of the Kitemark
- suggesting that the BSI gives an assurance of safety.

The candidate could have gained higher marks had they gone on to expand their answer by:

- suggesting the types of testing the BSI carries out
- explaining that the BSI is a professional body of experts.

The candidate did not get marks for the last sentence as it simply repeats the information already given.

Summary

★ If you revise and practise answers, you will enter the exam confident that you will do your best.

Glossary

Abrasive a material used for cleaning, smoothing or polishing
Adhesive A bonding agent used to join materials
Aesthetics How we respond to the visual appearance of a product, in relation to its form, texture, smell and colour.
Alloy a metal made by combining two or more metallic elements
Anthropometrics The study of the dimensions of the human body, including arm and leg reach.

Batch production A method of production where a number of components are made all at once.
Biodegradable materials that can be decomposed by natural means
British Standards Institute (BSI) an organisation responsible for preparing codes of practice

Client The person or company for whom the product is designed and made
Composite a material that is made up of various parts, often layers, for example carbon fibre on a racing car.
Computer numerical control (CNC) Using digital information from a computer to control a machine.
Computer-aided design (CAD) Use of a computer programme to design a product.
Computer-aided manufacture (CAM) Use of a computer programme to manufacture a product.
Consumer The people at whom new products and services are targeted.
Control of Substances Hazardous to Health (COSHH) legislation covering the risks to people from harmful substances.
Critical evaluation judging the quality or value of something
Customer The person who buys and uses the product.

Environment external conditions or surroundings
Ergonomics The study of the relationship between products and their users, focusing on improving performance, comfort and ease of use.

Flat-pack kit A set of parts and fittings for the customer to assemble into a product, e.g. the IKEA bookcase.
Flow-line production a non-stop manufacturing process
Formative evaluation Use of a computer programme to manufacture a product.
Function The purpose of a product, i.e. what it does.

Gantt chart a project planning chart which maps tasks against time

Hardwood comes from trees that have broad open leaves and fruit
Hazard a thing likely to cause injury
Health and Safety Executive (HSE) Britain's Health and Safety Commission (HSC) and the Health and Safety Executive (HSE) are responsible for the regulation of almost all the risks to health and safety arising from work activity in Britain.

International Standards Office (ISO) the world's leading developer of international standards, from credit cards to chemical, they set levels of quality and performance

Just in Time (JIT) A system in which goods are made and delivered to order rather than being held in a warehouse.

Kitemark The symbol used to show a product is made to British Standards
Knock-down (KD) fittings The fittings used to enable flat pack furniture to be easy for customers to assemble.

Line The use of drawn lines to create shapes, patterns and moveme

Manufactured board timber sheets made by gluing particles or la of wood fibres together
Market place The place where products are sold.
Market survey An investigation to discover what consumers think about existing or proposed products.
Mass production A method of production in which large numbers identical products are made using mechanised techniques.
Material the substance of which a thing is made
Mechanism a system of moving parts that performs some function

One-off (bespoke) production When a product is made by one person to meet the exact wishes of the customer.

Patenting making an official claim on the design or invention of a product
Pattern an exact replica of a product to be made
Primary research Research that involves finding things out 'first ha by talking to people and visiting places
Process the steps or procedure in a task
Prototype A pre-production version of a product, used to check whether it meets requirements.
Pure metal metal that is not an alloy

Quality assurance (QA) A policy written to ensure that a product c be consistently manufactured to a set standard
Quality control (QC) Systems put in place to check the quality of t product during manufacture, e.g. gauges, visual checks.

Recycled a material that has been passed through a system again f further use
Rendered a drawing that has colour, tone or texture added
Renewable energy a source of power that can be replaced
Risk assessment taking steps to reduce a potential hazard

Scale of production The type of production, i.e. batch, mass, one-c
Secondary research Research that uses 'second hand' information sources such as books and the Internet.
Smart material a material that responds to an external stimulus i.e temperature
Softwood comes from trees that have needles and seeds contained cones
Solvent a liquid capable of dissolving another substance
Summative evaluation The critical evaluation of a task or product after it is completed to see if it has met the design specificatio
Sustainable a material or energy that is renewed as it is used
Sustainable development is the ability to meet the needs of the present without compromising the needs of the future
System a group of processes - outputs, inputs, controls and feedbac - that link together to form a whole process.

Target group The group of consumers that a new product is aimed
Thermoplastic A type of plastic that softens under heat and can be resoftened many times.
Thermosetting plastic A type of plastic which, once set, cannot be resoftened or melted.
Tolerance The upper and lower acceptable limits of a dimension i.e. 25 mm +/- 0.5 mm means 24.5 mm to 25.5 mm.

Index